Early Invention. A paddle-wheel
vessel. From a sixteenth-century edition
of Vitruvius (first century A.D.).

DR. WILLIAM GILBERT demonstrating his experiments to Queen Elizabeth

Makers of
SCIENCE

Mathematics   Physics

Astronomy

BY

IVOR B. HART

WITH AN INTRODUCTION

BY

DR. CHARLES SINGER

Second Impression

LONDON
OXFORD UNIVERSITY PRESS
HUMPHREY MILFORD
1924

Printed in England

An early use of steam power by Heron
of Alexandria
? First century A.D.

AUTHOR'S PREFACE

THE motives underlying the writing of this book have been fully set out by Dr. Charles Singer in the Introduction. It merely remains for the author to express his acknowledgements and to explain the limitations of the work. Apart from the mode of presentation and the choice of material, the book makes no claim to originality, and the author freely acknowledges his indebtedness to existing works on the subjects dealt with. A list of these is given in the bibliography at the end of the book.

This work is not intended as a series of detached biographies. It is hoped that the reader will find the various chapters linked to each other to form a chronological sequence of *some* of the broader movements in scientific history so far as the physical and the mathematical sciences are concerned.

Space has demanded a rigid limitation in the matter treated. No attempt has been made to include either the biological or the chemical sciences. For the same reason much of the history of physics and mathematics has necessarily been omitted, and the characters chosen for biographical treatment have been so chosen rather from the point of view of their suitability as ' pegs ' from which to ' hang ' the scientific history of their times than from any superiority over their contemporaries.

The author desires to express his sincere thanks to his friends Miss D. Turner and Mr. D. E. Williams for considerable assistance in the reading of the proofs and manuscript. More especially he is under a deep debt of gratitude to Dr. Charles Singer for continuous advice, encouragement, and helpful criticism throughout the whole period of the author's labours at the book.

IVOR B. HART.

February 1923.

INTRODUCTION

THERE was a time—not so very long ago—when the general scheme of education seemed stable and almost complete. To the discovery of the classics in the fourteenth and fifteenth centuries had succeeded that process by which the literary treasure of Greece and Rome became accessible. The change in man's outlook quickly affected education and the classical system established itself firmly in the schools and remained practically unchanged for wellnigh four centuries.

What an illuminating system it was and how much truth it provided! It was Rome, the legatee of Greece, that had tamed the barbarian and created civilization. It was to the Roman tongue that the languages of the peoples of Europe surrendered themselves and are still surrendering. It was Roman law that displaced and still displaces tribal custom. It was the religion, the sacred books of which were written in Greek and the organization of which was fashioned in Rome, before which the tribal rites had receded. It was the Art and thought of Greece which seemed so clearly to be the ancestor of much of what was best and most beautiful in life. The consciousness of such an inheritance, even when corrupted by ages of barbarism, gave men a sense of the fullness of their own past. Purified by scholarship and philosophy it provided a complex and ennobling scheme of life.

The educational system that thus arose served as the fundamental training until almost our own time. Only with extreme slowness did new elements enter into the situation and the advent of science had for long surprisingly little effect upon education. The science of the sixteenth, seventeenth, and eighteenth centuries was mainly the affair of amateurs, of men trained in the old system who happened to interest themselves in phenomena. For them the classical education, the only complete and thought-out system of the day, was still the best available. The ideas of Copernicus and Vesalius and even those of Galileo, Kepler, Boyle. and Newton, were no obstacle. The great physical synthesis established by such workers, while it emphasized the separation from the Middle Ages—which seemed ever darker and darker as knowledge advanced—brought antiquity nearer to men of the early modern period. If the physics of Aristotle fell, yet much of his philosophy remained. Plato was untouched and Greek letters and art stood yet as the model of all that was the most beautiful. Latin was still the *lingua franca* of the learned. Greek was the language of that ancient wisdom which was so evidently the ancestor of the science of the day. In the eighteenth and even in the earlier nineteenth century, a classical education was by no means a bad preparation for a scientific career.

Two factors disturbed the situation, one practical and one spiritual—firstly, certain later developments of the Industrial Revolution and, secondly, the realization of the vastness and complexity of man's past.

I say later developments of the Industrial Revolution because the earlier developments, like the earlier developments of modern science, had comparatively little influence on the manner of thinking. The earlier factors in the Industrial Revolution, such as the introduction of stone-coal, the flying-shuttle, the spinning-jenny, steam-power, and new means of the preparation of iron, certainly greatly increased the amenities of life and had their influence on the manner of living, but they had no great effect on the intellectual situation. These early advances were almost all technical—inventions rather than discoveries—innovations depending on the application of known principles and not involving the introduction of new principles. It was at a later stage, when a high degree of technical training became a common demand, that the effect on the educational situation began to be felt.

The unsettling elements in science, as in industry, hardly began until the nineteenth century. The views of Dalton on the atomic nature of matter were expressed in the first decade. The idea of the infinite complexity of matter was furthered by the chemical discoveries of Davy, by Frauenhofer following up Wollaston's work on the spectrum, by Mitscherlich's disclosure of the existence of isomorphism, by Pelletier's synthesis of organic compounds, and by Faraday's researches in electricity — all appearing before the first half of the century was over. In 1850 came the work of Joule which laid the experimental basis of the modern doctrine of energy.

In Biological science the movement was a little later. Until the work of Ehrenberg in the thirties and forties the knowledge of minute life had remained much where Leeuwenhoek had left it. With new and improved instruments was revealed an unexpected variety and complexity of living things. The cellular theories of Schleiden and Schwann—developed by Henle, Kölliker, and later by Virchow—at last introduced effective general ideas into the conceptions of vital phenomena. It was, however, the evolutionary view of Darwin and his followers that finally destroyed, in the decades after 1860, the possibility of thinking of a world in which, outside the Bible, the whole debt lay to Greece and Rome. With the spread of evolutionary views in the second part of the nineteenth century, with the development of archaeology and especially with that department of pre-historic archaeology that had been founded by Boucher de Perthes, with the enormous increase in the complexity of scientific knowledge, and with the demand for specially trained scientific workers, entirely new needs arose. It was no longer true that the old classical education supplied a clue to man's history, nor did it aid for vocational purposes.

Classical learning in the old sense as the staple of education was thus perhaps inevitably doomed. But Science—I use the word for the moment in its restricted meaning—though it may *displace* the Humanities, could not and cannot *replace* them, for it cannot provide us with any clear record of how we have developed mentally. For this we must turn to History, but History not in the sense in which that word is customarily employed as equivalent merely to Political History, nor even in the wider sense of Sociological History. It is the history of mankind as a whole that we need, the history of civilization, the history of man's thoughts, of man's knowledge, of man's self.

Such history, we may hope, will ultimately take its place as the central item in the curriculum even of the elementary schools. Into that history will be interwoven the stories of Greece and

Rome, but these will be presented not for themselves but as part of a greater whole. The task of preparing such a work is a very great one and it must be many years before it will be forthcoming. There are large areas of knowledge which must be reduced to compassable form before it can even be attempted. In the meantime and as a preliminary stage we must look to separate works on different aspects of history. The history of the earlier stages of man's development as well as an account of the technology of a later stage have been admirably set forth in an elementary fashion by Mr. and Mrs. Quennell. There are several elementary text books of Economic History available. The history of Religion finds, or should find, its interpretation in the Sunday school. There is still, however, very great need for an elementary account of the development of Art throughout the ages and almost as great a need for a school history of Science.

For those whose education is mainly grounded in Science, and especially for that large and growing class that is destined to follow Science as a career, the History of Science—even apart from the reasons that have been urged—is itself surely an appropriate study. But there is another and more immediately practical ground on which we may plead for the introduction of History into the scientific curriculum. We are well accustomed to recognize that the store of acquired scientific knowledge is a general treasury from which all men draw, by which alone it has been possible for our material state to rise above that of the savage. Yet we seldom remind ourselves that the guardianship of this treasury, the heritage of all men, has always been in the hands of a very small band, and this has been so in all its wanderings. From the peoples of the ancient East it passed to the Greeks, then having dwelt awhile in Moslem lands it came to Italy, and during the last three hundred years it has at last penetrated to the West of Europe. In all these countries and at all these periods the organic apparatus by which new knowledge has been created has been the work of a mere handful. Surely the contemplation of the conditions under which these men worked and lived, the examination of their training and mental history, of their environment and manner of development, must be of value—even in the practical everyday sense—to those who would follow in their footsteps.

And the other side of the picture is also not without its application. The study of those social and economic and philosophical conditions that *fail* to produce effective scientific fruit, or that yield only bizarre and deformed products, has also its lesson. Some idea of the Science of these retrograde periods must also be included in any course on the History of Science, and should form an integral part of any scientific education worthy of the name. The scientific student would thus be grounded in the elements of what we may call the Embryology, the Physiology, and the Pathology of his special study.

But there is yet another aspect of the History of Science. Our scientific system of its nature claims an independence of all race, nationality, or creed. It is of all studies the most truly international. The scientific man may, better than most, claim that he is the true citizen of the world. Nevertheless, in all countries and at all periods there has been a certain local and temporal stamp in the Science that has been produced. These differences, however, concern the interests and processes of the scientist himself rather than the methods and aims of his science. Now among the methods of Modern Science there are certain new factors of an order that the world has not before seen ; and though he must be sanguine indeed who believes that the scientific treasury will always remain with its present guardians, yet these new factors give us good hope of a permanence in our scientific results and of a uniformity of scientific advance of a character the like of which history has not yet seen.

Those factors are bound up with the manner in which we record and present our knowledge as soon as it is acquired ; our mode of storing our treasures for ready accessibility. One great lesson of the history of science is that the influence of newly acquired knowledge varies greatly with its presentation. Much of the work of Thomas Young, for instance, one of the greatest scientific intellects that this country has produced, has needed to be redone, and modern discoveries are frequently ' re-discovered ' in his writings. The neglect of his material by later generations is largely the result of his own very imperfect method of presenting his work. With the mass of knowledge so vast and growing, with the evil and increasing tendency of the departments of knowledge to separate farther and farther from each other and to dwell each in its own house, the necessity for careful presentation of the material grows ever greater and greater. One practical advantage of even an elementary study of the history of science is that it may tempt the student to the perusal of the great classics of scientific investigation, to learn at first hand both the best methods of research and the most appropriate modes of presentment. A pressing need for such students is a work containing a series of extracts from the writings of the greatest investigators, which could be used as a sort of commentary on such a book as that of Mr. Hart, a work corresponding to the *Aus der Werkstatt grösser Forscher* of Dr. Friedrich Dannemann.

Under our present system there are two possible channels by which the history of science may reach the class-room, one is through science, the other through history. On the whole the men of science have proved themselves rather more active, if perhaps less effective, than the historians. We have several elementary accounts of the different sciences historically treated. Among the more recent is Dr. Lowry's excellent *Historical Introduction to Chemistry*. The self-imposed limitation of such works, however valuable they may be, prevents them from providing the philosophical insight and wide general interest of, for instance, Mr. F. S. Marvin's *Living Past*, which approaches the problem primarily from the historian's standpoint. For a school *History of Natural Science* as a whole we have to turn to the remarkable work of the venerable Mrs. Buckley Fisher (Arabella Buckley), first published in 1875.

Such works as those of Dr. Lowry, of Mrs. Buckley Fisher, and of Mr. Marvin naturally appeal to a more developed intelligence and to those who have already considerable command of the scientific material itself. For an earlier stage the biographical method is probably the best and most attractive. It has the advantage of fixing in the student's mind the work and names of the greater investigators, so that at a later stage he may be

tempted to examine the originals. It appeals too to the ' human '
side and does something to prevent the abstraction of the
scientific from other points of view. It literally brings science
into the home.

Works prepared on lines like these help to bring some sort of
continuity and unity into the educational scheme. They point
to a time when the central element in education will be a great
outline of history from which political history, civics, literature,
language, religion, art, science and other departments of knowledge will branch naturally, so as to give the student once again
a coherent view, as of old, of the great world into which he has
been born and the great heritage into which he has entered.

CHARLES SINGER.

University College, London,
31 *January* 1923.

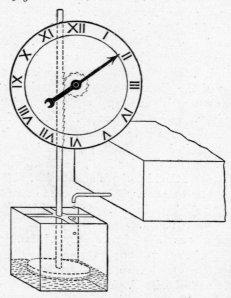

A water-clock described by Vitruvius and
worked by a water tank and float

CONTENTS

LIST OF ILLUSTRATIONS

I

ARISTOTLE

1. *The Beginning of Knowledge—The Ionian School*

DURING hundreds of years preceding the birth of Christ, at a time when the inhabitants of our own country were ignorant and uncivilized, there flourished in Greece a wonderful civilization, characterized by culture, scholarship, and skill in warfare. It is to this people that we must look for the first glimmerings of scientific knowledge. True, judging by present-day standards, the Greeks were in many ways ignorant. To them the world was a large flat surface surrounded by water ; and the sun was the God Apollo driving his chariot across the skies daily from east to west. But all things have their beginnings and our debt of gratitude to the ancient Greek philosophers for the wonderful heritage of learning which they have left to us cannot be over-estimated.

Confining ourselves, as we shall in this book, to the story of the progress of the physical and mathematical sciences, it may of course be argued that in fact the earliest knowledge of these subjects comes not from Greece but from Egypt, and Chaldea, and Phoenicia, and China, and even from India. While it is true that the beginnings of arithmetic may be found in Chaldea, and that an empirical and crude sort of geometry was in use in Egypt, these subjects were not developed in the abstract as sciences, but were purely a result of practical needs. Thus the periodic floodings of the river Nile, resulting as they did in the inundations of large tracts of land, created the necessity for a crude form of surveying, so giving rise to an empirical scheme of geometry. For example, observations on the rising and setting of stars enabled a north and south line to be laid along a plane midway between these points, and they could set out a right

angle by fastening ropes round three pegs to form a triangle
the ratio of whose sides were 3 : 4 : 5, and so on. Similarly the
trade relations between the Phoenicians and the Chaldaeans
made the use of some scheme of reckoning necessary in order to
facilitate barter, so giving rise to the beginnings of arithmetic ;
whilst a certain amount of observational astronomy was carried
on to assist navigation.

FIG. I.

The written records of all this are, however, very few, and much
is conjecture. But of the Greek initiation of these studies as
sciences, developed not from utilitarian motives but purely for
the sake of knowledge *per se*, there is no doubt whatever.

The Greeks were temperamentally well fitted for this mission.
They were of a naturally high order of intellect ; they were keen
observers ; the power of speculation was instinctive to their
being ; and above all they produced from amongst their numbers
great leaders of thought in whose hands these qualities could
not fail to make for tremendous progress.

Pre-eminent amongst these people were the Ionians, who added to the other qualities of the Greeks that of a love of adventure which prompted them to leave their homes and found colonies, with the result that they came into contact with other peoples, and with such culture as they found among these peoples. It was in this way that Thales of Miletus (640 ?–550 ? B. C.), rightly regarded as the founder of the Ionian school of philosophy, first developed a love of mathematics and science. We are told of him that business took him to Egypt, where he spent many years, and that when he returned to Miletus it was with an enthusiasm for the Egyptian sciences which caused him to abandon trade and to devote the remainder of his life to philosophy. As a result we may say of him that he introduced to the Greeks the serious study of geometry and of astronomy —a noteworthy achievement was his successful prediction of the solar eclipse of the 28th of May 585 B.C.—and he laid the foundations of the study of electricity by his observations on the electrification of amber by friction.

Amongst those who followed him we may mention Anaximander and Anaximenes, and more especially, Pythagoras of Samos (? 572–497 B. C.).

2. *The Pythagorean School*

The teachings of Pythagoras and of the brotherhood which he founded mark relatively a tremendous advance in mathematical and scientific knowledge. Arguing, for instance, that the sphere is the most perfect of all solid figures, the Pythagoreans were the first thinkers to assert the sphericity of the earth, the sun, and the moon. But perhaps to the average school-boy Pythagoras is best known for his discovery of the proposition with regard to the right-angled triangle (Euclid I, 47) commonly referred to as the ' theorem of Pythagoras '. The proof given by Euclid, and usually taught in schools, was of course original to Euclid himself, but perhaps it will not be out of place briefly to outline the demonstration which Pythagoras most probably employed.

Starting with the square $ABCD$ (Fig. 2) we may split it up into two squares EH and GF, and two equal rectangles AK and KC. Join GE. Hence we may say

$$AB^2 = EK^2 + GK^2 + 4\triangle AGE \dots\dots\dots\dots\dots(1).$$

But make $$BL = CM = DG = AE.$$

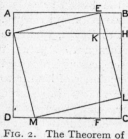

FIG. 2. The Theorem of Pythagoras.

Then it is easy to see that the figure $GELM$ is a square, and that the triangles AGE, BEL, CLM and DMG are all equal.

Hence we have
$$AB^2 = GE^2 + 4\triangle AGE \dots\dots\dots\dots\dots(2).$$

Equating (1) and (2) above, we therefore have

$$GE^2 + 4\triangle AGE = EK^2 + GK^2 + 4\triangle AGE,$$

whence

$$GE^2 = EK^2 + GK^2,$$

which proves the proposition.

The great advance which Pythagoras made in the study of number was also very stimulating. We see in his treatment of the subject a distinct geometrical bias. All numbers were regarded as either odd or even, and the odd numbers were called ' gnomonic '. A gnomon, of course, is a figure such as $ABCFKG$ in Fig. 2, derived from a square by removing from it a smaller square such as $GKFD$. Let us now see how Pythagoras built up his scheme of odd numbers.

Representing 1 by a dot thus $\bullet$, suppose we add *three* to form a square, $\begin{smallmatrix}\bullet & \bullet\\ \bullet & \bullet\end{smallmatrix}$. We now have $1 + 3 = 2^2$ (where before we had $1 = 1^2$). Now add *five* more dots at equal intervals, It will be noticed we have added a gnomonic figure, giving us $1 + 3 + 5 = 3^2$. The next gnomonic figure is got by adding *seven* dots at equal intervals, giving $1 + 3 + 5 + 7$ and so on, the general formula being

$$1 + 3 + 5 + 7 \dots\dots\dots + (2n - 1) = n^2.$$

Pythagoras spoke of the sum of the gnomons from 1 to $(2n - 1)$ as a *square number*, and he regarded an odd number as the

difference between two square numbers. This is evident from the following : $1+3+5+7\ldots\ldots+(2n-1) = n^2.$
Now add the next odd number, i. e. $(2n+1)$.

$$1+3+5+7\ldots\ldots+(2n+1) = (n+1)^2.$$

That is to say, $(n+1)^2 = n^2+(2n+1)$.

$$\text{i. e. } (n+1^2)-n^2 = (2n+1),$$

giving an odd number $(2n+1)$ as the difference between two square numbers.

To Pythagoras we also owe the beginnings of the study of *sound*. The story goes that while passing a blacksmith's shop he was attracted by the musical notes emitted by the anvil on being struck with the hammer, and subsequent experiments on the stretching force applied to strings of the same materials, length, and thickness, to produce notes whose intervals are fourths, fifths, and octaves were as $1 : \frac{3}{4} : \frac{2}{3} : \frac{1}{2}$. He also experimented on stretched strings of varied lengths, and found that the necessary length-ratio to produce an octave was $2 : 1$; to produce a fifth, $3 : 2$; and to produce a fourth, $4 : 3$.

3. *Plato and his Academy*

In due course the centre of Greek learning shifted from Ionia and southern Italy to Athens. Here the immortal Socrates thought and taught, and among his pupils was Plato, destined, like his master, to be recognized as one of the greatest of Greece's noble sons. Plato founded a school at Athens in a pleasant grove with shady walks and seats, and here he discoursed daily to his disciples and wrote those many dialogues for which he is justly famous. It was called 'Academy' after some almost forgotten hero Academus who is said to have once dwelt there.

It is not our purpose to give here a detailed account of the life of Plato. Great as a philosopher, he was not in the strict sense of the term a ' maker of scientific history '. Plato was, however, both a lover and a student of the science of geometry. Indeed he had caused to be written over the door of his Academy, in large capitals, the following inscription :

LET NO ONE PRESUME TO ENTER HERE UNLESS HE
HAS A TASTE FOR GEOMETRY AND THE MATHEMATICS.

Plato's claim to mention in this book lies in the fact that one of his disciples was a youth named Aristotle, whose later teachings were destined to exert a dominating influence over the 'western' world for nearly two thousand years.

Before, however, we pass on to a detailed consideration of the life and teachings of Aristotle, it is as well to note that it is to Plato that we probably owe some of the earliest additions to geometrical knowledge. He shares with Menaechmus the credit for creating the study of conic sections. Hitherto the circle had been the only curve which had been studied. But Plato per-

FIG. 3.   PLATO

ceived that if a cone be cut by a plane under certain conditions, the section obtained took the form of certain peculiar curves, and a little further study assured him that there were only three types of these, which he named the parabola, the ellipse, and the hyperbola.

A much later Greek follower of Plato (Proclus, A. D. 410–485) tells us that to Plato also belongs the credit for inventing that method of mathematical investigation known as 'geometrical analysis'—a process familiar to every school-boy. Given a certain problem or theorem, assume it to be true ; on this assumption deduce step by step a series of logical consequences, until a statement is reached which is definitely known to be true. Now retrace the steps one by one, and the required proof is obtained.

Most great men have their detractors and Plato was no exception to the rule. Thus an unjust charge was that he stole his knowledge from the valuable writings of Philolaus, a Pythagorean, which he had purchased in Sicily. The taunt was made by Timon in the following terms :

> You, Plato, with the same affections caught,
> With a large sum a little treatise bought,
> Where all the knowledge that you own was taught.

There is little doubt, however, that such charges were unjust and without foundation. At all events, whilst his detractors are comparatively unknown, Plato's fame will live for ever.

4. *Aristotle's Early Life*

Aristotle was born in the year 385 B. C. in the city of Stagira, in Macedonia. He was the son of Nicomachus, a celebrated physician of his day, and a favourite at the court of King Amyntas III. His parents died when he was but a youth, and he was left under the careful guardianship of Proxenus of Atarneus, who, recognizing in the lad an inherited taste for philosophy, sent him at the age of seventeen to Athens, knowing that with the ample fortune his father had left him he would be able to pursue his studies without financial embarrassments of any kind.

FIG. 4. ARISTOTLE

Accordingly we find Aristotle entered as a student in Plato's Academy, and here for twenty years he studied diligently, laying for himself the solid foundation for a great career which was to make scientific history. There is a story that his thirst for knowledge was so great that he even denied himself sleep in order to study. Diogenes Laertius tells us that to help him to reduce the amount of his sleep to a minimum, he always placed beside his bed a brass basin, and when he lay down to read and rest, he would hold in his hand extended over the basin a leaden weight. When he was overcome by sleep, the weight would fall from his inert hand, and the sound of its dropping into the basin would immediately awaken him.

Aristotle, so we are told by the same writer, was a young man who, in spite of such disadvantages as an effeminate lisping voice, small eyes, and ' spindle shanks ', took considerable pains over his dress and his appearance. He very soon established himself at the Academy as the most brilliant of a band of young students, all of whom looked up to him, and, it is said, frequently preferred his private opinion in debate to that of Plato himself.

On the death of Plato, in 347 B.C., the leadership of the Academy fell to his nephew, Speusippus, and possibly in consequence of this Aristotle left Athens, accompanied by Xenocrates, a fellow student. They went to Atarneus in Asia Minor, the home of Aristotle's guardian, and there formed a friendship with Hermeias, the remarkable prince ruler of that area, whose niece Pythias Aristotle afterwards married. Hermeias was shortly afterwards killed, and Xenocrates returned to Athens, whilst Aristotle and his wife went to Mitylene. Here they obtained the favour of King Philip of Macedon, at whose invitation our philosopher became tutor to the young prince Alexander, known to history as Alexander the Great.

It is not evident to what extent the Crown Prince was influenced by his tutor, but there can be no doubt about the satisfaction which this intercourse must have given to King Philip, for we read that, out of gratitude and affection for Aristotle, he ordered the latter's birthplace, Stagira, which had been laid in ruins in recent wars, to be rebuilt.

5. *The Peripatetic School*

In the year 336 B.C., King Philip was murdered, and Alexander was called to the throne of Macedonia. Aristotle's duties as tutor accordingly ended abruptly, and after an affectionate leavetaking he returned to Athens. Just at this time the leadership of the Academy had again fallen vacant owing to the death of Speusippus, and Aristotle, who considered his claims to be such as fully to entitle him to the position, found himself passed over in favour of Xenocrates. He therefore started an independent institution. He chose a spot known as the Lyceum, which was attached to the Temple of Apollo Lycaeus, and here he founded his new school. Its success was immediate. He was soon joined by some of the most distinguished members of the Academy, and for the next twelve years he gave himself up to speculations and researches in almost every branch of inquiry— researches the results of which completely dominated the world for the next eighteen hundred years.

At the entrance to the Lyceum there was a covered portico, or ' peripatos ', leading from which was a gravel walk with an avenue of trees, and it was Aristotle's custom to walk up and down this avenue with his pupils, and discuss with them the various problems which presented themselves for study. On this account his school was called the Peripatetic School, and his followers were spoken of as the Peripatetic Philosophers.

In later years Aristotle seems to have fallen foul of King Alexander, the difference arising out of his support of and interest in a distant relative named Callisthenes, who, it seems, had been brought up and educated by Aristotle. As a

FIG. 5. ARISTOTLE TEACHING as conceived by a late 13th-cent. illuminator.

result of his guardian's recommendation, Callisthenes had been accepted as historiographer to Alexander, but instead of playing the part of the polite courtier, he had expressed his real opinions somewhat too freely, and had openly condemned Alexander's attempts to impose upon his Macedonian subjects the worship of himself which he had been able to exact from the conquered Persians.

Alexander resolved to get rid of Callisthenes. He was suspected of being involved in an imaginary plot against the king's life, and was executed. This began, it is said, a period of active enmity between Aristotle and Alexander which only ended with the latter's death in 323 B. C.

Alexander's death was followed by an Athenian rising against the Macedonians, and this brought with it the final downfall of Aristotle. For despite his estrangement from Alexander, the people only remembered his friendly connexions with both the late king and Philip his father, and on a trumped-up charge of impiety against the gods, he was threatened with immediate prosecution. He accordingly withdrew with his disciples to Chalcis, where he remained until his death at the age of sixty-two, in the following year.

Aristotle was twice married, to Pythias, and after her death to Herpyllis, who survived him, and by whom he had a son, Nicomachus, and a daughter. Both marriages were happy, and his last will, still extant, testifies to the goodness of Herpyllis, and to the success of his first marriage by the request that his remains and those of Pythias should be placed in the same tomb. That he died in reasonably wealthy circumstances is also shown by the numerous bequests to his many servants and friends.

After his death it is said that the natives of Stagira, the city of his birth, erected altars to his memory, and paid him the tribute of divine adoration.

6. *Aristotle's Scientific Work and Teachings*

Let us now consider some of the teachings of this great philosopher. Much of his work deals with subjects which lie beyond the scope of this book—politics, ethics, and metaphysics. In all these subjects Aristotle's influence was great. However, we are concerned mainly with his influence in the mathematical and mechanical sciences, although, as a matter of fact, his main contributions were to the biological sciences. Here, indeed, Aristotle excelled, and the care he bestowed upon the tedious task of collection of specimens, and their classification into suitable groups, and the scientific efficiency of his descriptions, are such as to excite our admiration and respect.

What, then, were his teachings? As a preliminary to clear and ordered thinking, Aristotle realized that some scheme of classification of the sciences was necessary, and accordingly

began by adopting two broad divisions—Speculative or Theoretical Science, and Practical Science.   In the first division the
object is to ' know ', in the second the object is to ' do ', or to
know for the purpose of doing.

Aristotle now proceeded to subdivide his first group, Theoretical Science, into three main sub-groups.   The first of these he
called First Philosophy, corresponding to what we now speak of as
Theology, his second group was Mathematics, and his third Physics.
Aristotle's classification of the sciences is given diagrammatically
as follows :

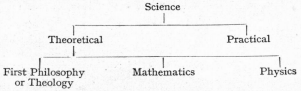

Turning then to his treatment of physics, and using the term
in its broadest sense, we find that Aristotle's pronouncements
contain a remarkable admixture of sense and what must now
appear as non-sense.

He taught that all terrestrial bodies are composed of four
elements—earth, water, air, and fire, although for celestial
bodies he introduced the idea of a fifth element.   That is to say,
he made an absolute distinction between ' celestial matter '
and ' terrestrial matter ', and he claimed as a fundamental
distinction between them that the natural motion of celestial
bodies was always circular, whilst for terrestrial bodies it tended
to be rectilinear.   Again, to talk of terrestrial matter as being composed of four elements implies a variety of possible combinations
and disintegrations within the limits of those four elements.
But not so with celestial matter, for which there was only
a single fifth element.   There could be, therefore, no such thing
as change of any kind in the sun or planets, and no break in
their uniformity.   No wonder, therefore, that it was a rude
shock for the Aristotelians when Galileo's telescope showed
irregularities on the moon, spots on the sun, and variability in
some of the stars.

Aristotle also developed a theory of gravity of a kind. Plato had already attempted such a theory, his idea being that a downward motion was really a motion towards the centre of the earth, and that there existed a tendency for all bodies to be attracted to larger masses of the same material. Hence, for example, a stone 'falls' to the earth, but a 'vapour' rises to the larger masses of vapour above. Aristotle, however, departed from this explanation by insisting on the distinctions between two classes of bodies—heavy bodies, which have a natural tendency to move 'down' towards the centre of the earth, and light bodies, whose natural tendency is to move 'up', and away from the centre of the earth. Further, the heaviest bodies tend to move nearer to the centre of the earth than the less heavy bodies. So, for example, earth being heavier than water, we expect to find the water over the earth, as indeed

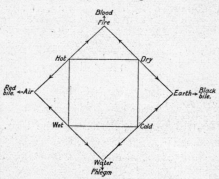

FIG. 6. Aristotelian elements

It should be noted that the addition of the four humours of blood, black bile, red bile, and phlegm was not due to Aristotle, but to the early mediaeval followers of the peripatician.

it is. Both, however, belong to the 'heavy' group of bodies. On the other hand, whilst fire and air both belong to the 'lighter' group, so that their natural tendency is 'up', yet, since fire is lighter than air, we get the air above the water, and the fire above the air and nearest to the celestial regions. This theory had at least the advantage of appealing to the imagination, and it went unchallenged.

Aristotle's treatment of the study of motion was very interesting. We have already seen that he speaks of two kinds of 'natural' motion—circular for celestial bodies, and rectilinear for terrestrial bodies. But confining ourselves to his treatment of terrestrial bodies alone, he classifies motions as 'natural' and 'unnatural'. There was no need for such a classification in the case of celestial bodies, whose motions could, according to Aristotle, be nothing but perfect and natural, so that they persisted in their uniform circular paths for ever. 'Falling' was a natural motion—so much so indeed, that 'falling' bodies were even accelerated, so very natural was this type of motion. 'Unnatural' motions, however, were those that were imposed upon a body by some external agency, and as a consequence, could not persist. Thus if a stone be thrown an unnatural motion is imposed upon it, and this being contrary to nature, the motion speedily diminishes, and the stone again comes to rest. We see here something in the nature of a principle of inertia.

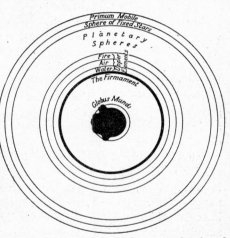

Aristotle's explanation of why falling bodies are accelerated is also extremely interesting. Motion, he says, is caused by something in contact with the body moved. The more persistent the contact

FIG. 7. Scheme of the Universe, as developed by the early mediaeval followers of Aristotle.

the more natural the motion, and the body will even get speeded up. Now, in the case of falling bodies, there is continual contact with the air, which therefore not only causes the motion, but produces an acceleration. From this followed, too, his famous doctrine that the acceleration depends upon the mass of the falling body—the greater the mass, the greater its acceleration, and it is amazing to think that a doctrine so fallacious as to be refutable by the simplest of experiments, held complete sway for centuries. It is a striking testimony to the thoroughness with which his doctrines ruled the civilized world.

To Aristotle is also due the famous statement 'that nature abhors a vacuum'.

Another point worthy of mention with regard to Aristotle's work in mechanics concerns his notions of the ' doctrine of force '. He definitely records, for the particular case when two forces are at right angles, the principle of the parallelogram of ' motions '—regarding the ' motions ' as being caused by forces, somewhat as follows : Supposing two forces, in a given finite ratio to each other, to act upon a body in directions at right angles, then assuming straight lines in those directions to be drawn to represent by their length the intensities of the two acting forces, then if the rectangle be completed, the diagonal will express in direction and quantity the resulting motion.

The value of this lies not so much in the arguments he employs, which are, in fact, of doubtful value, as in the statement itself. Enough has been given of Aristotle's teachings in physics and mechanics to indicate the general nature of his work, and the general trend of his scientific thought. But the reader must again be reminded that only a very small fraction of his teachings, even in the subjects dealt with, has been here included. Of his wonderful work on the study of animals, of his thoughtful discussion on the subject of geological change, and of his researches in embryology, no mention has been made, because space does not permit. Aristotle is, of course, known mainly for his teachings in social ethics and in moral philosophy. These are aspects of his activities with which we are not concerned in this book.

Aristotle lived over two thousand years ago. The history of science in the interval between then and now is studded with the brilliant work of many lives. It would not be untrue to say that the work of many of the pioneers of science has been far superior to the scientific work of Aristotle. Indeed it would even be true to say that in many respects Aristotle's influence was (partly perhaps owing to his ' mis- ' translators) retrograde. But where, throughout the whole of the period between then and now, can we find another case of a single scientist whose influence and whose teachings received such a blind and unanimous acceptance throughout the whole civilized world for so long a time after his death ? The record is truly an astonishing one, and fully entitles our philosopher to a prominent place as a pioneer of science.

II

THE SCHOOL OF ALEXANDRIA

1. *The School's Inception*

AMONG the many military achievements for which Alexander the Great became famous was the conquest of Egypt. This took place while Aristotle was teaching at Athens. Alexander, to commemorate his victories, founded a city on the southern shores of the Mediterranean Sea, and caused it to be named

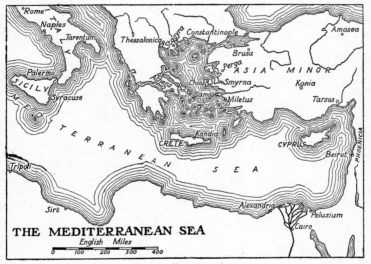

THE MEDITERRANEAN SEA
English Miles
0   100   200   300   400

FIG. 8.

Alexandria. Its success was almost immediate, and in a very short time Alexandria became a populous city and a flourishing port.

Now the death of Alexander was followed by the division of his empire among his more powerful officers, and fortunately for the world's subsequent scientific history, Egypt fell to the lot of one Ptolemy Lagus, who, powerful general though he had been, was also a lover of learning. As a consequence he soon gathered around him a fine band of philosophers and students.

On his death he was succeeded by his son, Ptolemy Philadelphus, who luckily inherited his father's wisdom and taste for learning—so much so, indeed, that he caused to be erected a magnificent block of buildings comprising a library, an observatory, and a school of science, and here philosopher after philosopher received his training. A solid foundation was laid to the study of mathematics and mechanical science, and a spirit of inquiry was fostered such as was unequalled in enthusiasm and achievement until the seventeenth century.

It is not our purpose here to give a connected history of the scientific achievements of those times. It is proposed, therefore, to make a selection of a few of the more remarkable from this Alexandrian School of philosophers, and to offer, as far as is possible in a brief space, a few biographical details in the hope that the reader may be stimulated to further study.

2. *Euclid*

Euclid was one of the great teachers of Mathematics in the Alexandrian School. Unfortunately, history records very little indeed of his life, such details as are available being derived from the writings of the later authors Pappus and Proclus. According to these, Euclid was born in Alexandria somewhere about the year 300 B.C. and he lived in the reign of King Ptolemy Lagus of Egypt. He was the first of a long line of eminent mathematicians, and was the source of inspiration, through the medium of his writings, for such later men as Eratosthenes, Archimedes, Apollonius, Ptolemy, and a host of others. Proclus tells us that Euclid was a man of courteous bearing and agreeable behaviour, and was much liked by King Ptolemy. The king once asked him if there was a shorter way of studying Geometry than by his Elements, and he received the answer ' There is no royal way to Geometry '.

His best-known work is the Elements, in which he presents a complete system of elementary geometry. But it must not be supposed that he was the creator of a system of elementary geometry. Indeed, from the point of view of the mathematical and physical sciences, the development of the study of geometry by a long succession of illustrious philosophers constitutes one of the chief features of the Greek age in scientific history.[1] We have already referred to Thales and the Pythagoreans, and mention should also be made of Hippocrates of Chios (470–400 B. C., not to be confused with Hippocrates of Cos, the father of Medicine), the first-known compiler of a book of ' Elements ', and the discoverer of the theorem that the areas of circles are to one another as the squares of their diameters, through which he introduced to the Greeks the fascinating and insoluble problem of ' squaring the circle ' ; of Eudoxus (408–355 B.C.), who discovered the great theory of proportion which forms the basis of Euclid's Book V, and who was the originator of the well-known ' proof by exhaustion ' ; [2] of Archytas of Tarentum (430–360 B. C.), who addressed himself to the study of the problem of ' doubling the cube ', as a consequence of the finding of two mean proportionals between two given lines, and who greatly advanced the study of the geometry of three dimensions ; of Menaechmus (c. 350 B.C.), who shares with Plato the credit for the discovery of the three conic sections ; and of Theatetus and others.

Euclid's ' Elements ' were therefore, with the exception possibly of Book X, rather in the nature of a ' review of the position '— a linking together of the works of his predecessors into a united whole. His task was splendidly accomplished and, quite apart from the question of the suitability of the presentation of his scheme of geometry to boys and girls for instruction, the wonderful sequence of ordered demonstrations, deductions, and truths, the thoroughness and the clarity which permeate, with one or two exceptions only, the whole of his work, have excited the wonder and the admiration of the whole of the civilized world from his day to ours.

The ' Elements ' consist of fifteen books, but it is now generally recognized that the last two are not Euclid's own, but have been

[1] In this connexion the reader is recommended to read Allman's *Greek Geometry from Thales to Euclid,* Dublin, 1889 ; and the recently published *History of Greek Mathematics* by Sir T. L. Heath (Oxford, Clarendon Press, 1922). [2] See p. 37.

added to the other books, probably by Hypsicles (about A. D. 150); for they are certainly not up to the same standard as the first thirteen. It is probable that the ' Elements ' are a combination of at least two distinct works, for they deal not only with geometry, but also with the theory of arithmetic and its applications to geometry. As is well known, the first four books treat of plane figures, the fifth of magnitudes in general, the sixth of the proportion of plane figures, the seventh, eighth, and ninth of the fundamental properties of numbers, the tenth of the theory of commensurable and incommensurable lines and spaces, and the remainder of the theory of solids.

There are weaknesses here and there, and of course in schools there are now taught systems of geometry more suited to the needs of boys and girls. Nevertheless as a philosophical scheme of geometry, Euclid still remains unchallenged.

Euclid gave great prominence to the problem of ' squaring the circle '. That is to say, to draw by geometrical methods a square equal in area to a given circle. The problem arose from the famous demonstrations of the proportionality of the areas of circles to the squares of their diameters, and of the volumes of spheres to the cubes of their diameters. The point is of interest from the fact that this problem so attracted the attention of the mathematically inclined of those days as to give a refreshing and in many respects fruitful stimulus to the study of mathematics in general and geometry in particular.

Euclid clearly saw the relationship between geometry and arithmetic—that is to say, between the properties of plane figures, lines, &c., and the numerical figures representing their dimensions. Thus, for example, it is well known that a right-angled triangle may be drawn whose sides are $3''$, $4''$, and $5''$. It is proved geometrically that the square (i. e. the actual rectilineal figure known as a square) on the hypotenuse is equal in area to the sum of the squares on the remaining two sides. But it is also obvious that the corresponding relationship is true with regard to the numerical figures representing these lengths, namely, in the example chosen above,

$$5^2 = 4^2 + 3^2 :$$

It is much to Euclid's credit that he fully grasped the significance of this, that he generalized the problem, and that he realized to what important developments he could extend this idea.

Plato, it is interesting to note, is credited with having found the general rule by which such a relationship could be found between whole numbers. Let n be any number, then we always have the three whole numbers. $2n$, n^2-1, and n^2+1 such that

$$(n^2+1)^2 = (2n)^2 + (n^2-1)^2$$

so that any triangle whose sides are drawn proportioned to these numbers *must* be right-angled.

Euclid's thorough treatment of the comparison of areas, based on his famous Proposition 47 of the First Book (originally the invention of Pythagoras) led naturally to an attempt to express the areas of curvilinear figures in terms of rectilinear figures, and a proper appreciation of this is necessary if the true significance of Euclid's work is to be realized. For we find here the first applications of the idea of 'limits'—and of course the study of 'limits' may fairly be regarded as the starting-point of what we vaguely speak of to-day as 'higher mathematics'.

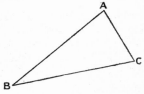

Fig. 9. Euclid's Proof by Exhaustion.

The simplest case of limits is seen in the well-known method of proof by 'exhaustion' discovered by Eudoxus [1] (fourth century B.C.). As an example take the proof of the proposition that 'the angle opposite the greater side is greater than the angle opposite the lesser'. Omitting all preliminaries, and referring to the figure, in which AB is given greater than AC, Euclid says 'The angle B must be either greater than, equal to, or less than the angle C'. He states *every* possibility, and then proceeds to consider each in turn.

Using, for the sake of brevity, the usual mathematical symbols, he says:—First suppose $\angle B > \angle C$.

$\therefore$ By the previous proposition, side $AC >$ side AB.

But this is impossible, by hypothesis.

The choice is accordingly narrowed down.

[1] See p. 35.

Secondly, suppose $\angle C = \angle B$.

$\therefore$ the triangle is isosceles, and $AC = AB$.

This again is impossible.

He has exhausted all the possibilities except one.

In other words, *he has approached the limiting case*, and the only remaining possibility must be true.

The principle of superposition, so beautifully developed by Euclid, is bound up with his treatment of the comparison of areas, and we will give just one further example of Euclid's use of the idea of limits—the case of the circle—before we pass to another of the great Alexandrian School of philosophers.

If a regular polygon—say a pentagon—be inscribed in a circle,

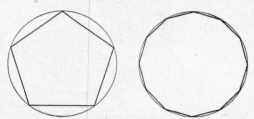

FIG. 10. Application of Idea of Limits to Area
of a Circle.

it is obvious (*a*) that the perimeter of the pentagon is less than the circumference of the circle, and (*b*) that the area of the pentagon is less than the area of the circle. Further, the differences are relatively considerable in each case.

But suppose we inscribe instead a regular polygon of many more sides—say twelve. Statements (*a*) and (*b*) above remain true, but the differences are now much smaller than before.

It is seen that the more we increase the number of sides of the inscribed polygon, the more nearly does the figure coincide with the circle, so that the polygon will in the limit become the circle. Euclid clearly realized, however, that the limit can never actually be reached (a very important point) but can only be approached more and more closely by continually increasing the number of sides in the inscribed polygon.

3. *Archimedes*

The name of Archimedes stands out as one of the most illustrious of the philosophers of the Alexandrian epoch. From the point of view of the mathematical and physical sciences, he ranks superior to Aristotle, for while the latter propounded doctrines and theories which, long dominant as they were, have now been more or less completely abandoned, the discoveries and doctrines with which the name of Archimedes is associated are being taught in schools to this day. His record is a standing example of the true greatness which may be achieved by a life devoted to one particular branch of scientific study. In the history of Mathematics and Mechanics, Archimedes deserves a very high place indeed.

Fig. 11.   ARCHIMEDES

We know very little of his life. He was possibly a contemporary of Euclid, and was born in the city of Syracuse, in Sicily, about the year 287 B. C., at a time when Hiero was its king. He received his education at Alexandria, probably under Euclid himself, and this is an interesting testimony to the fame which the School of Alexandria had achieved. For a journey from Sicily to Alexandria, particularly for a youth such as Archimedes must have been at that time, was no light undertaking. It was a very different thing from travelling as we know it to-day, having regard to the size and type of the ships of those days.

Archimedes very quickly established a reputation, and his future career became clearly marked out for him. He returned to his native city, and here he stayed for the remainder of his life, devoting himself whole-heartedly to study, experiment, and research.

Archimedes is best known for his work in hydrostatics and mechanics, but his work in the field of pure mathematics is equally important and praiseworthy. Working from the consideration of the subject of limits so ably begun by Euclid, he found a means of obtaining the areas of figures bounded by some of the conic sections. As an example let us consider his treatment of the parabolic surface ABC. If we inscribe in it the triangle

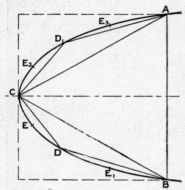

ACB, and if in the segments which it leaves we inscribe triangles CBD and ACD_1, then it is known that the combined area of CBD and ACD_1 is equal to one-quarter of the triangle ABC.

Again, if in each of the four smaller segments now left, triangles CDE, DBE_1, &c., be inscribed, the sum of the areas of these four triangles is one-quarter of the sum of the former two triangles. Suppose we continue this process. The next set of eight triangles have

FIG. 12. Archimedes' Evaluation of the Area of a Parabolic Surface by Method of Limits.

a united area one-quarter of the previous four, and so on. Obviously, in the limit, we shall have completely covered the area of the original figure with sets of triangles such that if we represent by 1 the area of the triangle ABC, then the area of the whole figure will be represented by the sum of the series

$$1 + \tfrac{1}{4} + \tfrac{1}{16} + \tfrac{1}{64} + \tfrac{1}{256} + \tfrac{1}{1024} + \&c.$$

taking in an infinite number of terms.

Now Archimedes knew that the sum of this series ' to infinity ' works out to exactly $\tfrac{4}{3}$, and so he deduced that the area of the parabolic curve in question must be four-thirds of the area of the triangle ABC, or what is the same thing, two-thirds of the area of the circumscribing rectangle.

This is only one, of course, of many similar investigations for which we are indebted to Archimedes. One of his most celebrated demonstrations was as to the famous relationship between the surface areas and volumes of a sphere inscribed in an equilateral cone, and a cylinder circumscribing a sphere. To Archimedes, too, is due the well-known evaluation of π, the ratio of the circumference of a circle to its diameter. Actually, his investigation proved that this ratio was less than $3\frac{10}{70}$ and greater than $3\frac{10}{71}$ to 1.

The curve known universally as Archimedes' Spiral was undoubtedly developed by him, but the original idea appears to have been suggested to him by his friend Conon. This curve may be defined as the locus of a point which moves uniformly towards or from the centre of a circle along its radius, at the same time as the radius revolves uniformly. Thus in the figure, let OA be the rotating radius. Consider successive eighths of its length. As the moving point in succession reaches these positions, marked 1, 2, 3, 4, &c. along the radius, the line OA is itself revolving, and taking up the positions 1, 2, 3, 4, &c., round O. The construction for drawing the curve is therefore obvious, and may possibly afford the reader some amusement.

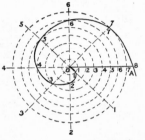

FIG. 13. The Spiral of Archimedes.

4. *Archimedes' Teachings in Mechanics*

Turning from the activities of Archimedes in pure mathematics to those in mechanics, we come upon another rich field of investigation. This is particularly the case in that branch that we speak of as statics, or the study of forces in equilibrium. His outstanding discovery is the principle of the lever. ' Give me ', said he, ' where to stand, and I will move the earth.' His line of reasoning, beginning with the truth that two equal masses suspended at the ends of a uniform rod suspended at its centre will balance each other, is flawless in its logic and accuracy ; and from this he proceeds to a careful study of centres of gravity, and works out a number of standard cases.

But perhaps the most famous of Archimedes' discoveries are those which deal with hydrostatics, a subject which had been somewhat neglected by his predecessors. The story of the discovery of what is now generally called the Principle of Archimedes, namely, that a solid body when immersed in a liquid ' loses ' a portion of its weight equal to the weight of the liquid it displaces, has many different versions, of which the following is one.

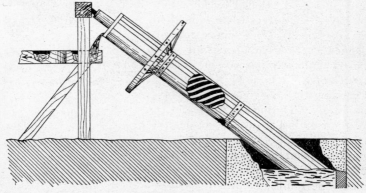

Fig. 14. The Screw of Archimedes.

It seems that Hiero, the King of Syracuse, intended to make an offering to the gods of a golden crown, and he accordingly engaged an artificer skilled in such matters to fashion one, the king supplying the gold for the purpose. In due course the crown was finished and delivered. The weight was found to be correct, but for some reason, the artificer came under suspicion of having appropriated some of the gold for himself, substituting for it an equal weight of silver. To Archimedes, therefore, was entrusted the task of discovering whether this suspicion was justified.

Archimedes was a very absent-minded man. So absorbed was he at times in the problems which interested him that he would frequently lose all sense of his immediate surroundings. He was in such a fit of abstraction one day over the problem the king had set him when he went to his bath, and he did not notice at first that the bath was full to the brim with water. He went in, and the first inkling of the fullness of the bath came when the water overflowed ; like a flash the full significance of its meaning came to him. He could not contain himself for excitement, and forgetting in the absorption of his enthusiasm that he was both wet and naked, he jumped out of the bath, and ran through the streets shouting ' Eureka ! Eureka ! ' (I have found it ! I have found it !)

As a matter of fact, his discovery was twofold and led later to his very able work on floating bodies. He saw first that when a body was immersed in a vessel of liquid, it displaced its own bulk of liquid, and secondly, that its ' loss ' in weight was equal to that of this displaced ' bulk ' of liquid.

He now saw how to tackle the problem he had been set. He obtained two balls, one of gold and one of silver, each weighing the same as the crown. He noticed that the two balls were of different sizes, because gold is heavier than silver, so that less of it would be required to make up the same weight as the silver. But he could tell this exactly by taking a basin of water, and noting the height of the water in it, and then immersing say the gold ball. The water rose by displacement, and he marked the new level. He now took out the gold ball and placed in the basin the silver ball. The water now rose *higher* than before owing to the silver being lighter, and occupying more room, and he noted the new level. Finally, he took out the silver ball and inserted the crown. The level of the water was now higher than for the gold, but lower than for the silver, thus proving that the crown was made of material lighter than gold and heavier than silver. Clearly, it contained both gold and silver, and the artificer stood condemned. Further, by making a series of balls of gold and silver mixed, all of the same weight as the crown, but each containing different proportions of gold to silver, and immersing each in turn, Archimedes was able to find one which would cause the water to rise to the same height as obtained in the case of the crown, and so he was able to say exactly how much gold had been stolen.

Archimedes was gifted with much mechanical skill, and this taken in conjunction with his theoretical knowledge, enabled him to devise many ingenious contrivances, one of the most famous of which was a form of pump known as the Cochlea or 'Screw of Archimedes'. This simple device was in effect a pipe twisted in the form of a corkscrew. It was held inclined with one end dipping below the water to be pumped up. It was then made to revolve about its axis, thus drawing the water up at each successive winding of the 'screw' until it came out at the top.

He is also reputed to have made a sort of glass model of the universe—a sphere of glass through which the heavenly bodies could be seen in motion—presumably by revolving the sphere on its axis. The truth of this is doubtful, though it is asserted that he ordered a record of it to be engraved on his tomb, together with his discoveries concerning the geometrical properties of the sphere and cylinder.

The poet Claudian wrote an epigram on this reputed invention, of which the following is a translation :

> When in a glass's narrow space confin'd,
> Jove saw the fabric of th' almighty mind,
> He smil'd and said : Can mortal art alone
> Our heavenly labours mimic with their own ?
> The Syracusan's brittle world contains
> Th' eternal law, which through all Nature reigns,
> Fram'd by his art see stars unnumber'd burn,
> And in their courses rolling orbs return.
> His suns through various signs describe the year,
> And every month his mimic moons appear.
> Our rival's laws his little planets bind,
> And rule their motions with a human mind.
> Salmoneus could our thunder imitate,
> But Archimedes can a World create.

Another contrivance with which Archimedes has been credited was an arrangement of 'burning-glasses', or mirrors, which he caused to be trained on to the hostile Roman Fleet then lying outside the harbour, but there is considerable doubt as to the truth of this.

These were troublous times for Sicily. The Roman power was then in the early days of its expansion, and Marcellus was Consul at Rome. The siege of Syracuse with which is associated the latter days of our philosopher occurred during the second Punic war. Reference has already been made to the absent-minded reveries into which Archimedes permitted himself to sink, and it was this which, unfortunately, cost him his life. The story is well known.

In spite of all the heroism of the besieged people, and of all the mechanical skill and ingenuity of their great philosopher, Syracuse at last fell, taken by storm in the year 212 B. C. Marcellus, in recognition of the respect due to the fame of Archimedes, had given strict orders that his life was to be spared, and that he was to be accorded due honour. But alas, the attack took place at a moment when Archimedes was engrossed on a geometrical problem for which he had traced a figure on the sand. A common soldier rushed up, and demanded his name. He was told to be gone and not to spoil his circle, whereat the soldier slew him.

If this story can be trusted, it is literally true, therefore, that Archimedes died 'in harness'—he was the scientist to his last moment.

Many of his works are lost, but the following list of those of which we know speaks for itself : Two books of the Sphere and Cylinder—The Dimensions of a Circle—Of Equiponderants, or Centres of Gravity—Of Spheroids and Conoids—Of Spiral lines—The Quadrature of a Parabola—Of the Number of the Sand—Of Bodies that Float on Fluids.

It is difficult to give adequate praise to the brilliant qualities of this great man, and we will conclude merely with the opinion that his work and record amongst the ancients may justly be likened to the achievements of Newton in later times.

5. *Ptolemy*

As a final example of the great philosophers of the Alexandrian period, we now proceed to an account of the life and works of Claudius Ptolemaus, or Ptolemy, as he was more commonly called. He was no relation to the line of kings who founded the famous school, Ptolemy being in fact quite a common name of the period. He was born about a hundred years after Christ

FIG. 15. CLAUDIUS PTOLEMAUS and BOETHIUS
Imaginative portraits by RAPHAEL
See note on p. 14

at Pelusium, in Egypt. The Alexandrian school had by that time passed through many vicissitudes. Egypt had become a province of the Roman Empire, and for a long time the study of science had received a serious set-back. The Roman taste lay more in the direction of poetry and moral philosophy and the study of law. But a revival came later with the advent of the Emperor Marcus Aurelius Antoninus, who, luckily, was of a philosophical turn of mind. A fresh impetus was now given to scientific study and research, and a new band of thinkers picked up the loose threads in the web of knowledge and began to weave them anew. Ptolemy, Diophantus, Pappus, and Proclus all belonged to this period, and each in his own way added renewed lustre to the glory of Alexandria.

Ptolemy is known to fame chiefly as an astronomer. Astronomy had been sadly neglected for the previous three hundred years, the last work of any importance having been done by Hipparchus, who in particular had compiled a valuable star catalogue. Ptolemy revived the study. He collected the works of Hipparchus and his predecessors, and built out of them a complete celestial system which, based as it was on Aristotelian doctrines, received blind and undisputed acceptance for centuries. We speak of it to-day as the Ptolemaic System, and it was set forth in detail in a great work called the ' Great System ', originally written in Greek. It was translated by Arabian astronomers under the title 'Almagest' (al = Arabic for *the*, magest = Greek *megiste*, greatest), and it is by this name that it is usually known nowadays. (The Latin translation was many centuries later than the Arabic, and was first made from the Arabic.)

At the root of his theory are the teachings of Aristotle, to which we have already referred, that the motions of the celestial bodies are ' perfect ', and that the most perfect type of motion is circular. It is almost tragic to think that Ptolemy made his teaching to fit this theory, for there is no doubt that with all the ability and originality displayed by him in his writings, the history of astronomy would have made very different reading but for the influence of Aristotle on his premises.

The earth, said Ptolemy, was a sphere, and was at the centre of the universe, and was immovable. His arguments as to why the earth is spherical were perfect, and are much the same as are taught in schools to-day ; there was nothing in the teachings of the peripatetic philosophers to prevent this. But for the rest, he was indeed blinded by their teachings, which included the doctrine that lighter bodies move more slowly than heavier ones. This being so (notice he did not say, ' If this were so '), he argues that if the earth were to move, the loose bodies upon it, including of course the air, being lighter than the earth would be left behind, which obviously was not in fact happening. Hence he satisfied himself that the earth was immovable. But if the earth is immovable, and is spherical in shape, then indeed it must be poised in space. We can imagine with what wonder and delight Ptolemy reached this striking conclusion. But the remainder of his theory followed almost automatically from the Aristotelian doctrines of motion in a circle.

As a matter of simple observation, the sun and moon and stars were seen to rise in the east and set in the west daily. The explanation by relative motion due to the earth's rotation could

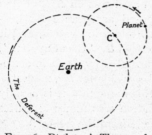

not even enter into the argument, since it had been shown that the earth was immovable. Therefore the celestial bodies were in motion, and their motion being 'perfect' they must be moving in circles round the earth, for the absolute uniformity with which the stars were seen to move could only be possible if the earth were the centre of their rotation.

FIG. 16. Ptolemy's Theory of the Motion of Planets.

Ptolemy was a careful observer of the heavens. His observations did indeed appear to bear out his theory. But the movements of those stars which had long been known as the planets, or wanderers, could not be so easily explained. Ptolemy, with that blind faith in the fundamental assumptions in his theory, therefore sought out some other scheme of circles which would answer the purpose of explaining these more complicated motions. He hit upon the idea of the planets revolving in a circle round a *moving* centre *C* (Fig. 16), this centre having, in fact, a circular orbit about the earth. This circular orbit he called the *deferent*, and by a careful choice of dimensions, this did in fact explain sufficiently approximately the variable motions (in some cases, as is well known, retrograde in the skies, instead of 'forward') of the planets, of which five only were known in those days. It is not necessary for us here to go further into the details of this theory. Readers who are sufficiently interested will have no difficulty in obtaining all the information they desire from astronomical text-books. Sufficient has been said to enable the reader to appreciate the fertile genius of Ptolemy in presenting to the world a complete and self-contained theory as to the structure of the universe.

There is, however, one point of interest which we must here interpose. Some four hundred years before Ptolemy's days there had flourished a Greek philosopher named Aristarchus of Samos, whose great achievement was the putting forward of a theory that the *sun*, and not the earth, was the centre of the universe, and that the earth revolved round the sun in a circular orbit. Here was something almost approaching the truth, ' in a nutshell ', yet unfortunately it met with no favour. The voice of the Aristotelian school was too strong, and so the views of Aristarchus were lost. Many centuries were to pass before they were destined to be revived by Copernicus.

Ptolemy's activities were not confined to astronomy,

FIG. 17. PTOLEMY as conceived by GIOTTO.

and he greatly distinguished himself as a geographer. The book he wrote on this subject was indeed, for centuries afterwards, the standard work on the subject. It contained maps of all the known parts of the world, and described countries as far apart as India, China, and Norway. Our own country was described under the name of Albion. Lines of latitude and longitude were marked on his maps, calculated on the basis of rules devised by an earlier geographer of great fame, named Eratosthenes, and the whole book indicates clearly the patient student and the diligent scientist.

To Ptolemy is also ascribed—perhaps wrongly—a work on

Optics.   The chief feature of this book is a valuable inquiry into the subject of refraction.   There is no doubt that in this pursuit he was actuated by a desire to understand and allow for the influence of this phenomenon in the displacement of the heavenly bodies from their real positions, but whatever his motive, the results were invaluable.   Actually, Euclid was the real pioneer of the study of light, and was responsible for the statement that light travels in straight lines.   Ptolemy went much farther.   He carefully worked out the angles of refraction corresponding to all angles of incidence from 0° to 80° for rays from air to water, and from air to glass, and from these results he built up a theory of astronomical refractions which worked out very well indeed in practice.   He did not, however, deduce a generalized law of sines such as we all use to-day.

According to Gauricus, one of the commentators on his life, Ptolemy died in the seventy-eighth year of his age.

6. *Last Days of Greek Science*

We have so far confined ourselves to special examples of the great thinkers of the Alexandrian School, but before leaving this subject we must draw attention to a few other names of those who contributed to the greatness of this later phase of Greek scientific history.   Thus we have the celebrated Apollonius of Perga (265–190 B.C.?), probably contemporary with Archimedes, whose researches on conic sections carried the subject far beyond the point at which it had been left by Plato and Menaechmus ; Ctesibus and his contemporary Hero of Alexandria, who were both successors of Archimedes in their study of such various mechanical appliances as the forcing pump, the air-gun, the water clock or clepsydra, the siphon-fountain, &c., and the theodolite ; and Posidonius, who wrote on the tides and interested himself in the subject of atmospheric refractions.

But with the Roman ascendancy the period of intellectual decline was now definitely in evidence.   Great as were the Romans in war, social ethics, literature, and above all perhaps in law, they were emphatically not scientists.   The scientific activity which recommenced with the advent of the Emperor Marcus Aurelius Antoninus did not persist, and beyond such isolated exceptions as the astronomer Gallus, the historian Pliny, the geographer Strabo, and the physicist Seneca (whose *Naturalium quaestionum libri VII* was used as a text-book throughout the Middle Ages), we come upon a rather barren era.

In the study of mathematics the record is a little brighter, for with this era is associated the famous name of Diophantus, often referred to as the founder of the study of Algebra.   He lived probably early in the fourth century A. D. and he greatly enriched the world by his refreshing methods of analysis.   He was preceded by Pappus, a geometrician of great power, whose misfortune it was to be surrounded by a people in whom the taste for geometry was seriously on the decline, and was followed by Theon (*c.* A. D. 370) and his daughter Hypatia, both able commentators of the fifth century.

Finally we must mention Boethius, the great Roman writer of the sixth century, who formed the main link in the slender chain which connected up mediaeval science with the Greek ages.   He was essentially a commentator, contributing nothing original (except perhaps in music), but writing on the mathematical sciences as he knew them from his studies of the original Greek sources.

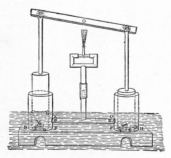

FIG. 18.   'A Fire Engine.'

III

ROGER BACON

I. *Science in the Middle Ages*

THE history of science in the Middle Ages makes but sorry reading. It was, so far as science is concerned, a period of ignorance, misunderstanding, and neglect. The decline of the Roman Empire brought with it an inevitable decay in the Alexandrian School. The influence of Greek learning gradually faded. Then came the final fall of the Roman Empire, and with it the last flickerings of philosophical inquiry in Europe came to an end.

But although the light of learning had left Europe, it had not left the world altogether. For it now began to burn brightly in the East. The Nestorians, Moors, Jews, Syrians, and other Arabic-speaking peoples [1] had always exhibited a leaning towards scientific inquiry, and when later the military hordes of the Mohammedan rulers pushed their conquering way into Spain and northern Africa, these peoples knew better than to destroy the valuable records which they found. Instead they translated many of these works into their own language, and derived therefrom an encouragement to further inquiry which brought many fruitful results. Foremost among the Arab leaders responsible for this enlightened policy we may mention the Caliphs El-Mansour, Haroun El-Raschid, and El-Mamoun in the eighth and ninth centuries A. D. It was the last of these, in fact, who ordered in A. D. 827 the translation to be made of Ptolemy's great work into Arabic which passed under the title of the 'Almagest'.

---

[1] The Arabs themselves were not philosophers, as is popularly supposed, and what is spoken of as Arabian learning is attributable almost entirely to subject peoples under the Arabs who wrote in the Arabian language, and it is through this fact that the misconception has grown up.

Accordingly, during this period, we read of a number of Arabian philosophers pursuing their researches diligently in Astronomy, Mathematics, Physics, and Alchemy (that ' mystic' forerunner of chemistry), and making valuable contributions to the world's knowledge in these subjects.   In particular mention should be made of the great Moorish philosopher Alhazen, who flourished in Spain in the eleventh century, and who produced well-known

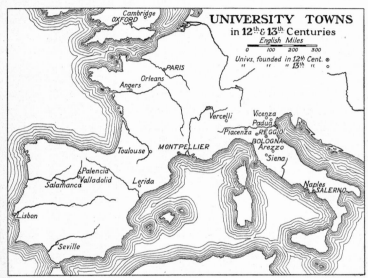

Fig. 19.

works on Optics (he tells us of lenses, or rather segments of glass spheres, and their magnifying powers) and Geometry.

Meanwhile, as we have already pointed out, Europe had sunk to its lowest depths of intellectual ignorance and inertia.   There were no original writers, and very few readers.   Such very little learning as existed was confined to the clerics.   At most it comprised a few bad Latin translations of the writings of Aristotle, together with the works of Pliny, and the teachings in these books were accepted without question.   Such records of other ancient teachings as survived were relegated to the unused shelves of the monastic libraries. From one point of view this was fortunate, for, in an era of tumult and disorder, the monasteries were at least regarded as sacred ground by all parties, and so the records were saved from an otherwise inevitable destruction.

The effect, however, of this scientific activity of the Arabic-speaking peoples was to stimulate a few of the more enlightened men of the West to curiosity. As a consequence, the books of the ancients were taken down from the shelves of the monastic libraries, and they were studied anew, and the men who shared in this now became the pioneers of a new movement of restoration. Amongst these should be mentioned Gerbert, a monk from the Netherlands, who in the tenth century journeyed to Spain, to acquire at first hand the wisdom of the Moors. Under the title of Silvester II he afterwards became pope, and the story of his life appears as a ray of light in a world of darkness.

The first real signs of a return to intellectual activity in Europe was the establishment in various centres of the institutions known as universities. This began in the twelfth and was at its height in the thirteenth century. To these universities students and teachers began to gravitate in increasing numbers. All the European nations were represented, and Latin was the universal language employed. One of the most famous of these universities, particularly from the point of view of science, was at Paris, where, although it had long before been the seat of some considerable learning, a university was constituted in the year A. D. 1101. The favourite studies pursued at these universities were almost entirely theology and metaphysics, and the prevailing influence was of course Aristotelian. There was no attempt made to seek out new truths, or to question old dogmas, and the blind worship of the Peripatetics was general throughout Europe.

It was in such a world, and in such an atmosphere, that there was born, to the glory of England and of science, a man destined to rise superior to his times. As herald of a new era of inquiry and activity the memory of Roger Bacon, visionary and scientist, will live for ever.

2. *The State of Philosophy in the Dark Ages*

It will help us to appreciate the value of Roger Bacon's scientific record if we review the general position in which philosophy found itself in the eleventh and twelfth centuries. So far as the problem of the nature of the universe, and of man's place within it, is con-

cerned, the governing views were those laid down by Plato in his *Timaeus,* as translated by Apuleius and commented upon by Chalcidius, and included that central doctrine around which practically the whole of mediaeval science was built—that of the 'macrocosm and microcosm'. This doctrine taught that man's fate was governed by a completely knowable interplay of the forces of nature and character. The microcosm, man, reflected the macrocosm,

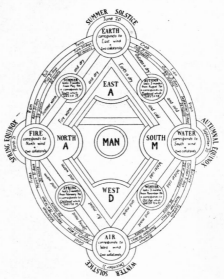

Fig. 20. Byrhtferth's Microcosm and Macrocosm.

the world around him, and the problem which presented itself to the 'dark age' and 'mediaeval' philosophers was the manner and the extent of this reflection, and the study of this subject was known by the name of 'astrology'. Having derived the problem from Plato, the development of it was largely governed by Aristotle's views as to the structure of the universe. The later Greek philosophers taught that for the cause of changes in bodies on the earth below, one had to look for parallel changes in the heavens above. They held that such *regular* alternations as that of night and day,

winter and summer, growth and decay, were governed by the
regular movements of the stars in circles ; whilst on the other
hand the many variable and less predictable elements of daily
life and experience were governed by the *irregular* planetary
movements.   Writer after writer elaborated on all this, until
the position by the end of the tenth century was very much as

FIG. 21.   Leaf from a 7th-cent. Greek MS. believed
to have been used by Grosseteste.

is shown in the figure on p. 55, after Byrhtferth (*c.* 1000).
The reader will notice from this figure how the Aristotelian
doctrine of the four elements had become incorporated in this
scheme.

    This, then, was the position and the standpoint of the world
of philosophy in those days, and it will be noticed that the
astrology which grew up from it, and at which we are nowadays

somewhat hastily wont to scoff, was a perfectly natural and inevitable outcome of the times. It was destined later to degenerate into a charlatanism which was to bring it into deserved disrepute, but in the early Middle Ages it was a pure philosophy, and as such must command our respectful attention.

We have mentioned how the spirit of learning, slowly and haltingly, began to revive when Graeco-Arabic culture began to percolate through into Europe ; and by the thirteenth century,

FIG. 22. A Scribe at work.

during what is known as the ' scholastic period ', a new spirit was beginning to assert itself, fostered by such people as Alexander of Hales (*d.* 1245), Robert Grosseteste (*d.* 1253), Albertus Magnus (1193–1280), and St. Thomas Aquinas (1225–74). The universities had by now been firmly established, the Greek language was beginning to be studied, and the scientific works of Aristotle were becoming more accessible.

For the development of this new spirit much credit is due to a group of Franciscan Friars who, headed by the great Robert Grosseteste, afterwards Bishop of Lincoln, studied and wrote upon

mathematics, optics, natural philosophy, literature, and the
foreign and ancient languages. It was as a member of this band
that Roger Bacon did much of his work, and so to him and his
labours we now turn.

3. *Roger Bacon*

Roger Bacon was born near Ilchester, in Somersetshire,
probably in the year 1214, and appears to have belonged to
a wealthy family of ancient and honourable descent, whose
members later sacrificed their fortunes in the cause of King
Henry III in his struggle with the Barons from 1258 to 1265.
He began his studies at home at the early age of thirteen years,
and then proceeded to the University at Oxford. Here he
attended the lectures of Edmund Rich (subsequently Archbishop
of Canterbury), on Aristotle, and he quickly asserted himself as
a young student of unusually brilliant qualities. Whilst at
Oxford he came under the influence of another of Rich's pupils,
Robert Grosseteste. Grosseteste had made a careful study of
the Greek language, having had the advantage of intercourse
with a Greek monk, and at his promptings Roger Bacon also
sought to learn this language, and so to gain access to a wealth
of scientific literature which must have stood him in excellent
stead in his later career. One of the great claims of Roger on
our memory is the attention that he drew to the importance of
getting good texts of the existing scientific works translated
direct from the Greek.

Following the fashion of the times, Bacon passed on from
Oxford to Paris, then the premier university of Europe and the
centre of attraction for the intellectual world, and he had here
a most distinguished career.

He returned to Oxford in 1250, and embarked upon an extended course of study and research over a very wide field. He
pursued his investigations far beyond the stage in which he found
his subjects, which were accordingly greatly enriched by his
labours. He spent, he tells us, no less a sum than two thousand
pounds in the course of twenty years on books, instruments, and
apparatus—a prodigious sum, having regard to the value of

money in those days, although as a matter of fact much of this sum was contributed by his friends and admirers.

During this period he was undoubtedly at the height of his fame. But fame brings with it its penalties. There were those who envied Bacon, and there were others who were even ready to do him injury, particularly after the death in 1253 of his most influential patron, Bishop Grosseteste. It must be remembered

Fig. 23. ROGER BACON with a pupil taking observations from a window.

that Bacon lived in a very ignorant age. The real students were few indeed—the quacks and pretenders many. The Church was the dominating influence of the time, and looked askance at the practice of what were vaguely termed the ' magical arts'. It was this fact which was seized upon by Bacon's traducers as their opportunity to encompass his downfall.

One can well understand that it was easy for these people to persuade the men who ruled in the Church of that day how closely allied to the practice of magic was the use of retort stand and crucible. Unfortunately, too, Friar Bacon had written of the clergy with more candour than tact. He had spoken freely of their ignorance and their want of character, and had even gone so far as to write to Pope Innocent IV on the subject of the necessity for a reformation. These were hardly the writings which his enemies would peacefully receive, but Friar Bacon, like so many other pioneers of science, was a conscientious thinker, and he had the courage of his convictions. Indeed, it is contended that his motive in embracing a monastic life was to obtain such increased leisure for research as to enable him to achieve discoveries that would be ' of the highest consequence to the honour and peace of the Church '. For, he continued, ' the surest method of extirpating all heresies, and of destroying the Kingdom of Antichrist, and of establishing true religion in the hearts of men, is by perfecting a true system of natural philosophy '.

As a reward for his pains, Bacon found himself inhibited from lecturing to the students of the University by command of the General of the Franciscan Order, Bonaventura the ' seraphic ', as he was afterwards called. Later, in 1257, he was sent to Paris and was kept in close confinement at the Franciscan house near the Porte Saint-Michel. Here he stayed, under strict surveillance, for ten long years.

There seemed at first but little possibility of his release, but, after a few years, Bacon heard that there had been sent to England a papal legate, one Guy de Foulques, a man who for his time was singularly broadminded. Guy had heard of the great philosopher, and this, added to the fact that his political tendencies in England were on the side of King Henry III and against the Barons, brought him into sympathetic contact with Bacon's family.

In 1265 Guy de Foulques was elected Pope under the title of Clement IV, and Roger, when he heard this news, saw at last opportunity of release. Knowing the new Pope's philosophical tendencies, he sent him a petition in the course of which he proposed ' out of a reverence due to his high dignity, which ought to engage him in seeking to procure the benefit of the whole world, he was willing, as far as the impediments he laboured under would permit, and his memory would allow, to deduce a regular system of true philosophy to the utmost of his power '. His offer fell on willing ears, and in the year 1266 the Pope wrote to his ' beloved son, Friar Roger named Bacon, of the Order of the Friars Minor ', inviting him to send, with all speed, a copy of his works.

Roger Bacon set to work on his self-imposed task. To appreciate its magnitude, we must remember that he was a prisoner, and that for years he had been without instruments, with probably very few books, and without the assistance of expert copyists. His only materials were his excellent memory and his indomitable courage. In the space of eighteen months he produced the three large treatises on which the main part of his reputation is based. They were called the *Opus Maius*, the *Opus Minus*, and the *Opus Tertium*, respectively. They gained him his long-sought release. In the year 1268, after an absence of over ten years, Bacon was at last permitted to return to Oxford.

A fresh period of fruitful intellectual activity now set in for our philosopher, and in 1271 he produced the first part of an encyclopaedic work called *Compendium Studii Philosophiae*. His freedom was, however, doomed to be once more limited. Bacon always had his enemies, and the well-known friendliness of the Pope to him was his only safeguard against attack. But unfortunately, Pope Clement IV died very soon after, and the storm clouds of biased and jealous ignorance once more gathered. Once again Roger was arraigned on the charges of meddling with the magical arts. He was tried by the new General of the Franciscans, Jerome de Esculo. His writings were again condemned, and he was once more imprisoned in the Franciscan house in Paris. This was in the year 1278.

Bacon was now sixty-four and obviously less able than before to endure the rigours of confinement. He was again cut off from the opportunity of experiment and research, though possibly he was permitted access to books. It speaks much, therefore, for his courage and perseverance that during the fourteen years of this second confinement he continued to write books on a wide range of philosophical subjects.

Bacon was released in 1292. He was now an old man, but he was by no means broken. He returned to Oxford, to the college of his Order, and wrote his last great work, a Compendium of Theology. He spent his last days in peace and died in the

FIG. 24. AN ALCHEMIST AT WORK, by Pieter Breughel, 1558.

eightieth year of his age, on the 11th of June 1294. He was interred in the Church of the Franciscans, all trace of which has since vanished.

' Of this son of Oxford, who with his " almost prophetic gleams of the future course of science " had only a Pisgah sight of the promised land of long deferred discovery, we may say that " no man knoweth of his sepulchre unto this day ".' [1]

4. *Bacon's Scientific Writings*

Bacon's writings have come to light but slowly. With his death his books appear to have been suppressed, though luckily not destroyed. One of the earliest to be printed (at Paris in 1542) was a treatise *On the marvellous power of art and nature*, a book that was perhaps responsible for the accusations of ' magic' which were hurled at him during his life. One can imagine the effect on his contemporaries of the following striking passages which we reproduce from an old translation.

' First, by the figurations of art, there may be made instruments of navigation without men to rowe them, as great ships to brooke the sea, only with one man to steere them, and they shall sayle far more swiftly than if they were full of men ; also chariots that shall move with unspeakable force, without any living creature to stirre them. Likewise, an instrument may be made to fly withall if one sit in the midst of the instrument, and doe turne an engine, by which the wings, being artificially composed, may beat the ayre after the manner of a flying bird. . . .

' But physicall figurations are farre more strange : for by that may be framed perspects and looking-glasses, that one thing shall appeare to be many, as one man shall appeare to be a whole army, and one sunne or moone shall seem divers. Also perspects may be so framed, that things farre off shall seem most nigh unto us.'

When it is remembered that this was written in the thirteenth century, and that some of those ' visions' Bacon saw then have only achieved reality in the twentieth century, one may realize how far ahead of his times he must have been.

By many educated people Bacon is best remembered for his supposed connexion with the invention of gunpowder. There

---

[1] John Sandys, *Roger Bacon*, British Academy, vol. vi, 1914.

is no doubt that he was a close student of the subject of alchemy, the forerunner of chemistry. Alchemy was a serious business in his days. It was a study largely developed by the Arabians, and may be said to have had a twofold object—the transmutation of all metals into gold, and the search for the elixir of life. John Freind, a seventeenth-century scientist and student of Bacon, claims that the Friar succeeded in discovering a tincture of gold for the prolongation of life.

With regard to gunpowder, we find the following passage in his *Secrets of Nature and Art* : ' From Salt Petre, and other

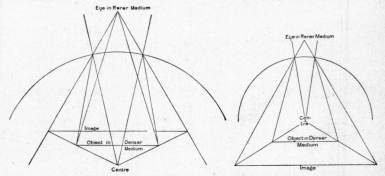

Fig. 25. Diagrams of Roger Bacon to illustrate optics of lens.

ingredients, we are able to make a fire, that shall burn at what distance we please.' Then again later :

' That sounds like thunder, and corruscations, may be formed in the air, and even with greater horror, than those which happen naturally ; for a little matter, properly dispersed, about the bigness of a man's thumb, makes a dreadful noise, and occasions a prodigious corruscation, and this is done in several ways ; by which a city, or an army, may be destroyed after the manner of Gideon's Stratagem, who having broke the pitchers and lamps, and the fire issueing out with an inexpressible noise, killed an infinite number of the Midianites.'

There is no doubt whatever, in view of these passages, that Bacon must have been fully aware of the formula for the composition of gunpowder, and such a formula has been found in a cryptogram in his work.[1]

[1] See A. G. Little, *English Franciscan Studies*.

Bacon was not a mathematician in the highest sense of the term, that is to say, although he made himself familiar with the subject in so far as it had then been developed, he made no original contributions to it, his interests being rather in the direction of its applications. Nevertheless, he had a true perspective of its value, on which he never ceased to write, and he referred to it as ' the gate and the key ' of all the other sciences.

Bacon, too, was skilled in astronomy, though he followed the universal rule of his day which regarded the movements of the stars as affecting the lives of men. He was, in fact, a believer in astrology, and he even held that the origin of religions depended

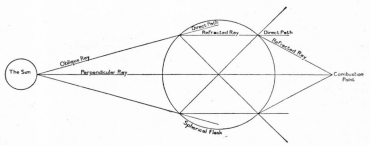

FIG. 26. Diagram of Roger Bacon to illustrate optics of burning-glass.

upon the conjunction of the planets. Yet in spite of the fact that we now know astrology to be nonsense, the superiority of Bacon as an astronomer over his contemporaries is indisputable.

Finally we come to Bacon's work in ' Opticks '. Here again there is no doubt of his brilliance. There is ample evidence that he was acquainted with the properties of lenses and spherical mirrors. The extract given below speaks for itself. It comes in a part of his *Opus Maius*, where he is discussing the angle subtended to the eye by the image of an object as viewed through a refracting plane or spherical medium. He applies to this discussion such cases as the crooked appearance of an oar in water, and again he describes how a piece of money in the bottom of a basin which is concealed by the rim may be made visible by pouring in water, and he discusses why the sun and the moon appear larger when near the horizon. He then proceeds as follows :

'If the letters of a book, or any minute objects be viewed through a lesser segment of a sphere of glass, or crystal, whose plane base is lade upon them, they will appear far better and larger. Because by the fifth canon about a spherical medium, its convexity is towards the eye, and the object is placed below it, and between the convexity and its centre, all things concur to magnify it. For the angle under which it is seen is greater and its image is also greater, and nearer the eye than the object itself ; because the object is between the centre and the eye ; and therefore this instrument is useful to old men, and to those that have weak eyes ; for they may see the smallest letters sufficiently magnified.'

Here clearly we have an attempt at the theory of spectacles, and we find in fact that the adaptation of lenses for use as spectacles was certainly an invention of his time.

Great controversy has raged around the question of whether or no Bacon knew of the telescope. The consensus of opinion is on the whole against the view that Bacon actually made or invented such an instrument. Nevertheless, his writings show that he was at least aware of the possibilities of lens combinations, such as have produced in later times both microscope and telescope. It shows how very far ahead of his times this great man lived and thought, for remember that it was actually not until the seventeenth century that the telescope was effectively constructed, and first turned to the skies by Galileo.

We have tried to impress upon the reader some real idea of the state of ignorance with which Bacon was surrounded, and without this it is impossible to do adequate justice to his memory. Bacon stands out as a bold champion of inquiry, experiment, and observation, and his life was a lasting protest against the 'trammels of prejudiced authority' which hindered progress in science and learning.

There is a general idea prevalent, and it finds encouragement in most commentaries on Bacon's life and work, that his efforts were wasted owing to the intellectual inertia of those around him. This view is, however, unfair and incorrect. 'Bacon was not an isolated phenomenon, but an important link in the chain of scientific development.'[1] For example, his pupil, John Pecham,

[1] See Little's *Studies in English Franciscan History*, Manchester, 1917, pp. 220–1.

lectured to the Franciscans at Oxford; Herber, also a lecturer there, carefully collected all Bacon's manuscripts; we find evidences, in the shape of 'school' copies of the *Perspectiva*, that this work was authoritative in the fourteenth and fifteenth centuries, and looking still farther ahead, both Columbus and Copernicus, through intermediary writings, were influenced by Bacon.

All honour, therefore, is due in these days to the man who, in the words of a great Oxonian, ' was perhaps the first of the long list of the victims of ecclesiastical persecution, and is associated with that illustrious band of patriots in the republic of letters and science who maintained the cause of intellectual and moral liberty against the odious encroachment of spiritual despotism.' [1]

IV

COPERNICUS

1. *The Revival of Scientific Inquiry*

WE have seen how the thirteenth century brought the first faint signs of the return of a spirit of inquiry. Slowly but surely this spirit developed, halting no doubt when it came into antagonistic contact with the accepted theological views of the time, but nevertheless gaining in impetus, until it attained a culminating pitch of brilliance in the seventeenth and eighteenth centuries.

One science there was which, even in the darkest days of ignorance and neglect, was never completely abandoned—the science of astronomy. And we need not go far to seek the reason for this. Astronomy was essential for the determination of the

[1] Baden Powell, in his *Historical View of the Physical and Mathematical Sciences*. See also articles by R. R. Steele and by C. Singer in *Studies in the History and Method of Science*, vol. ii, ed. C. Singer, Oxford, 1921.

dates of the Church festivals, the accurate celebration of which was a matter of great importance in mediaeval days. Moreover, bound up with the ignorant superstitions of the Middle Ages was a profound belief in the art of astrology. This art, sister to the science of astronomy, was regarded as being the more important of the two. Indeed, the value of astronomy was often measured solely by the assistance which astronomical observation could render to the astrological art. Later, when the claims and pretensions of astrologers had been exploded and their exponents held up to ridicule, this untenable system brought a measure of discredit upon the more legitimate science, but in the earlier days there is no doubt that much of the stimulus to astronomical inquiry was due directly to the superstitious interest in astrology.

Throughout the whole of this period the influence of Ptolemy in astronomy and of Aristotle in other departments of science was always paramount. Their teachings were brought into further prominence with the invention of the art of printing about the middle of the fifteenth century. Two names in particular are associated with these Ptolemaic teachings—they are George Purbach and his famous pupil, John Müller, of Königsberg (= King's hill), better known by his Latin pseudonym of Regio-montanus [1] (= King's mountain). Purbach was professor of astronomy at the University of Vienna about 1450, and he realized the necessity for an accurate translation of Ptolemy into Latin. He died before this project was very far advanced, but his pupil and admirer, Regiomontanus, carried on and completed the work. There is no doubt that this philosopher had serious doubts as to the truth of Ptolemy's fundamental statement that the earth was fixed, immovable, and the centre of the universe, but, in refraining from openly challenging it and working from it to its logical conclusion, he lost a great opportunity.

It was left for a quiet but thoughtful cleric to do this, and to begin for the world a new era of philosophical belief. As a conse-quence Nicolas Copernicus will go down in scientific history as the man who accomplished a revolution in astronomy by the final and complete overthrow of the Ptolemaic doctrine.

[1] The practice of the learned in latinizing their names was natural in view of the fact that they wrote in Latin.

2. *Nicolas Copernicus*

Nicolas Copernicus was born in the town of Thorn on the Vistula at the Prussian frontier, on the 19th of February 1473. His father, also named Nicolas, was a successful tradesman, and his mother was a sister of Lucas Watzelrode, afterwards Bishop of Ermeland, a relationship which turned out later to be a very useful one for the subject of our study.

Little is known of the childhood and early youth of Copernicus. It appears that his early education, chiefly in the Latin and Greek languages, was undertaken at home, but as soon as he was sufficiently proficient to profit thereby, he proceeded to the University of Cracow with the object of training for the medical profession. He soon discovered in himself a natural liking for mathematics and natural philosophy, and it was not long before he was working just as hard at these subjects as at medicine. His mathematical studies carried him into a discussion on the theory of perspective, and as a consequence he also became an able draughtsman.

FIG. 27. NICOLAS COPERNICUS

Having graduated at Cracow as doctor in both arts and medicine, Copernicus, after a short stay at his home in Thorn, proceeded first to Bologna, where he came under the influence of the astronomer Domenico Maria Novara, and then, at the age of twenty-three, to Rome, which was ringing with the name of Regiomontanus. Here Copernicus rapidly established himself as an earnest mathematician and astronomer, and it was not long before he experienced the signal honour of being instituted, before a full assembly of doctors and great men, professor of mathematics in the University of Rome.

Rome did not keep him at her University for very long, for his uncle, Lucas Watzelrode, Bishop of Ermeland, gratified at the position achieved by his nephew, invited Copernicus to return to his own country, and take up a canonry at the cathedral of Frauenberg. Before doing this, however, Copernicus went to the University of Padua, at whose medical school he studied till 1505.

He did not proceed immediately to Frauenberg, but resided first at the episcopal palace of Heilsberg as his uncle's physician. His early days here were none too comfortable. As so often happens when a man obtains a position by influence his presence was resented by some. But his natural gentleness, his love of peace and quiet, and his obvious scholarship soon had their effect, and on his appointment after his uncle's death to the canonry of the cathedral of Frauenberg he found himself in peaceful possession, honoured and respected. His daily routine was characteristic of the man. It was made up of three ' activities '—devotional exercises and the diligent performance of his divine offices, the tending of the sick poor who required his medical assistance, and the employment of all his spare time in philosophical study and meditation.

There were occasions when the peace and solitude of his daily routine were not permitted to Copernicus. He was occasionally called into consultation by those in charge of the affairs of the State. He had been chosen by the College of Canons as their representative in the State Assembly at Grodno, and although he never went out of his way to disturb the ordered scheme of his daily life, he never attempted to deny the State the benefit of his wisdom and learning when called upon to offer them. The following example is of peculiar interest in connexion with certain post-war problems. The many wars in which the country had become involved had considerably diminished the value of money, and had in consequence created much financial and economic distress among the people. The Diet was greatly concerned about this, and a committee of Senators were appointed to investigate the matter, but they had to confess themselves beaten. They appealed, however, to Copernicus for his advice and opinion. He accordingly drew up a rule for reducing to a definite standard all the various kinds of money then in circulation throughout the provinces of the kingdom, and this was immediately adopted by the Senate and inserted in its public Acts.

3. *Copernicus as an Astronomer*

Nicolas Copernicus is known primarily as an astronomer. He gave to the study of the heavens all the time he could spare from his normal duties. His instruments were few and poor, but this did not dishearten him. He proved himself a most patient and painstaking observer, utilizing his slender resources to the best of his ability. The modern observatory is equipped with a telescope known as a transit instrument. This is mounted on two massive pillars and can only swing in one vertical plane—the plane of the meridian, which is defined by a great circle passing through the north and south points and the point overhead ('zenith'). This is the plane which the sun crosses approximately at twelve noon. Sooner or later, in the course of every twenty-four hours, all stars cross this meridian, and the exact time at which this happens for any particular star is an important determination in astronomy. Copernicus had no transit instrument—telescopes were not yet invented—and so he arranged slits in the walls of his home through which, by suitably placing himself for observation, he could note the 'transit' of the stars across the meridian. Further, he measured the altitude of these stars above the horizon, at the moment of 'transit', by means of a quadrant which he devised, and which he set up in front of the slits or apertures mentioned.

Copernicus was soon attracted to a careful study of the motions of the planets. He recorded all his observations, and the tables of planetary motions which he compiled therefrom were easily the best of his times, and remained in general use for long afterwards. Of more importance than these tables was the train of thought to which his observations of the planets led him, for from it was gradually evolved that theory of the solar system universally referred to to-day as the Copernican System.

It is a matter of some interest to all students of science and of human nature to ask themselves the question, with regard to any important discovery, invention, or theory, ' What started the train of thought which led to the final achievement ? ' The answer is usually interesting, and frequently surprising. An accident, a dream, an apparent speck of dust in an instrument, the falling of an apple from its tree—how remarkable may be the results when these small things and simple occurrences are experienced by genius !

Rheticus, friend, pupil, admirer and commentator of Copernicus, tells us that the whole of his master's speculations arose from his observation of the planet Mars. He was profoundly impressed by the fact that its brightness and its magnitude varied so very considerably at different times. Now, according to the Ptolemaic System, unquestionably accepted, the earth, fixed and immovable, is the centre of the universe, and the sun and the planets revolve round the earth. If the reader refers back to Fig. 16 he will recall that according to Ptolemy the planets move round the earth in epicyclic orbits—that is to say, the planets move in circular orbits round a point C, which itself moves round the earth in a circular path known as the ' deferent ' circle. A planet, therefore, is not at a constant distance from the earth, but the variation is not very great. Copernicus felt very definitely that the marked variations in brightness and magnitude which he observed in Mars and in the other planets were out of all proportion to what might be expected from the Ptolemaic doctrine of the universe. Now Copernicus knew from the literature of the ancients of a theory of the solar system put forward by the distinguished Greek philosophers, Pythagoras (572–497 B.C.) and Aristarchus (310–230 B.C.), according to which the sun, and not the earth, is the centre of the universe, the planets, including the earth, revolving round the sun annually, and rotating about their axes diurnally. The teachings of Pythagoras and Aristarchus became completely submerged under the flood of the Aristotelian and Ptolemaic doctrines which formed the staple scientific material of succeeding ages. So the truth had laid hidden in obscurity for about two thousand years, till Copernicus again brought it to light. Let there be no misunderstanding about this all-important fact. Copernicus did not create the system which bears his name. He knew that its fundamentals had been given out to the world by Pythagoras, but the world had not listened.

Copernicus revived this theory, and so supported it with argument and exposition as to force its acceptance. Thus began a new era in scientific thought.

How did Copernicus work out his theory? Pondering over Ptolemy's writings, he was first struck by the somewhat laboured claim that with the earth immovable and fixed, the whole of the vast expanse of the heavens, with all the stars, sun, and planets, are carried completely round the earth every twenty-four hours. If there were no alternative explanation, Copernicus, too, would perforce have accepted it as true, but he realized clearly the elementary facts of relative motion. Thus, he instanced, when a ship is moving parallel to the shore in smooth water, to a person on board, the ship appears to be at rest whilst the objects on the shore move past the ship in the opposite direction from that of the ship's real motion. Scores of similar examples will readily occur to the reader.

Similarly, therefore, the daily movements of the heavenly bodies could be explained by supposing that it is not the celestial sphere which is rotating, but the earth which is rotating once in twenty-four hours in the opposite direction. Here were two alternatives. Which was the more plausible? Surely the simpler of the two, and so Copernicus definitely rejected the clumsy idea of a gigantic universe revolving round the earth. It remained for him to consider what logical consequences must follow from his acceptance of the other alternative.

To appreciate properly the frame of mind into which Copernicus had been drawn, the reader must again be reminded that the doctrines of Aristotle and Ptolemy were still paramount everywhere, and that it was tantamount to heresy to question even a single utterance of the great Greek philosopher. If Copernicus had not, so to speak, ' caught them out ' on one point, he probably would not have attempted to question any other point. Now Aristotle had taught that the earth was ' fixed, immovable, and the centre of the universe '. Copernicus had satisfied himself that, on the contrary, the earth was neither fixed nor immovable, but that it was rotating in space on its own axis. He, therefore, would be naturally led to ask himself, ' If Aristotle was wrong in stating that the earth is fixed and immovable, perhaps, too, he was wrong in declaring it to be the centre of the universe.' His observations on the varying brightness of the planet Mars

Fig. 28. AN ASTROLABE of 1574.

strengthened his doubts, and his reading of the Pythagorean view evidently settled them once and for all.

We find, then, after eighteen hundred years of unbroken rule, the first great departure from the teachings of Aristotle. The sun, declared Copernicus, is the centre of the solar system. Round it at varying distances revolved the planets, and these also rotated about their axes. Yet even with Copernicus the Aristotelian influence was strong. He made no attempt to break away from the ' circle-worship ' of the Greek philosopher, and said that the planets moved in circular orbits round the sun. Where observation showed a planet's motion to be inconsistent with this in its irregularity, he freely introduced Ptolemy's device of a ' deferent ' circle, and, indeed, before very long a complicated scheme of epicycles grew up, keeping pace in its increase of complexity with every improvement in observation, and it remained for Kepler in the next century to sweep all this away and substitute for it the simple ellipse.

The great achievement of Copernicus was, therefore, that he ' put the earth in its proper place ' in the cosmical scheme of things, and that although, as we shall see later, his suggestions were made with much timidity, he was the first to break away from the ' Aristotle-worship ' which had impeded scientific progress for so many centuries.

4. *De Revolutionibus Orbium Caelestium,* 1543

The book in which Copernicus stated and proved his theory that the sun is the centre of the solar system was published in the year of his death, 1543. It was called *The Revolutions of the Celestial Orbs,* and its publication was undoubtedly a landmark in scientific history. Yet we know that Copernicus began his speculations on the subject thirty years before this, and that the book had been practically completed by about 1530. Why, then, was there a delay of thirteen years in the publication of the book ? The story is very interesting and characteristic of the times in which Copernicus lived.

We have already referred to the strong hold of the Church upon the people of those days. Nothing could exceed the rigidity of its outlook or the iron of its discipline in those days, and its notion of the exalted place and functions of mankind in the universe demanded unquestioned recognition that the home of man, the earth, was fixed, immovable, and the centre of the universe. There is little doubt that if Copernicus had been anything but the retired, unobtrusive student and churchman, that if he had shouted his views from the house-tops, and had, as we sometimes put it nowadays, ' rushed into print,' his book would have been seized and destroyed, his views condemned, his teachings suppressed, and he himself punished. But Copernicus did not seek fame, and only those with whom he came into contact could gather, from direct conversation and discussion, the trend of his thoughts and his views.

There was, however, another factor of importance which made for delay in publication. Copernicus was himself a canon of the Church, and he was, moreover, deeply religious. As a true man of science he was above the narrow prejudices of his colleagues, but nevertheless he was strongly influenced against publication by his knowledge of the great offence it would give. His was too modest and gentle a nature easily to override such a consideration, and it accordingly took many years of earnest persuasion on the part of his friends and admirers before a reluctant permission to publish was drawn from him.

FIG. 29. TYCHO BRAHE

Justice to Copernicus demands that we should point out that there was in him no element of fear in the statement of his views. He dedicated his work to the Pope, Paul III, in a preface which concludes in the following terms :

'If there be some who, tho' ignorant of all mathematics, take upon them to judge of these, and dare to reprove this work, because of some passage of Scripture, which they have miserably warped to their purpose, I regard them not, and even despise their rash judgement. . . . What I have done in this matter, I submit principally to your Holiness, and then to the judgement of all learned mathematicians. And that I may not seem to promise your Holiness more concerning the utility of this work than I am able to perform, I pass now to the work itself.'

There is some irony, let us note in passing, in the fact that this eulogy, which greatly pleased Pope Paul III, was succeeded

FIG. 30. TYCHO BRAHE, in 1587, with his astronomical instruments
See note on p. 15

eight years later by a similar eulogy to his successor, Pope Sextus, in a preface to a Latin edition of Ptolemy's *Almagest*, and was received by the latter with equal pleasure.

The manuscript was entrusted by Copernicus to his friend and pupil, Rheticus, who took it to Nuremberg, where some years before he had printed a treatise by Copernicus, *Concerning the Sides, and Angles of Triangles, Planes, and Spheres.* Here the book was printed, and a copy was sent to the illustrious author. But while it was yet on its way, Copernicus, at the age of seventy years, was smitten by a paralytic stroke which rapidly weakened him. The book, the fruits of his life, arrived but a few hours before his death, on the 23rd of May 1543.

We may fittingly conclude this brief note on his life and work by a mention of the fact that in his early days Copernicus painted his own picture—a half-length portrait. This picture was given later to the famous astronomer and poet, Tycho Brahe, who placed it in his museum at Uraniborg over an inscription of which the following is a translation :

> Phoebus no more his bounding Coursers drives
> Sublime in Air ; the task to Earth he gives.
> Amidst the world enthron'd he sits in State,
> And bids the Heav'ns obey the Laws of Fate ;
> Yet thro' all Nature is his Aid the same,
> And changing Seasons still his Guidance claim.
> Erratic Stars have now their Courses known,
> By this rare System of the station'd Sun ;
> They stand, go retrograde, are swift, or slow,
> Just as the Earth directs them what to do.
> The great Copernicus (the Man behold),
> This heavy Orb in rapid Motion roll'd.
> But why, you'll say, was not his Wit portray'd ?
> But that is partly in the Heav'n display'd,
> Partly in Earth ; for neither can confine
> The boundless Searches of his daring Mind.
> Again you'll say—But half his Figure 's shown,[1]
> A Man so worthy to be wholly known.
> True ; yet 'tis he who bore the earth entire
> Thro' Space immense around the Solar Fire ;
> The spacious Earth in vain would hold the Man
> Who measures Heaven with his ample Span.

[1] Referring to the fact that the portrait was only half-length.

V

JOHANN KEPLER

1. *Early Life*

KEPLER'S chief claim to memory lies in his enunciation of the laws of planetary motion. The record of this faithful follower of science is remarkable. The whole of his life is one long story of domestic trouble, ill-health, and financial worry. Yet through all he displayed a genius and an enthusiasm for mathematics and astronomy which led him to the highest pinnacles of scientific achievement. Kepler was denied the joy of astronomical observation. In his youth a serious illness had permanently injured his eyesight. Telescopes and other instruments of observation were for him ' forbidden fruit '. He conquered, but his victory was won in the battlefield of geometry and statistics with the aid of his calculations, his drawing instruments, and above all his wonderful perseverance in the face of repeated failure.

FIG. 31.
JOHANN KEPLER

Johann Kepler was born at Weil in the Duchy of Würtemberg on the 21st of December 1571. His father, though probably of good family, was idle and unreliable; his mother ignorant and of violent temper. Moreover, Johann was a sickly child; and an attack of small-pox, which nearly killed him at the age of four, left him with an enfeebled constitution.

He went to a local school at a very early age, but it was not long before the first check to his studies appeared. It seems that his father had become surety for a friend who proved to be a defaulter. As a consequence he lost what little money he had and was obliged to keep a tavern. So we see the sorry spectacle of a future professor of astronomy withdrawn from school at the age of nine and employed as a pot-boy in his father's inn. For three years this state of affairs continued, but eventually, owing to the kindly intervention of friends, young Johann Kepler was enabled to attend a monastic school at Maulbronn. The ability which he displayed enabled him to be passed on, at the age of seventeen, to the University of Tübingen, where it was intended that he should prepare himself for the Church. Fortunately for the world, he here came under the influence of Michael Maestlin, then professor of mathematics at the university, who soon detected Kepler's genius.

Maestlin was an outspoken convert to the Copernican doctrine of the solar system, and in this doctrine Kepler may therefore be said to have been brought up. Its simplicity made a powerful appeal to his imagination, and he was its vigorous defender in lecture and debate. All this helped to build up for him a considerable reputation, so that when, in 1594, a professorship of mathematics fell vacant at the University of Graz, in Styria, it was immediately offered to Kepler, who accepted it with some hesitation. From the point of view of pay and prestige, astronomy was none too highly rated in the universities of those days, and the professors were expected to devote more time to the revelations of astrology than to anything else. It was because of this fact, and because of his bitter recollections of the acute poverty of his childhood that Kepler was so diffident in accepting the professorship, and he fully made up his mind that when anything better offered itself he would accept it.

2. *Kepler's Early Theories*

In 1597, at the age of twenty-six, John Kepler wooed and married a lady from Styria. It is not known whether he thought that, with her 'dowry' she might have eased his financial position, for she had been twice married before. Be that as it may, it proved none too happy a union. There were three children of the marriage, and Kepler's financial cares were on the whole considerably increased in consequence.

At Graz, he busied himself with speculations as to the general scheme of the solar system. There were at the time six known planets—Mercury, Venus, Earth, Mars, Jupiter, and Saturn, and Kepler knew that these were at successively greater distances from the sun. Moreover he knew that the farther a planet was from the sun, the slower seemed its motion. It was Kepler's strong feeling that there was in all this some governing scheme. The unravelling of this problem he made his life work. His final efforts were indeed crowned with brilliant success, but his first theory, developed at Graz, was fantastic. He was a keen student of geometry, but his mathematics, in those days of astrology, were not unnaturally tinged with mysticism. Between six planets there are five spaces, and for some reason or other Kepler felt that this held the clue which he sought. The five spaces led him to think of the five symmetrical solid figures— the tetrahedron, the cube, the octahedron, the dodecahedron, and the icosahedron, with four, six, eight, twelve, and twenty faces respectively. Accordingly his scheme took the following form. Beginning with a sphere to represent the earth's orbit, he drew round it a dodecahedron, and round this another sphere to represent the orbit of Mars ; about that a tetrahedron, and around that a larger sphere for Jupiter ; about that a cube, and round that a final sphere for the orbit of Saturn. Again, returning to the sphere representing the earth's orbit, he drew within that an icosahedron, and inside that another sphere for Venus ; inside that an octahedron, and finally inside that a sphere for the orbit of Mercury.

Kepler's delight is well worth recording. ' The intense pleasure I have received from this discovery can never be told in words. I regretted no more the time wasted ; I tired of no labour ; I shunned no toil of reckoning, days and nights spent in calculation, until I could see whether my hypothesis would agree with the orbits of Copernicus or whether my joy was to vanish into air.'

Kepler published his theory (as to the absurdity of which it will suffice for us to point out that we now know of eight large planets and a host of planetoids) in 1596 in a book called

Mysterium Cosmographicum, and it brought him the enthusiastic applause of a wondering world. Of more immediate importance to Kepler, however, was a cordial invitation which he now received from a man at Prague who was destined to affect his whole future career. This man was the famous Tycho Brahe.

Tycho Brahe may justly be termed the pioneer of accurate astronomical observation. He was a Dane of noble family, and had created in 1576 with the co-operation of his King, Frederick II, a wonderfully equipped observatory at Uraniborg Castle, in the Island of Hven, near Elsinore. Here he laboured for twenty years, accumulating the most complete records of planetary observations thus far existing. Naturally his success brought him enemies, and when Frederick died in 1596, his successor was induced to withdraw his patronage from Tycho, who accordingly retired to Prague, in Bohemia. Here, under the patronage of Rudolph II (who, as befitting the times, valued his services as an astrologer rather than an astronomer) he continued his wonderful record of observations.

To Kepler, then, Tycho extended a cordial invitation to come to Prague and test his fantastic theory with the observations in Tycho's possession. Tycho was not a follower of Copernicus but he nevertheless had sound advice to offer Kepler. ' Do not build up abstract speculations concerning the system of the world,' he advised, ' but rather first lay a solid foundation in observations, and then by ascending from them, strive to come at the causes of things.'

Kepler paid his visit, studied the records, and did not hesitate to abandon his theory when he realized it was not consistent with the accurate observations he knew himself to be handling. But he had earned the respect of his host, and when his professorship at Graz was rendered exceedingly uncomfortable owing to a religious change in the régime of the University, Kepler (who was a Protestant) gladly accepted in 1601 the offer of a post as imperial mathematician to King Rudolph II, his duty being to assist Tycho Brahe. This was a wonderful combination of talents. Tycho was a splendid observer, but a poor mathematician, Kepler was a splendid mathematician but a poor observer ; both had unbounded enthusiasm for their work and admiration for each other. What might they not have achieved together had the alliance continued ! But it was not to be. Tycho had never recovered from the disappointment of his dismissal from Uraniborg, and he died soon after Kepler joined him.

3. *Kepler as Physicist and Geometer*

All this time, Kepler was in continuous financial straits, and periodically he was seized with illness. Tycho's generosity had tided him over his troubles, but at his colleague's death they broke out afresh. Bohemia was in a sorry state at that time ; misgovernment and wars had brought the national exchequer to a low state and Kepler's salary was more often promised than paid. Yet he stuck to his post. A solemn duty had been entrusted to him by Tycho on his deathbed. Tycho, engrossed in the preparation of an elaborate set of planetary tables, had charged Kepler to complete them, and they were to be known as the Rudolphine Tables, in honour of his patron. They entailed enormous work and considerable expense. The latter consideration involved such delay that Kepler perforce had time to devote to other matters.

In 1604, he published a work called *Paralipomena in Vitellionem*,[1] in which the question of refraction came up in connexion with the theory of lenses. The telescope had but recently been invented, and Kepler clearly saw the necessity for such investigations. He tried to work out a relation between the angle of incidence and the angle of refraction. All schoolboys know of Snell's Law, which says that the ratio of the sine of the angle of incidence to the sine of the angle of refraction is a constant for any given pair of media. For glass, for example, this ratio, known as the refraction index, comes out somewhere about 1·5. Kepler did not discover this law, though there is no doubt but that his work inspired Snell to take up the subject so successfully. He did, however, discover a useful approximation to it. In the

---

[1] Vitello was a thirteenth-century Polish philosopher who commented on Alhazen and studied the subject of refraction.

case of glass, *when the angle of incidence is small*, he found the ratio of the angle of incidence to the angle of refraction is almost always about 1·5. Thus in the figure (Fig. 32) the angle of incidence, measured in radians, is the ratio arc $\dfrac{Ip}{IO}$, whereas the sine of this angle is the ratio perpendicular $\dfrac{IP}{IO}$, and it is at once evident that provided the angle i is small, there will be little difference between the arc Ip and the perpendicular IP. Similarly, of course, for the angle of refraction $\hat{r}$. The approximate truth of Kepler's rule is therefore established. For the purpose which Kepler had in view, namely the application of the subject to the case of the telescope, the rule as he stated it sufficed, for (as shown in Fig. 33) an object P viewed through such an instrument will necessarily involve only a small angle of incidence.

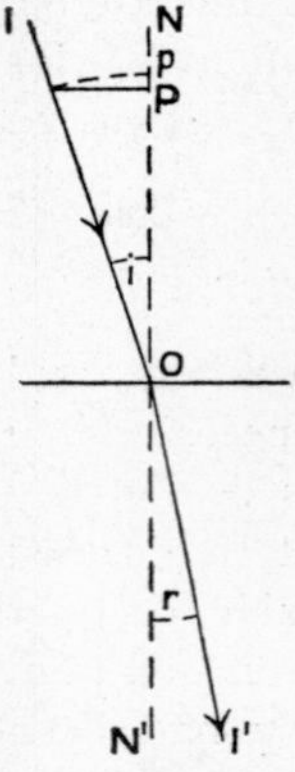

FIG. 32. Showing Kepler's approximate Law of Refraction for Glass.

Kepler also studied atmospheric refraction, and greatly improved on the treatment of this subject by Ptolemy. He worked out an approximate formula to allow for this error for all angles from 0° to 90°.

FIG. 33. Illustrating the application of Kepler's Rule of Refraction to the Telescope.

It is convenient at this stage to do homage to Kepler's great influence on his contemporaries in the realms of mathematics, and particularly in geometry. This branch of mathematics had suffered some neglect at the expense of a great advance in algebra, the theory of equations, and trigonometry. The seventeenth-century revival in geometry was largely due to the influence of Kepler. In chapter 4 of his *Paralipomena*, for example, he introduced to the world of mathematics for the first time what has been called the *principle of continuity*.

As an instance of this, he regarded the circle as a special case of the ellipse. For, keeping the major axis AA' (Fig. 34 (a)) of constant length, suppose we construct a series of ellipses with the two foci SS' (Kepler was the originator of the term ' focus ') successively closer together, we find that the minor axis becomes longer and longer, making the ellipse resemble the circle more and more closely, until we reach the limiting case in which the foci coincide with the centre, when the curve becomes a circle.

We have another example when we regard the parabola as continuous with the ellipse. This is seen by keeping A and S (Fig. 34 (a)) fixed, and gradually moving the other focus S' and the extremity A' farther and farther to the right. In the limit, when S' is at an infinite distance to the right, the curve becomes a parabola.

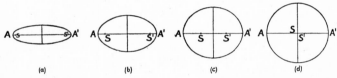

(a)   (b)   (c)   (d)

FIG. 34. Kepler's Principle of Continuity. The circle as a special case of the ellipse.

In 1615 Kepler published a book called *Stereometria*. He was led to some investigations on the volumes and areas of certain solid forms through noticing by accident the blunders made by an ignorant gauger in measuring his wine casks. Kepler submitted a large number of solids for the solution of geometricians, only solving a few himself. It speaks much for his influence, however, that these suggestions were at once taken up by others. Kepler, in his own solutions, introduced the idea of infinitesimals as an application of the law of continuity. This was really a simple extension of the method of limits in vogue as far back as the days of Euclid and Archimedes, but it had far-reaching consequences later, for it paved the way to the invention of the calculus by Newton and Leibnitz. By way of illustration of Kepler's introduction of the term ' infinitely small quantity ', a single case will suffice. He regarded a circle as being made up of an infinite number of triangles all with vertices at the centre O (Fig. 35) and with infinitely small bases on the circumference. The sum of the areas of the infinitely small triangles gives the total area of the circle, whilst the sum of the lengths of the infinitely small bases gives the length of the circumference.

4. *Kepler's Later Life*

Meanwhile Kepler's financial worries and domestic miseries were continual. His salary was always in arrears, and it was with difficulty that he could make both ends meet. His wife was suffering from long fits of despondency, and finally, in 1612, a series of misfortunes produced a crisis in his affairs. His patron, King Rudolph, died, and his salary now ceased. But worse was to come. Within a very short time, all his children fell ill, and small-pox carried off one of them. A few days later his wife also died. Yet when his fortune seemed at its lowest ebb, he was offered a professorship at the University of Linz, and without hesitation he accepted it, and off to Linz he went with his two remaining children, leaving due to him a sum of 8,000 crowns in respect of arrears of salary.

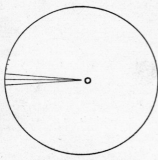

FIG. 35. Showing application of Infinitesimals to the area of a Circle.

There was little money in a professorship, and at Linz he had to supplement his income somehow. So he published a sort of Old Moore's Almanac, and told people's fortunes, and generally practised the arts of the astrologer in a way which in these days would have earned for him a prosecution, at any rate in England.

Having settled in Linz, Kepler did a somewhat bold thing in view of his unhappy experience of married life. He deliberately looked round him for a second wife, and he set about it very thoroughly and scientifically. There were, it seems, no less than eleven candidates for the privilege, and Kepler, statistician to his finger-tips, carefully set forth his estimate of the merits and demerits of each! That he was honest in all this, and free from any mercenary motives, is evidenced by the fact that he chose the poorest of them all—an orphan girl without dowry. Apparently it turned out a much more satisfactory marriage than his first one, though judging from the fact that his wife bore him seven children, his continuously scanty resources must have been taxed to the uttermost in his efforts to pay his way. Always something seemed to turn up to increase his difficulties. Thus, about this time, news reached him that his bad-tempered old mother had managed to get herself accused of sorcery at her home in Würtemberg. She was found guilty and was condemned to imprisonment and torture. Kepler hurried off to Würtemberg to intercede on her behalf, and although he failed to obtain her release, he at least saved her from torture. It took him another twelve months, however, before he could get her released from prison. She died shortly after, bellicose to the last.

At the same time Kepler was applying his mind to the problems of the solar system, and one by one, at long intervals, he gave to the world his three wonderful laws of planetary motion (see p. 89).

Nor did Kepler forget his promise to Tycho Brahe to complete the Rudolphine Tables of planetary motions. Year after year he worked at these, all the time puzzling as to how to raise the necessary funds for their publication. Time and again he applied to the court for assistance, but always without result. Yet strange to say, with all his poverty, with all his yearnings for the wherewithal to discharge his debt of gratitude to his dead friend and benefactor, when an opportunity did arise for him to take up a lucrative and honourable position, he refused because it entailed his leaving his own country to go to England. In 1620 Sir Henry Wotton, English Ambassador to Venice, a man of very wide culture and interests and a poet of no mean merit, invited Kepler to come to England, guaranteeing him a good post and an enthusiastic reception. But the prospect of life in a foreign country among a strange people appears to have been too much for him ; and this refusal came in spite of the fact that he had but recently incurred the violent displeasure of the Church for publishing a work on the Copernican System—a book which having been promptly banned, did not even yield him the sorely needed financial benefits from its sales.

Yet Kepler never abandoned his determination to publish his Rudolphine Tables, and at last, tired of further waiting, he determined to find the money himself. How he succeeded remains a mystery. It has been asserted that he had accumulated a secret hoard of money, the fruits of years of fortune-telling as an astrologer ; but it is difficult to believe that he deliberately and unnecessarily subjected his wife and children to years of miserable poverty in the accumulation of such a hoard. Be that as it may, however, the Rudolphine Tables were published, and published handsomely too, in 1627. They were of the utmost importance. Their accuracy rendered them indispensable to the navigators of the seventeenth century, by whom they were used for practically the same purpose as is served to-day by the Nautical Almanac. Even had he produced nothing beyond this Kepler would deserve our lasting remembrance.

But the publication of the Tables left Kepler a broken man. The long strain of ill-health, poverty, worry, and constant study began to have its effect, and at last, in November 1630, in his sixtieth year, whilst on his return from a fruitless mission to Prague for the purpose of recovering the money so long due to him, he caught a chill and died. He was buried in St. Peter's Church at Ratisbon, and it is no credit to the country of his birth that so little was done to perpetuate his memory. ' A century ago a proposal was made to erect a marble monument to his memory, but nothing was done. It matters little one way or the other whether Germany, having almost refused him bread during his life, should, a century and a half after his death, offer him a stone.' [1] It matters little indeed. Kepler's true monument is not of stone. It stands in those brilliant laws of planetary motion which gave to the world for the first time a complete view of the cosmic scheme as far as it concerns the solar system of which our earthly home forms so integral a part.

5. *Kepler's Laws of Planetary Motions*

We will conclude our study of Johann Kepler by a consideration of his three laws of planetary motions. He had always felt that there was some profound law which controlled the motions of the planets round the sun. ' There were three things ', he wrote, while still at Linz, ' of which I pertinaciously sought the causes why they are not other than they are : the number, the size, and the motion of the orbits.' He fully realized the fundamental importance of his self-imposed task, and in his book, *Treatise on the Motions of the Planet Mars*, he took care to ' warn off ' the anti-Copernicans : ' If any one be too dull to comprehend the science of astronomy, or too foolish to believe in Copernicus without prejudice to his piety, my advice to him is, that he should quit the astronomical school, and condemning, if he will, any or all the theories of philosophers, look to his own affairs, and leaving this worldly travail, go home and plough his fields.'

Kepler's materials were the invaluable records of Tycho Brahe's observations, and his own knowledge of geometry. His was essentially the method of trial and error. Every conceivable relationship between distance, the rate of motion, and the path of the planets he tested in the light of Brahe's results, only to reject them one after the other. Through all he saw one ray of hope. ' I was comforted,' writes he, ' and my hopes of success were supported, as well by other reasons which will presently follow, as by observing that the motions in every case seemed to be connected with the distances, and that when there

[1] Sir O. Lodge, *Pioneers of Science*, London, 1893. It is fair to note that the Germans have since made partial amends in the issue of a complete edition of Kepler's works, *Joannis Kepleri Astronomi Opera Omnia*, Dr. Ch. Frisch, Frankfurt, 1883, 9 vols.

was a great gap between the orbits, there was the same between the motions.' Like Copernicus, Kepler followed in particular the movements of the planet Mars, these being sufficiently rapid to provide adequate data for testing purposes. What was the correct orbit of Mars? He soon convinced himself that if it were a circle, then at any rate the sun could not be at its centre. After much labour he got a step farther. He noticed that when the planet's distance from the sun diminished, the planet went faster, and when the distance increased, it went slower, and this brought him to the idea that *the planet must sweep out equal areas in equal intervals of time.* Suppose, therefore, that he were to represent the orbit by a circle, with the sun not at the centre (Fig. 36), would the planet under such conditions sweep out equal areas in equal times? He tested it for innumerable positions of the sun, but it never quite fitted. He next tried an oval orbit, but this, too, never quite fitted the facts. At last, however, he hit upon the right solution. *Why not try an ellipse?* He tested it with Brahe's observations, and it fitted beautifully. At last the long-sought secret was his. *The path of the planet is that of an ellipse with the sun at one focus, and the variations in speed are such that in equal times the planet sweeps out equal areas.* A reference to Fig. 37 will at once show the idea. *S*, representing the sun, is at the focus of an ellipse *ABCD* &c. This ellipse represents the orbit of any planet. Then obviously the distance of the planet will be a minimum at *A* and a maximum at *F*, and observation shows that the

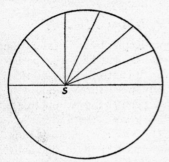

Fig. 36. Kepler's test of a circular orbit with the sun not at the centre.

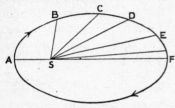

Fig. 37. Illustrating Kepler's First Two Laws of Planetary Motion.

speed of motion is, on the contrary, a maximum at A and
a minimum at F, so that, if A, B, C, D, E, &c., be the positions
of the planet at equal intervals of time, and we join these points
to S, then the areas swept through by the planet will be respectively ABS, BCS, CDS, DES, and EFS, and *these areas are found
to be exactly equal.*

Kepler was fully entitled to his triumph, but his work was
not yet complete. He had yet to unravel the relationship which
he felt existed between the distances of the different planets
and their average speeds round the sun. Why he felt such
a relationship to exist we can hardly say, but he had a feeling
that simple mathematical laws were traceable in all natural
phenomena. He had little to go upon. It was part of his genius
that he felt intuitively that not only was there such a relationship, but also that he would find it out sooner or later. And
find it out he did, though later rather than sooner. Let him
speak for himself :

' What I prophesied two-and-twenty years ago, when I discovered the five solids among the heavenly orbits (see p. 81)—
what I firmly believed long before I had seen Ptolemy's " Har-
monies "—what I had promised my friends in the title of this
book, which I named before I was sure of my discovery—what
sixteen years ago, I urged as a thing to be sought—that for which
I joined with Tycho Brahe, for which I settled in Prague, and
for which I have devoted the best part of my life to astronomical
contemplations, this at length I have brought to light. It is not
eighteen months since the first glimpse of light reached me,
three months since the dawn, very few days since the unveiled
sun, most admirable to gaze upon, burst out upon me. Nothing
holds me ; I will indulge in my sacred fury ; I will triumph over
mankind by the honest confession that I have stolen the golden
vases of the Egyptians to build up a tabernacle for my God, far
away from the confines of Egypt. If you forgive me, I rejoice ;
if you are angry, I can bear it ; the die is cast ; the book is
written ; to be read either now or by posterity, I care not which ;
it may well wait a century for a reader, as God has waited 6,000
years for an observer. . . .

' If you would know the precise moment, the idea first came
across me on the 8th of March of this year, 1618 ; but, chancing
to make a mistake in the calculation, I then rejected it as false.
I returned to it again with new force on the 15th of May ; and

it has dissipated the darkness of my mind, by such an agreement between this idea and my seventeen years' Labour on *Brahe's Observations*, that at first I thought I must be dreaming, and had taken my result for granted in my first assumptions. But the fact is certain, *that the proportion existing between the periodic times of any two planets is exactly the sesquiplicate proportion of the mean distances of the orbits.'*

And now let us put this into simple language. Kepler's discovery was this : *that for all planets, the squares of the times of revolution round the sun are as the cubes of the mean distances.* Let us try it, for example, in the case of Mars.

The data are as follows, taking the Earth's distance as one unit, and the Earth's year (i. e. time of one complete revolution) also as unity :

Earth's Distance from Sun . . 1·000 units

Mars' ,, ,, ,, . . 1·5237 ,,

Earth's Period of Revolution . . 1·000 years

Required, the period of revolution for Mars. We have by Kepler's Third Law

$$\frac{(\text{Mars' Period})^2}{(\text{Mars' Distance})^3} = \frac{(\text{Earth's Period})^2}{(\text{Earth's Distance})^3}$$

Hence

$$\frac{(\text{Mars' Period})^2}{(1·5237)^3} = \frac{1^2}{1^3}$$

Mars' Period of Revolution $= \sqrt{1·5237^3}$

$$= 1·8808 \text{ years.}$$

which is true.

And so with all planets.

This then was Kepler's life work, and no more fitting tribute to his memory could be given than to conclude this chapter with a restatement of his laws :

Law 1. All the planets move round the sun with elliptic orbits with the sun at one focus.

Law 2. The radius vector, or line joining the planet to the sun, sweeps out equal areas in equal intervals of time.

Law 3. For all planets, the square of the time of one complete revolution (or year) is proportional to the cube of the mean distance from the sun.

VI

WILLIAM GILBERT, FATHER OF MAGNETIC PHILOSOPHY

1. *The Founding of Experimental Science*

In the sixteenth century two names stand out clearly in the initiation of a revolution in scientific method.   They are William Gilbert of Colchester, the father of the magnetic philosophy, and Galileo Galilei of Pisa, the founder of modern physics. With these two we must now concern ourselves.

Fig. 38.   WILLIAM GILBERT

To the average schoolboy of to-day, with his organized scheme of studies, an integral part of which is concerned with experimental work in properly equipped laboratories, the conditions under which the sixteenth-century student of natural philosophy studied his subject must indeed seem strange.   The text-books were almost entirely inferior translations of Aristotle ; the lectures were frankly Aristotelian ; the experiments performed were nil. Such a thing as a laboratory was unheard of.   When a problem came up for solution, the treatment was simple.   What did Aristotle say about it ?   The point was looked up in the text-book, and whatever the Greek Philosopher said was accepted with absolute finality. Against the centuries-old judgement of Aristotle, not only was there no appeal, but there was no thought of appeal.   If, for example, the question is asked, ' Which falls to the ground the quicker from the same height, a heavier body, or a lighter one ? ' the natural answer to-day is, ' Let us drop them and see '. In those days such an answer was unthinkable. Instead they would say, ' Let us see what the ancient philosophers said'. The position was even worse than this, as we shall see in the next chapter, when we deal with Galileo. For if such a scientific revolutionary were to suggest, ' Well, let us drop them, if only to verify what these

Fig. 39. Gilbert's figure of a smith at his anvil
See note on p. 15

men said', he was branded as a heretic. The very suggestion implied a wicked doubt as to the wisdom of the ancients. Obviously, only by rude shocks could such a stumbling-block to scientific progress be swept away.

The name of William Gilbert, the first eminent man of science in England since Roger Bacon, must fittingly go down in scientific history on account of his brave stand for verification by experiment. He did not hesitate to trounce his opponents in outspoken terms. Referring to his reasons for delay in the publication of his results, he writes in the preface to his *De Magnete*:

' Why should I submit this noble science and this new philosophy to the judgement of men who have taken oath to follow the
opinions of others, to the most senseless corrupters of the arts,
to lettered clowns, grammatists, sophists, spouters, and the
wrong headed rabble, to be denounced, torn to tatters, and heaped
with contumely ! To you alone, true philosophers, ingenuous
minds, who not only in books but in things themselves look for
knowledge, have I dedicated these foundations of magnetic
science—a new style of philosophizing.'

And again later :

' To the early fathers of philosophy let due honour be paid,
for by them wisdom has been handed down to posterity. But
our age has detected and brought to light many facts which they,
were they alive, would gladly have accepted. Therefore have
I not hesitated to expound by demonstration and theory those
things which I have discovered by long experience.'

2. *Biographical Details*

William Gilbert (he himself wrote it Gilberd) was born at
Colchester in 1544. He was the son of Jerome Gilberd, a man
whose family had resided for centuries in Suffolk, but who had
migrated to Colchester. Jerome was greatly respected by his
fellow townsfolk, and in 1553 he became a free burgess of the
town. Later he rose to be the Recorder of Colchester. He had
four or five sons, of whom, curiously enough, two were called
William. The one with whom we are here concerned was, how ·
ever, the elder of these. Gilbert became a student at St. John's
College, Cambridge, at the age of eighteen years, and probably
began his academic career by studying mathematics. He took
his degree of B.A. in 1560, became a fellow of his college in
1561, and proceeded to his M.A. in 1564, afterwards becoming
a mathematical examiner. But evidently he had now seriously
turned his attention to medical science, for in 1569 he graduated
as M.D. and on the 21st of December of the same year he was
made a senior fellow.

Gilbert now left Cambridge, and as was the custom of educated
men of his day he travelled on the Continent, especially with
a view of visiting Italy, the intellectual centre of the world in

the sixteenth century. He returned to England in 1573, and settled down to the practice of medicine in London. In this he was very successful, quickly establishing himself as a practitioner of repute. He was elected a Fellow of the Royal College of Physicians in 1573, and later to the position of Treasurer to the College. He had for some time held the appointment of physician-in-ordinary to Queen Elizabeth, and in order the better to combine his duties in this office with those of his private practice, he took a house on St. Peter's Hill, near St. Paul's Cathedral. This house became the rendezvous of a Society or College of philosophers, probably the first of its kind in Europe, and certainly the first in this country. There is no doubt, too, that here was the scene of most of his famous experiments and researches, at first in chemistry, but later in electrical and magnetic phenomena. His reputation grew prodigiously, both as a physician and as an experimentalist, and may be said to have reached its highest point in 1600. This year saw him elected President of the Royal College of Physicians, it saw the publication of his epoch-making book, and finally, it was in the same year that he received the appointment of Chief Physician to the Court of Queen Elizabeth.

As a consequence Dr. Gilbert gave up his house on St. Peter's Hill, and joined the Court about February 1600. The publication of *De Magnete* had a mixed reception. Offending, as the preface naturally did, very many of his scientific contemporaries, there were nevertheless those who were greatly impressed by its contents. In his *Magneticall Advertisements*, 1616, William Barlowe speaks of a letter he received from Gilbert which reads,

' There is heere a wise learned man, a secretary of Venice, he came sent by the State, and was honourably received by Her Majesty. He brought me a Lattin letter from a gentleman of Venice that is very well learned, whose name is Johnnes Franciscus Sagredus ; he is a great magneticall man, and writeth that hee hath conferred with divers learned men of Venice, and with the readers of Padua, and reporteth wonderful liking of my booke.'

The great Galileo was certainly emphatic in his praise, ' I extremely admire and envy the author of *De Magnete*,' wrote he, ' I think him worthy of the greatest praise for the many new and true observations which he has made, to the disgrace of so many vain and fabling authors, who wrote not from their own knowledge only, but repeat everything they hear from the foolish and vulgar, without attempting to satisfy themselves of the same by experience.'

Queen Elizabeth died in March 1603, but her successor, James I, retained William Gilbert in his office of Chief Physician to the Royal Court. But his service under his royal master was of very short duration, for Dr. Gilbert died on the 30th of November, of the same year. His death probably occurred in the town of his birth, Colchester. He bequeathed his books, instruments, loadstones and other minerals to the College of Physicians, which was then housed at Amen Corner. Unfortunately all were destroyed in the Great Fire of 1666.

In his *Worthies of England*, 1662, that delightfully semi-conscious humorist Thomas Fuller writes thus of Gilbert:

' He had the *clearness* of *Venice glass* without the *brittleness* thereof ; soon *ripe* and long *lasting* in his perfections. He commenced doctor in physick, and was physician to Queen Elizabeth, who stamped on him many marks of her favour, besides an annual pension to encourage his studies. He addicted himself to chemistry, attaining great exactness therein. One saith of him that he was *stoicall*, but not *cynicall*, which I understand reserv'd but not morose ; never married, purposely to be more beneficial to his brethren, such his *loyalty* to the queen, that, as if unwilling to survive, he dyed in the same year with her 1603. His stature was tall, complexion cheerful, an happiness not ordinary in so hard a student and retired person. He lyeth buried in Trinity Church, in Colchester, under a plain monument. Mahomet's tomb at Mecha is said strangely to *hang* up, attracted by some invisible loadestone ; but the memory of this doctor will never *fall to the ground*, which his incomparable book, *De Magnete*, will *support* to eternity.'

3. *De Magnete*

The complete title of Gilbert's treatise, published in London in 1600, was ' De magnete magneticisque corporibus, et de magno magnete tellure ; Physiologia nova '. (' Of the magnet and magnetic bodies, and of that great magnet the earth ; a new physiology.') Quite apart from the fact that this book threw a flood of light upon a hitherto little-known subject, it insisted with much-needed emphasis on the urgent necessity for an experimental basis to scientific inquiry. If for no other reason, this plea, backed by the example of his own experiments, entitles Gilbert to a permanent place in the history of science. When an argument or a statement is verifiable by experiment, then, Gilbert holds, its truth must stand or fall by the result of the experiment, performed not once alone, but many times over, to eliminate chance errors, and to be the more convincing.

For example, Giovanni Battista Porta, an Italian philosopher, had taught that iron rubbed with diamond behaves in exactly the same way as if it had been rubbed with loadstone. That is to say, it would be endowed temporarily with the property we speak of to day as ' polarity ', so that when suspended freely it would come to rest pointing to ' magnetic ' north and south. Gilbert administers his chastisement to Porta in the following terms :

' We made the experiment ourselves with seventy-five diamonds in presence of many witnesses, employing a number of iron bars and pieces of wire, manipulating them with the greatest care while they floated in water, supported by corks ; but never was it granted me to see the effect mentioned by Porta.'

Gilbert's doctrine of the experimental method of investigation may well be expressed in his own words :

' In the discovery of secrets and in the investigation of the hidden causes of things, clear proofs are afforded by trustworthy experiments rather than by probable guesses and opinions of ordinary professors and philosophers. In order, therefore, that the noble substance of that great magnet, the earth, hitherto quite unknown, and the exalted powers of this globe of ours may be better understood I shall first of all deal with common magnets, stones, and iron materials, and with magnetic bodies, and with the near parts of the earth, which we can reach with our hands and perceive with our senses. After that I shall proceed to show my new magnetic experiments, and so I shall penetrate for the first time into the innermost parts of the earth. . . .

' Whoever wishes to try the same experiments, let him handle the substance, not carelessly, but prudently and deftly, and in the proper way, and when the thing does not succeed let him not in ignorance denounce my discoveries, for nothing has been set down in these books which has not been many times performed and repeated.'

Some slight knowledge of magnetism and frictional electricity certainly dates back to the time of Thales of Miletus.[1] Thales probably knew something of it from the fact that amber (the Greek word for which, *elektron*, has given us our word 'electricity'), when rubbed, attracts such things as small pieces of paper. He also knew of the magnetic properties of ' lodestone '. But he considered that both were possessed of ' soul '. This was typical of the ideas held by many of his successors all through the Middle Ages. The phenomena of magnetism were mingled in men's minds with the fancies of magic to an almost hopeless degree.

' The lodestone was accused of producing melancholy, of making love philtres, of losing its power when rubbed with garlic, and regaining it when smeared with goat's blood, of declining to attract iron in presence of diamond.'

One by one Gilbert took all such statements and by the rigid test of experiment he proved each to be so much nonsense. But his work was by no means confined to the mere refutation of other people's statements. Take the case of frictional electricity as an example. His extensive tests showed that amber was not the only substance which when rubbed would attract very light objects. Using a carefully pivoted light needle as his attracted object, he held up in succession various substances which had been rubbed. Some immediately attracted the needle, such as glass, jet, sulphur, sealing-wax, resin, diamond, sapphire, opal,

[1] See p. 21, ch. i.

and amethyst. To these he gave the name of 'Electrics'. Others, such as marble, ebony, ivory, flint, pearl, coral, and the metals, he termed 'non-electrics'. This classification was, as we now know, incorrect; but Gilbert did not know of the properties of electrical conductivity and insulation, or he would have realized that what he termed a non-electric could in fact be electrified by rubbing, provided it were properly insulated.

In the realms of magnetism Gilbert's achievements were of the highest importance. Indeed, apart from his pioneer work as an exponent of experimental methods, he will always be remembered as the first to realize that *the earth is itself a magnet*. We know

FIG. 40. Showing Non-mag-netized Needle.

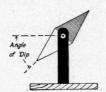

FIG. 41. Showing Magnetic Dip.

that in Europe the mariner's compass, originally a piece of load-stone floated by means of corks in a vessel of water so as always to point nearly north and south, was used by Peter Peregrinus as early as 1269. But no one knew *why* a compass always pointed in one direction. Again, the phenomenon known as 'dip' had been recently discovered by George Hartmann of Nuremberg (1489–1564). If a needle be suspended about its centre of gravity, so as to be able to rotate freely about a horizontal axis, then it should be able to come to rest in a horizontal position (Fig. 40). But if the needle is magnetized, we find that, when made to rotate in the plane of the magnetic meridian (that is to say, in the plane which includes the 'magnetic' north and south poles), it never comes to rest in a horizontal position, but instead the north pole of the magnet 'dips' downwards, the angle its axis makes with the horizontal being called the 'angle of dip' (Fig. 41). An instrument for detecting and measuring this is known as a 'dip-circle', and the first account of such an instrument was given by Robert Norman, a compass-maker, in his book, the *Newe Attractive*, printed in London in 1581. It was known, moreover, that the angle of dip differed from place to place, and in the region of the equator it was zero.

The explanation of these phenomena was given by Gilbert, who said that the earth is itself a big magnet. He had asked himself whether it were possible for a magnet to be of spherical shape, and he fashioned one of iron and magnetized it by rubbing it with loadstone. Not only did he find that it behaved like a magnet, possessing its magnetic poles, but also that, on bringing up to it a carefully-suspended small magnetic needle : (1) the needle always came to rest with one of its poles pointing directly to the opposite pole of his 'terrella' (as he called his spherical magnet), and (2) the suspended magnet came to rest at various angles of 'dip' with respect to the terrella, varying from ninety degrees at the poles to zero dip at points midway between the poles (Fig. 42). Gradually the full significance of this came to Gilbert's mind.

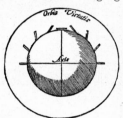

FIG. 42.   One of Gilbert's Terrellae.
See note on p. 16.

The earth itself is a giant magnet, with magnetic poles in the region of the geographical north and south poles, and from this fact all the commonly observed phenomena of compass-property and dip were at once explicable. Since like poles repel each other, and unlike poles attract, a suspended magnet will obviously come to rest with its *north-seeking* pole pointing to the earth's magnetic north pole. Gilbert insisted on the proper use of the terms 'north-seeking' and 'south-seeking' poles, rather than 'north' and 'south' poles, rightly realizing that since unlike poles attract, then if we speak of the earth's 'north' magnetic pole, the end of a magnet facing it must necessarily be the opposite 'south' pole, unless the term 'north-seeking' be introduced.

So, by the logic of experiment, all the myth and magic which the mystery-loving philosophers had called in to explain why the needle points north were swept away. Speaking of this, Gilbert remarks in his book :

' The common herd of philosophers, in search of the causes of magnetic movements, called in causes remote and far away. Martinus Cortesius . . . dreamt of an attractive magnetic point beyond the heavens, acting on iron. Petrus Peregrinus holds that direction has its rise at the celestial poles. Cardan was of the opinion that the rotation of iron is caused by the star in the tail of the Ursa Major. The Frenchman Bossard thinks that the magnetic needle turns to the pole of the zodiac. . . . So has ever been the wont of mankind : homely things are vile ; things from abroad and things afar are dear to them and the object of longing.'

In spite of its value, Gilbert's *De Magnete* suffered neglect after his death. The reason is perhaps that with all the care and accuracy of his experiments, he strained the applications of his theory of terrestrial magnetism. He was a strong supporter of the Copernican system, and in his anxiety to assist this with his own arguments, he ' overdid ' it. Thus, for example, he tried to prove that magnetism was the actual cause of the earth's rotation on its axis. Such assertions as these considerably damaged his reputation after his death, so that there was no reprint of *De Magnete*, after that of 1638, for more than two hundred and fifty years ; and for all this time the memory of this true pioneer of science lay neglected.[1] In 1889 a ' Gilbert Club ' was formed in London for the purpose of celebrating the tercentenary publication of *De Magnete*, and the work was retranslated and published, whilst in recent years the late Sylvanus P. Thompson has made an exhaustive study of his writings.

[1] It is interesting to note that Descartes in his *Regulae* (probably written in the winter of 1628–9) refers two or three times with obvious admiration to Gilbert's work on the magnet. The *Regulae* was unfinished, and was first published in a Flemish translation in 1684, and in Latin in 1701 in *Opuscula Posthuma*.

VII

GALILEO GALILEI, FOUNDER OF EXPERIMENTAL SCIENCE

1. *Early Life*

GALILEO GALILEI was born at Pisa, in the province of Tuscany in Italy, on the 18th of February 1564. His father, Vincenzo

Galilei, was an impoverished Florentine nobleman of much culture, high ideals, and breadth of mind. He was a poor man, and he was naturally anxious that his son should adopt some definitely lucrative career. He saw his little Galileo exhibiting marvellous ingenuity in making toy contrivances, and he was much troubled by the thought that his son might wish to take up a scientific career. Vincenzo knew how hard it was to make a living in such a career, and he determined

FIG. 43. GALILEO

that if he could divert Galileo's mind from any such tendencies he would do so. Accordingly he decided to make of his son a cloth-dealer. Luckily fate was against him. Galileo went to a convent school, and whatever he did, he did well. His father gave up the unequal struggle. The idea of making a merchant of such a boy was preposterous. A university career was inevitable; but at least, if he must take up a profession, then it should be as lucrative as possible. All this pointed to the medical profession, so to the University of Pisa went Galileo, at the age of seventeen years, to study for his medical degree.

However, fate would not be denied. Mechanical skill was there, and mathematical genius was there. Galileo knew no mathematics, but his genius could not be suppressed. Thus during a service in the Cathedral at Pisa, his attention was diverted from his devotions by the swinging of a chandelier above him. Its regularity of movement set him thinking. Galileo timed its swings. He had no watch—such things had not yet been invented—so he felt his own pulse and used that as his time-index. What particularly interested him was the fact that, although the oscillations were dying down, the time of swing yet remained unchanged. This fact is now universally recognized as what is known as the principle of *isochronism* in pendulums, and is applied in the working of the modern clock. But Galileo's interest in it at the time was purely medical. He experimented at home with a metal ball suspended by a string of varying length, and found that the *time* of swing changed with the length—it was faster for shorter lengths and slower for longer. The outcome was his invention of the ' pulsilogium '—an instrument for recording the pulse-rate of a patient (Fig. 44). It was a simple enough contrivance. By rotating an index or pointer, a simple pendulum was wound up or unwound until its time of swing just coincided with the pulse-rate of the patient. The scale over which the pointer moved was graduated to give a direct reading of the number of beats per minute. One day Galileo, while calling on a friend of the family, one Ottilio Ricci, a mathematical tutor to the Court of Tuscany, accidentally heard through an open door a lesson in Euclid being given to some pages. That chance lesson decided Galileo's fate. He begged his friend to give him some lessons, and soon he was deeply engrossed in his new-found joy ; for joy it was to him. It was not long before he had mastered Euclid's first six books. Nor was it long before the elder Galileo saw how things were going, and the career of medicine was finally abandoned.

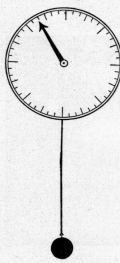

Fig. 44.   Galileo's Pulsilogium.

Galileo now gave himself up whole heartedly to a study of mathematics and physics. Among other things, he became a close student of Archimedes, and he wrote a thesis on the ' hydrostatic balance ', suggesting improvements on the Syracusan philosopher's original design. This brought Galileo to the notice of Guido Ubaldi, at that time the premier mathematician of Italy, and through him to Ferdinand dei Medici, grand duke of Tuscany. It was the patronage of this latter gentleman which secured for him, at the age of twenty-six years, his first professional appointment—that of professor of mathematics in his own university of Pisa.

2. *Galileo at Pisa*

Galileo was not long in asserting for himself that independence of mind which we have seen to be so rare in those days. He was not indeed alone in his indictment of Aristotelian physics. For example, the writings of Copernicus were making silent headway amongst somewhat timorous adherents, who seldom spoke out, so many were there to offend. Galileo, however, did not hesitate. With a born genius for experiment, a trenchant pen for the recording of facts, and an honesty which refused to permit his conscience to sanction as fact that which his laboratory proved to be fiction, there could be only one result.

Galileo's older colleagues knew nothing of experiments. The very idea implied to them a sort of hideous witchcraft—a profanation of the sanctity of the Aristotelian doctrine. One part of the doctrine, it will be remembered, stated that a heavy body will fall to the earth more rapidly than a lighter one. Thus a 100 lb. weight will fall in one-hundredth the time it will take a 1 lb. weight to fall through a given distance. One would scarcely dare claim much pluck or originality for the idea of dropping two such weights simultaneously from a given height in order to put the great Aristotle to the test ; yet this simple experiment was in fact one of the outstanding achievements of scientific history. It is astonishing to think that such an experiment had not been deliberately performed for at least two thousand years. Thinkers had come and gone, yet this absurd fiction of the great Greek philosopher had persisted through the ages. And the men who were considered *par excellence* the great minds of the sixteenth century refused the evidence of their own senses ! It is a problem for the psychologist.

The story of the experiment at the leaning tower of Pisa is well known. It speaks volumes for the vigorous personality of young Galileo that he got his audience together at all. There is real humour in the thought. What an unwilling audience they must have made ! What angry mutterings must have accompanied the preliminaries as this young upstart slowly mounted the tower. And then, no doubt, a hush of unwilling expectancy as the signal was given for the simultaneous release of heavy and light weights. Surely it is difficult to believe that these aged philosophers had not, at some time or other in their lives, seen two such weights drop in more or less the same time. They must surely have felt, in their heart of hearts, that they were fighting a losing fight, and that this young firebrand of a Galileo was a true herald of a new era.

Fig. 45. Leaning Tower of Pisa

Crash ! With simultaneous thud those two weights did indeed reach the ground at the same time. It was truly a great moment in the history of the world. Yet the blind prejudice of an unreasoning hero-worship was too strong even for the evidence of the senses of sight and sound. ' Let us go home again ', said they, ' and look it up.' So back they went to their old books, and there sure enough it was—a heavy body falls faster than a lighter body. Besides, and the thought was like balm to their wounded sensibilities, does not the Church sanction the views of the great Aristotle ? So the net result of it all was that whilst they secretly feared Galileo, they openly disliked him. It was but the beginning of his career, yet his enemies multiplied rapidly.

Galileo persevered in his study of motion—particularly the

motion of falling bodies. He saw clearly that falling bodies have accelerated motion—that is to say, the velocity is increasing. He sought out what was the law of this increase in velocity. He soon satisfied himself that *the velocity is proportional to the time of falling* ; that is to say, that a falling body received equal increments of velocity in equal increments of time. He tested this experimentally by means of an inclined plane—a board twelve yards long, down the centre of which was cut a trough one inch wide. This trough was lined with smooth parchment so as to minimize frictional errors. A highly polished and well-rounded brass ball was allowed to run down this plane, and the time was carefully noted for a wide range of varying inclinations. Galileo had no clock with which to measure time, but he was too gifted an experimentalist to be beaten by that fact. He arranged a water pail with a small outlet at the bottom. The escaping water was caught in a cup, the period of flow being timed to begin and end for the exact duration of his experiment—namely, the period of roll of his brass ball down the inclined plane. He then carefully weighed the water, and of course this weight was a measure of the time of descent of the ball down the inclined plane.

Galileo found that, within the limits of experimental error, the *distance of descent was proportional to the square of the time.* This is in accordance with the well-known formula for falling bodies

$$S = \tfrac{1}{2} g t^2.$$

Galileo had no difficulty in realizing that the results for the inclined plane would apply equally to falling bodies, since by gradually increasing the steepness of slope to ninety degrees, the latter case emerges as a special limit of the general problem.

Galileo, too, was the first to realize that the path of a projectile in space is a parabola. This was not a new problem. Early writers on gunnery had remarked that for certain distances of the objective, the gun must be pointed upwards ; whilst Thomas Digges, in his *New Artillerie*, published in 1591, had pointed out that the ball had a downward tendency right from the beginning of its course, and that it was the persistence of this tendency which ultimately produced a deflexion from the original direction. Galileo's contribution to the problem was of a much more positive character. He had shown that for a falling body the fall was proportional to the square of the time. Representing then equal increments of time by *AB*, *BC*, *CD*, *DE*, &c. (Fig. 46), if *BF* be the fall in the first interval, the fall in twice the time would be four times *BF*, namely *CG*, and in three times this interval the fall would be *DH*, equal to nine times the fall *BF*, and so on. So that if *AB*, *BC*, *CD*, &c. represent also the equal *forward* displacements of the projectile ejected initially in a horizontal direction, then in fact the successive actual positions in space occupied by the projectile at these equal intervals of time would

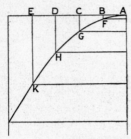

be *A*, *F*, *G*, *H*, *K*, &c., and this path Galileo had no difficulty in showing to be a parabola. It will be noticed that actually Galileo was making use here of the principle of the composition of forces, but he did not definitely enunciate this, evidently not fully recognizing its scope.

FIG. 46. Illustrating Galileo's method of proving that the path of a projectile in space is a parabola.

One other important principle in mechanics was brought out by Galileo at this period, in his *Della Scienza Meccanica*, published in 1592. It is concerned with the theory of mechanical powers, and his statement in effect was this : that a force which can move a weight of two pounds through one foot will also move a weight of one pound through two feet. That is to say, the lighter the weight to be overcome, the greater is the distance in the corresponding ratio through which the force will move it, but under no circumstances can this advantage be exceeded.

This is a most important proposition in Statics, and was one which, much about this time, was also being investigated by the famous Stevinus, of Bruges, from a somewhat more practical standpoint.

The days of Galileo at Pisa were numbered, as things were fast reaching a climax. He had, by his outspoken criticisms, multiplied his enemies rapidly. The end came as a result of a difference he had with one Giovanni dei Medici, an influential personage who had invented a scheme for cleansing the port of Leghorn. Galileo's opinion was sought, and honest man that he was, he condemned it outright. Later experience of the scheme fully justified Galileo's condemnation, but the mischief was done. The inventor was mortally offended, and his hostile influence proved too strong for Galileo, who was compelled to resign his chair at Pisa. The death of his father at this period left him with some responsibility in the matter of assisting to provide for his sisters, so that when in 1592 the Senate of Venice offered him the professorship of mathematics at the University of Padua, Galileo eagerly accepted, and so began for himself a new era of brilliance and fame.

FIG. 47. Galileo's Thermometer.

3. *Padua*

Galileo went to Padua in 1592 in no chastened spirit. Pisa was his native city, and the call of home was strong in him. There is no doubt that he keenly felt his exile, for such it really was. Yet he threw himself whole-heartedly into his professional duties. His inaugural lecture was a triumph of eloquence, and his fame rapidly increased. People of the highest rank flocked to hear him, and his school of natural philosophy was filled to overflowing, so that frequently he had to abandon his class room and lecture in the open air.

One of the first-fruits of his labours at Padua was the invention of what was perhaps the first thermometer. This consisted of a flask *A* with a long narrow neck (Fig. 47), inverted, with its end *B* dipping into a small reservoir of coloured water. Some of the air within the flask having been withdrawn, the decreased pressure of the air so produced causes the water to rise in the neck. The position of the head of the column was indicated by a scale *SS* at the side. The effect of heat is much greater upon air than upon water, and hence, when the temperature rose, the liquid fell in the stem, and vice versa. The chief error in this instrument arises from the fact that not only does the position of the liquid in the stem depend upon the temperature, but also upon the barometric pressure. Galileo, however, was probably unaware of this, as the barometer was not invented till about 1642.

It was whilst Galileo was at Padua that he began to come into world-wide prominence as a disciple of Copernicus. It is evident that, so far as his public lectures were concerned, he made no attempt in the first years of his professorship to depart from the current Ptolemaic hypothesis as usually taught. He first testified to his belief in the Copernican system in 1597, when he wrote to Kepler to thank him for a copy of the latter's *Mysterium Cosmographicum*. ' I have been for many years ', wrote he, ' an adherent of the Copernican system, and it explains to me the causes of many of the appearances of nature which are quite unintelligible on the commonly accepted hypothesis.' He then goes on to explain why, in spite of this belief, he has remained silent. ' I have collected many arguments for refuting the latter ; but I do not venture to bring them to the light of publicity, for fear of sharing the fate of our master, Copernicus, who, although he has earned immortal fame with some, yet with very many (so great is the number of fools) has he become an object of ridicule and scorn.'

Galileo was not wanting in courage, but his appointment at Padua was for a term of six years only, and he evidently had no intention of jeopardizing his prospects of re-election. Presumably he was justified, for in 1598 he was not only re-elected, but his salary was considerably increased, and he felt more secure in consequence.

There was, however, another fact—a black incident in the history of the Church of those days—which must have profoundly influenced Galileo against too free a pronouncement of his Copernican views. Giordano Bruno, an eminent philosopher, had boldly pronounced for Copernicus. This, as we all know, was regarded as heresy by the Church, and Bruno took refuge from anger by residing for a time in the republic of Venice.

Nevertheless, in 1594 Bruno was tried and convicted and cast into prison. He refused to recant. At last, after six years, it became evident to the ecclesiastical authorities that imprisonment would not suffice, and so this martyr of science was passed on to 'have his soul cleansed'. He was condemned to death at the stake, but he remained true to his convictions to the last. ' You who sentence me ', said he, ' are in greater fear than I who am condemned.' There is something really fine about Bruno's dying words. ' I have fought, that is much—victory is in the hands of fate. Be that as it may, this at least future ages will not deny me, be the victor who he may—that I did not fear to die. I yielded to none of my fellows in constancy and preferred a spirited death to a cowardly life.'

His death was a shock to all high-minded people who dared to think about it at all. Padua, now a tram-ride from Venice, was near enough then for Galileo to have been profoundly affected by the whole affair. We know he was a Copernican, but it was some years after the death of Bruno before he ventured to be really outspoken on the subject.

At first he confined his denunciations to the general Aristotelian philosophy of the immutability of the heavens. An almost ideal opportunity offered itself in 1604, when a brilliant new star literally blazed into view. Such stars appear at varying intervals in the skies, and astronomers speak of them as *novae*, or temporary stars. They are obvious evidences of great cosmic upheaval of some kind or other, and they are the subject of considerable speculation and scientific interest whenever they appear.

So far as Galileo was concerned, here was a splendid object-lesson for his obstinate pro-Aristotelian contemporaries. Here in the ' unchanging ' heavens (for the heavens in the old view were the seat of all that is changeless) was shining with a brilliance far exceeding that of Jupiter at his brightest, a something where there had been nothing ! A star where there had been no star ! What was Aristotle's immutable sky worth in the face of this ?

Before enraptured audiences of greater numbers than ever before, Galileo discussed this phenomenon and pointed the moral. His opponents took up the challenge, and Padua became the storm-centre of a controversy which could only carry Galileo one way ; and so we find him boldly proclaiming for Copernicus and his system, and definitely committing himself to a campaign in which, as we shall see later, the whole of the forces of the Church were arrayed against him, and which brought tragedy to his later life.

4. *The Telescope*

It was a trick of fate which placed at this period a most powerful weapon in Galileo's hands, and enabled him to adduce illustration after illustration in support of his pro-Copernican campaign. In 1609 he heard interesting rumours of a remarkable contrivance which had been devised in Holland, whereby objects, viewed through the instrument, appeared to be enlarged and brought considerably nearer than they actually were when seen by the naked eye.

There has been much controversy as to the origin of the telescope. We know that lenses had been used as long ago as Roger Bacon's time as an aid to vision, but the actual combination of lenses to produce a telescope was an invention of the beginning of the seventeenth century. There have been many claims for the honour of the invention. On the whole, evidence appears to favour the claims of Hans Lippershey, a manufacturer of spectacles in Middelburg, as having been at least the first *to produce* such an instrument. Details are regrettably vague. It is said that the necessary combination of lenses was accidentally arranged by one of Lippershey's apprentices, and was regarded by the spectacle-maker rather as a toy than anything else. In some vague way, the novelty began to be talked about, and in due course rumours of it reached Galileo. The significance of such an instrument as a weapon of science was fully evident to him. The problem of its design haunted him, and he could not rest until he had solved it. His only data for a solution were the existing treatises on the structure of the eye, and his own vague knowledge of the theory of lenses. But these with his genius for mechanical contrivance sufficed. He sat up for a whole night, and before the morning he had solved the problem. His own words are definite enough. Writing to a relative, he said :

' I have a piece of news for you, though whether you will be glad or sorry to hear it I cannot say. . . . You must know then, that two months ago there was spread a report here that in Flanders some one had presented to Count Maurice of Nassau a glass manufactured in such a way as to make distant objects appear very near, so that a man at the distance of two miles could be clearly seen. This seemed to me so marvellous that I began to think about it. As it appeared to me to have a foundation in the Theory of Perspective I set about contriving how to make it, and at length I found out, and have succeeded so well that the one I have made is far superior to the Dutch telescope. It was reported in Venice that I had made one, and

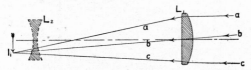

FIG. 48. Effect of a Lens on Rays of Light.

a week since I was commanded to show it to his Serenity and to all the members of the senate, to their infinite amazement. Many gentlemen and senators, even the oldest, have ascended at various times the highest bell-towers in Venice to spy out ships at sea making sail for the mouth of the harbour, and have seen them clearly, though without my telescope they would have been invisible for more than two hours. The effect of this instrument is to show an object at a distance of say fifty miles, as if it were but five miles.'

It is worth noting that the Dutch instrument was of a totally different type from that which Galileo designed. The former gave an inverted image ; the latter an erect image. Galileo's type of instrument is still in use in the opera-glass. The principle of Galileo's telescope is shown in Figs. 48 and 49. To avoid confusion it will suffice to remember that the effect of interposing a lens in the path of a ray of light is to produce a bending or refraction towards the thicker part of the lens. Thus in the Fig. 48, if a, b, and c are rays from a distant object, the lens L_1, will bend the bounding rays *a* and *c inward* (because the lens is thickest in the middle) and will give an image I_1. Such a lens is spoken of as a convex or converging lens.

Suppose now we prevent the formation of this image by interposing a concave or diverging lens L_2 (as shown dotted in Fig. 48). The effect of this interposition is shown in the next figure. The rays are not permitted to come to focus at I_1, but are each bent outward towards the thicker portion of the lens L_2, the divergence being the greater as we get farther from the middle of the lens. That is to say, ray *b* is bent farther down than *a*, and *c* farther down than *b*. Consequently the rays emerge *diverging*, as in *a'*, *b'*, and *c'*, in Fig. 49. The eye looking along these rays sees

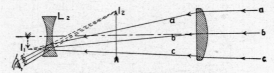

Fig. 49. The principle of Galileo's Telescope.

the image where the rays, produced backward (as shown by dotted lines in the figure), come to focus, and it will be seen that the result is a much more magnified image I_2 than was produced by the first lens L_1 alone. Such an image is known as a virtual image, and it is erect or upright instead of inverted as was I_1. Galileo's original instrument gave a magnification of three and his second of eight. It was not long before he had considerably extended these magnifications, and with his assistants he became very expert in telescope manufacture. He presented some to various noblemen, and some he sold, and with such unbounded delight and wonder was this novelty received that an admiring senate promptly increased his salary to one thousand florins and granted it for the duration of his life.

It should not be difficult to realize how astonishingly impressive the invention of this instrument must have been to those privileged to gaze through it for the first time. To see a ship where the naked eye sees nothing, to see a man a mile away smiling or making some slight movement ordinarily invisible at a distance ;

such experiences must of course have appeared wonderful to all concerned. Of far more importance is it that when Galileo turned his instrument to the heavens at night, he discovered new wonder after new wonder, and each new fact helped to controvert the Aristotelian philosophy, and afforded added proofs of the truth of the Copernican doctrine of the solar system as modified by Kepler.

A few examples of these discoveries—there are too many to deal with within the compass of this book—will suffice. Thus Aristotelians had regarded the face of the moon as being steadily even and uniformly bright. Galileo found instead the irregularity, both in surface and in brilliance, of mountain and crater and

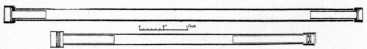

FIG. 50. Diagram to illustrate the proportions of Galileo's First Telescopes.

valley and sea. The reference to Galileo's observations is clearly indicated in Milton's *Paradise Lost* :

> . . . the moon, whose orb
> Through optic glass the Tuscan artist views
> At evening from the top of Fesolé,
> Or in Valdarno, to descry new lands,
> Rivers or mountains in her spotty globe.

Again, the Aristotelians said that all heavenly bodies revolved round the earth. Yet Galileo turned his telescope to Jupiter and to his amazement and delight discovered four moons revolving round it. The extravagances of opposition which these observations elicited read to-day like a childish novel. Thus Sizzi argued that since these moons were invisible to the naked eye, therefore they can exercise no influence on the earth, and therefore they are useless, and, therefore, they do not exist. Another opponent went farther. He absolutely declined to look through the telescope at all.

' Oh, my dear Kepler,' writes Galileo, ' how I wish that we could have one hearty laugh together. Here at Padua, is the

principal professor of philosophy whom I have repeatedly and urgently requested to look at the moon and planets through my glass, which he pertinaciously refuses to do. Why are you not here? What shouts of laughter we should have at this glorious folly. And to hear the professor of philosophy at Pisa labouring before the grand duke with logical arguments, as if with magical incantations, to charm the new planets out of the sky.'

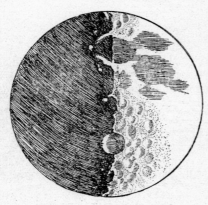

FIG. 51. The Moon as seen by Galileo, 1609–10.

One further instance may be quoted. Galileo examined the surface of the sun, and saw spots. Heinous offence! He examined them and saw them moving, and so proved the rotation of the sun on its own axis. A thoughtful monk named Scheiner verified these observations, and communicated an account of the spots to the superior of his order. And what was he told for his pains? 'I have searched through Aristotle', wrote the superior, 'and can find nothing of the kind mentioned. Be assured, therefore, that it is a deception of your senses, or of your glasses.'

5. *Florence*

Meanwhile Galileo's fame grew. He was the idol of the Venetian Republic. We have seen that in 1609 he had his salary doubled and confirmed for life. In Padua, too, children had been born to him—one son, Vincenzo, and two daughters, one of whom, Polissena, was afterwards to become the comfort of his old age. Yet he was never quite happy in Venetia. Galileo was a Tuscan, and for him Tuscany spelt home and Venetia exile. The people of Tuscany, too, had long since regretted that they had driven this great man from them. Galileo had never quite lost touch with Pisa, and when his position at Padua had become reasonably secure, he began paying holiday visits to his native home, and thus came into friendly contact with the Grand Duke of Tuscany, Cosimo II. Cosimo expressed the popular desire in his efforts to induce Galileo to return to Tuscany, and in 1610, after the famous discovery of Jupiter's satellites, he offered our philosopher the appointment of Mathematician and Philosopher to the Grand Duke, and Galileo accepted.

It was a fateful decision. The joy of freedom from the daily routine of lectures and the remembrance of long years of yearning for a return to his native country overrode all other considerations, and so we find him in 1610 installed in the city of Florence, there to continue his career of successful research in astronomy and mechanics.

Why was it such a fateful decision ? Galileo was a Copernican in a land which was officially anti-Copernican ; and where the Church ruled, to dabble with doctrines which it regarded as heresies was to play with fire. It was not so very many years since Bruno was burnt at the stake for such an offence. In Venice Galileo had been reasonably safe. It was a land of relative tolerance in religious matters. But Tuscany was different. It came more under the influence of Rome. And so behind Galileo's return from a land of freedom to a land of religious tyranny there lurked tragedy.

Of course the Venetians were much offended at his departure from them, and rightly so. It was scarcely a year since they had voted Galileo an annuity for life. They had always treated him well, and his departure hurt them. So Galileo left behind him many enemies amongst those who had been his friends.

In 1611 he paid a brief visit to Rome, and was enthusiastically received. On his return to Florence, he turned his attention to the subject of hydrostatics, and published an excellent treatise on floating bodies. This was followed by more astronomical activity. He discovered and commented on Saturn's remarkable ' appendages ', later known as Saturn's rings ; he wrote upon the problem of the determination of longitude ; he discovered the phenomenon known as the 'libration of the moon'. And all the time he attacked the Aristotelian philosophers with unceasing vigour ; and meanwhile his clerical enemies were at work, trying to stir up Rome against him.

They were so far successful that Galileo was in 1615 summoned to Rome to explain his views. He went. It was a delicate situation, fraught with possibilities. He found himself arrayed against the cream of the Aristotelian talent of the day. But he excelled in argument and carried his points. If only he could have remained in the presence of his opponents no doubt all would have been well, for Pope Paul V was well-disposed towards him. When, however, he withdrew from the debating chamber the magic of his arguments went with him, and the College of Cardinals decided definitely to ban the writings of Copernicus and Kepler, and to instruct Cardinal Bellarmine to reprimand Galileo for his support of their doctrines. This was

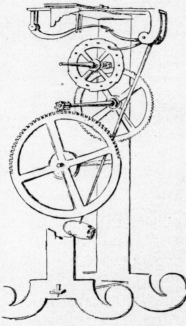

Fig. 52. Facsimile of design for a pendulum clock.

done, and on the 26th of February 1616 Galileo found himself enjoined, under the threat of imprisonment and torture, ' to abandon and cease to teach his false, impious, and heretical opinions'. Galileo bowed to the inevitable ; he gave his promise and was permitted to return to Florence.

6. *The Inquisition*

The years which followed Galileo's return to Florence were peaceful enough in their way. He vigorously continued his researches but carefully avoided anything which would give offence to his watchful enemies. He was getting on in years, and at this period of his life found much comfort in the proximity of one of his daughters, who had become a nun in the Convent of St. Matthew at Arcetri, just outside the town of Florence. So Galileo took a small villa in Arcetri, and here he passed much of his time, frequently visiting the Convent and when unable to do so maintaining a steady correspondence with his daughter. Her letters to her father, many of them still extant, constitute a most touching record of this period of the philosopher's life.

So we come to the year 1623, to the death of the Pope Paul V. He was succeeded by Urban VIII, who, as Cardinal Maffeo Barberini, had been one of Galileo's cordial friends and well wishers. His elevation to the Papacy was a source of much gratification to Galileo, who hoped that the new régime would spell for him an era of tolerance. One of his friends tactfully sounded the Pope on his behalf, and as a result advised Galileo to come to Rome to offer to the Pope his personal congratulations. Galileo came, and the visit was a success. So much so, that on his return to Florence, he found that Urban VIII had dispatched a letter of commendation to Ferdinand, Cosimo's young successor to the ducal throne of Tuscany.

' We find in Galileo ', wrote he, ' not only literary distinction, but also the love of piety, and he is also strong in those qualities by which the pontifical good-will is easily obtained. And now, when he has been brought to this city to congratulate us on our elevation, we have very lovingly embraced him ; nor can we suffer him to return to the country whither your liberality calls him, without an ample provision of pontifical love. And that you may know how dear he is to us, we have willed to give him this honourable testimonial of virtue and piety. And we further signify that every benefit which you shall confer upon him, imitating or even surpassing your father's liberality, will conduce to our gratification.'

This was surely a splendid testimonial, and it was only natural for Galileo to hope that the tide had turned, and that he might at last venture a little more outspokenly to record his real thoughts and opinions. However, Galileo made the fatal mistake of forgetting to differentiate between the Pope himself and the powerful ecclesiastical authorities who surrounded him. It was a mistake for which he was to pay heavily.

He now set to work and prepared the great book of his life. It was called *Dialogues on the Ptolemaic and Copernican Systems*, and he completed it by the year 1630. The form which this work took was determined by the fact that in 1616 he had been made to promise, under threat of imprisonment, never to teach the Copernican doctrine. He wrote what purported to be an impartial discussion in dialogue form, between Salviati, a Copernican, Simplicio, an Aristotelian, and Sagredo, a sort of good-natured chairman. It is claimed by some writers that this work was in no way antagonistic to the promise which had been extorted from him, but it is difficult to believe this. At best one can only say that if it did not conform to the spirit of the promise, it did to the letter. The fact remains that as a pretence to a detached impartiality it was little more than a pretext, for throughout the work Salviati has much the better of the argument. It was a brilliantly written work, and was undoubtedly a masterpiece of common sense and a fine literary effort, but it did not deceive Galileo's enemies. Indeed it is remarkable that he ever got so far as to obtain preliminary permission to publish the book. Looking at it from their very narrow and prejudiced point of view, the permission to publish could only have been due to some very careless bungling on the part of the Master of the Sacred Palace, the man who acted as censor in these matters. The book appeared in 1632, and was dedicated to the Grand Duke of Tuscany. It was received by an eager public and read with avidity. It was then realized by the Master of the Sacred Palace that he had blundered, and he at once ordered the sequestration of the book. Too late Galileo saw how strong were the forces against him, and in spite of such friendly assistance as the Grand Duke Ferdinand and others tried to offer, the tide of fury was irresistible.

Even Pope Urban, former friend and well-wisher of Galileo, turned against him. His Holiness was persuaded that the character of Simplicio was intended as a deliberate caricature of himself. Galileo was peremptorily summoned to Rome on a charge of heresy. He was now an old man, his health was failing, the plague was abroad and it was winter. In those days the journey from Florence to Rome was no light undertaking, and Galileo pleaded for delay. His plea was refused and he arrived in Rome in February 1633. He was permitted to be received as the guest of his old friend Niccolini, the Tuscan ambassador, but he was recommended to keep indoors. The proceedings of the Inquisition were protracted till June. They were of course conducted in secret. Throughout this time Galileo's friends urged upon him the advisability of submission. It must have been a time of mental torture for the aged philosopher. What was he to do? How could he, in the circumstances in which he was placed, do other than remember the fate of such men as Bruno? The old man, broken in spirit, gave in, and declared his ' free and unbiassed ' willingness to recant. Clothed in the regulation garb of the penitent, he was brought before the assembly of cardinals to receive the judgement of the Inquisition. They condemned his works, but out of their mercy and in consideration of his voluntary recantation, they extended to him their gracious pardon, and merely imposed the sentence of imprisonment at the Papal discretion.

Then followed the famous recantation :

' . . . But because I have been enjoined by this Holy Office altogether to abandon the false opinion which maintains that the sun is the centre and immovable, and forbidden to hold, defend, or teach the said false doctrine in any manner, and after it hath been signified to me that the said doctrine is repugnant with the Holy Scripture, I have written and printed a book, in which I treat of the same doctrine now condemned, . . . that is to say, that I held and believed that the sun is the centre of the universe and is immovable, and that the earth is not the centre and is movable ; willing, therefore, to remove from the minds of your Eminencies, and of every Catholic Christian, this vehement suspicion rightfully entertained towards me, with a sincere heart and unfeigned faith, I abjure, curse, and detest the said heresies and errors, and generally every other error and sect contrary to the Holy Church, and I swear that I will never more in future say or assert anything verbally, or in writing, which may give rise to a similar suspicion of me. . . .'

What are we to say of this disgraceful scene ? Who, dispassionately reading the facts, can do aught but feel deeply for the pathetic victim ? Who can but feel profound indignation against an organization which could act thus in the name of God ? Yet in common fairness the reader should be reminded that, so far as the Church was concerned, there was in reality no *motive* of either punishment or persecution behind what might be called the ' theory ' of the Holy Inquisition.

' The Inquisition was not a court of justice to try heresy as a crime ; but rather a sort of spiritual board of health, whose office was to apply a salutary remedy, possibly a painful one, to stop the contagion of error, and if possible, to restore the heretic to the pale of salvation. The object was not conviction, but submission : not truth, but profession : this being once obtained, by whatever means, the sole end was accomplished.' [1]

Knowledge of Galileo's almost world-wide influence as a scholar and a philosopher prompted the most elaborate methods of bringing to the notice of Europe the full text of the recantation. It was read to all congregants from every pulpit ; it was read to all students by the professors at universities ; it was read publicly to all Galileo's friends and sympathizers in his own town of Florence.

7. *Galileo's Last Years*

The Pope interpreted the sentence of imprisonment mercifully. So far as close confinement was concerned, it lasted but four days, after which he was permitted a modified exile in the palace of the Archbishop Piccolomini at Siena.

Meanwhile the anxieties of the trial had broken the health of Galileo's daughter. As she lay dying, her last wish was naturally to see her father, so Galileo asked for permission to return to

[1] Powell's *Historical View of the Mathematical and Physical Sciences,* 1834, p. 177.

Arcetri. The wish was mercifully granted, and for the last time the two were permitted to see each other. A few days later she died. The grief-stricken old man now asked to be permitted to return to Florence, but fear of his possible influence at the scene of his former triumphs brought a stern refusal and a warning that he must content himself with confinement in the Villa Arcetri. So here he stayed on, broken by grief and by the infirmities of old age. Nevertheless, his intellect was as brilliantly active as ever, and he returned to his work. He devoted the next few years to the study of dynamics, and in his famous *Dialogues on Motion*, published under great difficulties (owing to the ecclesiastical ban on his works) in Amsterdam in 1636, he consolidated his earlier work on the subject at Pisa, and did all the spade work which later resulted in the enunciation of Newton's Laws of Motion, justly considered to be the foundation of the study of mechanics.

Virtually a prisoner—his own son was appointed to act as his warder—and with rapidly failing health, Galileo was at last seized with blindness. He accepted this misfortune, as he had done so many others before, with philosophic resignation.

'Your dear friend and servant, Galileo,' he wrote to Diodati in 1638, 'has been for the last month perfectly blind, so that this heaven, this earth, this universe, which I by my marvellous discoveries and clear demonstrations have enlarged a hundred thousand times beyond the belief of the wise men of bygone years, henceforward is for me shrunk into such a small space as is filled by my own bodily sensations. So it pleases God ; so also shall it therefore please me.'

Apparently he was now considered to be somewhat less dangerous to civilization, as we now find him permitted to receive friends. The highest in his own country vied with the eminent men of all other parts of Europe to do him homage and to express sympathy and admiration for him. Among others, by a strange irony of fate, Milton, doomed to blindness himself, visited Galileo. All who came were delighted to find his gift of conversation and old charm of manner unimpaired by his bodily infirmities. But the end was approaching. To his blindness there was added deafness, and at last he was seized with a low fever. He died on the 8th of January 1642, aged seventy-eight years.

Even in death his persecution was continued. At first the authorities refused him burial. Later they sanctioned an obscure burial, but permitted no monument over his grave. They then disputed his will, and even this did not suffice. They seized all the unpublished manuscript in the possession of his family, and what little they actually returned was 'offered up' as a 'burnt offering' by Galileo's grandson, Cosimo, as a preliminary act of devotion at the beginning of his career as a missionary.

Nowadays there exists a monument to his memory in the church of Santa Croce at Florence. Yet what finer monument to Galileo's memory can there be than the old leaning tower at Pisa—that silent witness of a great experiment by the man of whom it may truly be said 'he was the founder of experimental science'.

An age which still believed in witch-craft. Two Witches discovered.

VIII

RENÉ DESCARTES AND CO-ORDINATE GEOMETRY

1. *Early Life*

CONTEMPORARY with the latter half of Galileo's career there lived a man who, without rising to the brilliance in experiment and invention of the great Italian philosopher, nevertheless played a very significant part in the scientific history of the seventeenth century. René Descartes was a Frenchman of wide attainments, who greatly enriched the world by his writings in many branches of knowledge. He was a great metaphysician and he had also an important influence on biology. He wrote the first textbook of physiology. To him we are indebted for the origin of that branch of mathematical inquiry known as co-ordinate or analytical geometry.

FIG. 53. RENÉ DESCARTES

René Descartes was born at La Haye, near Tours, on the 31st of March 1596. He was the younger son of Joachim Descartes, a wealthy man of wide culture and noble lineage, who was accustomed to spend six months of the year at Rennes, in the local 'parliament' in which he was a councillor, and the remaining half on his family estate of Les Cartes, at La Haye.

There were two misfortunes attendant on the upbringing of young René. One was the death of his mother soon after he was born. The other was the fact that he was a delicate child. Bereft of her gentle guidance, and granted every wish by an over-anxious father, he developed a mild selfishness which displayed itself throughout his later life. Joachim Descartes was sufficiently wealthy to deny his children nothing ; they were brought up in the lap of luxury. He was, however, an observant man, and it was not long before he detected in René signs of unusual ability. Most healthy children continually ask questions. But the everlasting stream of questions which this child asked—there were no encyclopaedias for parents in those days—were almost too much for the harassed father. The type of question showed a high order of mentality in the child, and the elder Descartes jokingly called him ' the philosopher '.

At the age of eight René was sent to the Jesuit school at La Flêche, and was placed under the tuition of Father Charlet. The discipline and the education in this school were both excellent, and Descartes had little difficulty in mastering the ' learned languages and polite literature ' which formed the backbone of the course of studies there. He was allowed much licence on account of his delicate health. Thus he was permitted to remain in bed late in the mornings. This was a habit which persisted with him throughout his life, and he tells us that the best of his thinking was always done there ! Yet in spite of all the advantage offered by his school, and of the ease with which he mastered any work which was put before him, René Descartes seemed to derive no personal satisfaction from his studies. He developed neither enthusiasm nor hobbies, and if one can use the expression with regard to a youth of fifteen or sixteen, he seemed very much bored with life. His was evidently a very difficult personality, and with all its excellences, the Jesuit school at La Flèche failed to discover his sympathies.

When René left school in August 1612, it was without the slightest inclination on his part to pursue his studies any farther. For a short time he devoted himself to outdoor exercises, ' in learning to ride the great horse and to fence, and other such like actions suitable to his quality '. His health, however, did not permit him to continue this for very long, and so he was sent under the care of a kind of companion-tutor to Paris, there to play the gentleman in a manner befitting his station. The tutor-companion seemed to have had very little to do other than to ensure by a sort of judicious chaperonage, that the generous formula as to behaviour which Joachim Descartes had laid down for his son—namely, absolute freedom from all restrictions consistent with virtue and quality—was properly carried out.

2. *The Call to Science*

Descartes' whole upbringing had been that of an idle gentleman of wealth and station, and he had never taken life very seriously. Denied nothing, and thrown when still but a youth into the gaieties of Parisian life, and into the companionship of pleasure-loving people of his own age, it is probable that but for that abnormality of personality which had proved a puzzle to his tutors at school he might have sunk to a low level of profligacy. Evidently that same something in his character which bored him at work equally bored him at idle pleasure.

Conflicting forces, indeed, appear to have been at work during his stay in Paris. In 1615 he met with two men who influenced him strongly. One was Claude Mydorge, and the other an old friend of his schoolboy days, Father Marin Mersenne. Both were mathematicians of some note, and both saw the genius latent in the idler. They succeeded in rousing him to a liking for mathematics and philosophy sufficient to persuade him to devote himself to a detailed course of study. The effect was no doubt lasting, but at the time it seemed little more than a spurt, for in 1616 we again find him in the hands of his former friends, who appeared to have lured him back to the world of fashion. But this lapse did not last very long, and soon Descartes looked around him for a career of some kind. For men of his social standing, however, there was very little choice. The Army and the Church were practically the only alternatives. There was nothing of the churchman about René Descartes, and so the problem solved itself. Accordingly in 1617 he joined the army of Prince Maurice of Orange as a volunteer, and he became involved in the campaign then in progress between the Spanish and the Dutch.

It was whilst he was stationed in the garrison town of Breda, during a period of truce between the two armies, that a very significant incident occurred in his life. It seems that an anonymous person had mounted a placard in one of the main streets of the town, challenging the world to find a solution to a problem in geometry. Such challenges were to become very frequent later on in the same century, and indeed were destined to be the medium for considerable research in mathematics ; but in Descartes' early days a challenge of this kind was a distinct novelty.

Chance prompted him to stop and look at the placard. It was written in Dutch, and he was unfamiliar with the language, so he stopped the first passer-by with a request to translate the notice to him into French or Latin. As luck would have it, this passer-by was Isaac Beeckman, Principal of the Dutch College at Dort, and he offered to supply the translation on condition that Descartes would attempt a reply. Descartes took the problem home to his quarters and worked at it for a few hours, and to his delight succeeded in obtaining a correct solution. It was a revelation to him. He had enjoyed the tussle, and had discovered in himself a mathematical ability which he had not suspected, despite his previous work with Mersenne. He took the solution to Beeckman, who, too, was delighted with it, and a warm friendship sprang up between these two.

The remainder of Descartes' stay in Breda was very fruitful. He had little to do in the way of military duties, and he devoted himself to mathematical study and discussion in an ever-growing circle of friends of a philosophic turn of mind. Among other things he wrote a treatise on music. He would definitely have abandoned his military career, but family tradition impelled him to stay on. However, he tired of Breda, and took advantage of the beginning of the Thirty Years' War to leave Holland and volunteer early in 1619 in the army of the Duke of Bavaria.

So we find him at Neuberg after a season of campaigning on the Danube, and here, on the night of the 10th of November 1619, there occurred that emotional experience which determined his future career as a philosopher and mathematician. Something turned his thoughts in the direction of mathematics, and presumably he was thinking of a possible relationship between the hitherto separate subjects of algebra and geometry. The idea suddenly flashed through his mind of the fixing of a point in a plane by referring it to two lines at right angles to each other. His powerful mental vision fastened on this, and upon all the possible developments to which it could give rise, and soon the idea became an obsession. That night, so he tells us, he dreamt three separate dreams which he regarded as a clear call to him to abandon his former mode of life, and to take up the mission of developing his new line of mathematical reasoning, and from that to explain the mystery of the universe.

3. *Holland—The Vortex Theory*

Descartes did not immediately abandon his military career, but he never lost sight of his great idea and his new purpose. The campaign of 1620 was a busy one for him. He was present at the sieges of Prague, Pressburg, Tirnaw, &c., but he was rapidly tiring of this kind of life, and in 1621, after the raising of the siege of Neuhausel, he resigned his commission and definitely abandoned the profession of arms. He was twenty-six years of age, and even now he did not settle down. For five years he travelled, dividing his time between sight-seeing and the study of mathematics.

In 1626 he returned to Paris, a very different Descartes from the one who had lived an aimless life of gaiety there ten years before. He shunned his old haunts, and devoted himself to the theory and construction of optical instruments, which, it will be remembered, were attaining general prominence about this time. Soon his presence began to be known, and men of science and learning sought him out. Cardinal de Bérulle, the Pope's Nuncio, in particular was much impressed by the general trend of Descartes's views, and successfully urged upon him the task of devoting his life seriously to their development and presentation to the world. Descartes acquiesced, and decided to take up his residence in Holland for that purpose, and thither he went in 1628, the year which may be regarded as the real beginning of his active career as a scientific publicist in mathematics and philosophy.

What were his methods ? He was not a member of the experimental school of Galileo and Gilbert. He had very little to do with the laboratory, except perhaps in his work on anatomy. His methods were essentially those of the mathematician. He would start with a statement of fact—an enunciation of a definite principle, and working from it, he would develop, step by step, a logical sequence of deductions until he had built up a complete scheme. He was in a sense a pioneer of the mathematical study of nature. ' Comparing the mysteries of nature with the laws of mathematics, he dared to hope that the secrets of both could be unlocked with the same key.' To guide himself in developing his scheme of work, he compared the problems of nature to a tree of which metaphysics was the root and physics the trunk. The three chief branches dealt with the external world (mechanics), the human body (medicine), and human conduct (morals), and to these subjects he rigidly confined himself.

As a result of his first four years of labour in Holland, Descartes had practically completed a work which he called the *System of the World*. It contained his theory of ' vortices ' which was later to bring him the widest possible notice. Yet he never published it. The reason is interesting. The book neared its completion in 1633, just at the time of Galileo's famous trial before the Holy Inquisition at Rome, followed by the recantation. The news took Descartes by surprise. He was not of the stuff of which heroes are made. He had no ambitions for any conflict with the Church, for he had no illusions as to its power. He liked his theories, and he liked publicity, but he had no desire for martyrdom. So he decided at once against publication. He wrote to Father Mersenne : ' I confess that if the opinion of the earth's movement be false, all the foundations of my philosophy are so also, because it is demonstrated clearly by them. It is so bound up with every part of my treatise that I could not sever it without making the remainder faulty ; and although I consider all my conclusions based on very certain and clear demonstrations, I would not for all the world sustain them against the authority of the Church.'

He did not burn his manuscript, as he at first threatened to do, but extended it, for eleven years later, in 1644, he did in fact publish the book under the title of *Principia Philosophiae*, having found some ' formula ' which he thought might reconcile the Church to its acceptance. As a matter of fact it did not do so, and the work was placed on the ' Index ' of prohibited books. In spite of this, however, it obtained a wide publicity.

Descartes's theory of vortices caused a great stir in the world of philosophy. According to this theory, matter was endowed with the properties of extension, impenetrability, and inertia. Such matter, said Descartes, fills all space. This is the first point he makes. His second point is this, that every portion of this matter is endowed with motion, or the possibility of motion, in every conceivable direction. Arguing from this, he held that such a combination of motions made rectilinear or straight line motion absolutely impossible. On the other hand, there was a continual tendency to deflexion from such motion ; a continual tendency, in other words, to circular motion, and hence to the phenomenon we speak of as centrifugal force.

From this to the formation of multitudes of whirlpools or vortices was but one step, the lighter portions of matter forming the real vortex, and the heavier portions ' floating ' within ; and each vortex, in addition to its own rotary motion, is carried round bodily with its heavy nucleus. The universe, therefore, consisted of vast numbers of these vortices, all limiting and circumscribing each other.

Applying this to the Solar System, Descartes held that the planets (including the earth) are carried round in the great vortex of which the sun is the main nucleus. The normal pressure exerted on the planets by the ' light ' matter composing the solar vortex (the modern substitute for which is the ether) would tend to draw the planets (i. e. make them fall) into the sun, but this is counterbalanced by the equal and opposite and centrifugal force normally outwards. In the same way, each planet is itself the nucleus of a lesser vortex, and so on.

There is something very remarkable in the eager and almost universal acceptance which this theory received, particularly in

England. It will be noticed that *the theory leads to circular orbits only*, and yet Kepler had definitely established his laws of planetary motion beyond all doubt. There was evidently something in it which satisfied the philosophic hunger of those times, and it probably lies in the fact that the theory of vortices was a complete *theory with explanations*, as compared with Kepler's bald *facts without explanations*. It made a powerful and an effective appeal to the imagination.

In these days, Descartes's theory is a relic in the museum of scientific literature, but, abandoned as it is to-day, it served an important purpose then. From the time of Copernicus there had been attempts to break away from the Aristotelian tradition, yet no such attempt had received universal acceptance. In spite of all, Aristotle still held the field. But Descartes's theory of vortices brought about a remarkable change. Everybody accepted it, and almost in the space of a generation it began to be taught in the universities.

4. *Cartesian Mathematics*

In 1637 Descartes published at Leyden the book which contains his invention of co-ordinate geometry. Its full title was *Discours de la méthode pour bien conduire sa raison et chercher la verité dans les sciences*, but it is more commonly referred to as the *Discours*.

The first portion of the book is not devoted to mathematics, however, but to optics, and it is right that we should note the more important contributions he made in this subject. He took up the subject of refraction, and enunciated the law now spoken of as Snell's Law. It has been suggested that he derived this law from Snell.

Descartes next investigated the problem of the focus of a spherical lens. The usual formula given is

$$\frac{1}{v} - \frac{1}{u} = \frac{1}{f},$$

using the customary notation.

If the reader is sufficiently interested to follow up the proof of this simple formula, he will find that it is only an approximation, and that it is based on the assumption that all rays are taken very near to the axis. In fact there is no real point-focus to a spherical lens. There is instead a focal region, and Descartes tackled the problem of finding out what must be the shape of a lens to give a real point-focus. He proved the answer to be a curve of the fourth degree, and in certain cases a curve of the second degree, i. e. a conic. However, owing to the practical difficulties of workmanship in fashioning such a lens, Descartes's work was of little practical value in his own time.

Descartes also tackled the problem of the rainbow. This, so far as the primary bow was concerned, had already been explained by Antonio de Dominis, Archbishop of Spalatro, in 1611, in a work, *De Radiis Visus et Lucis*.

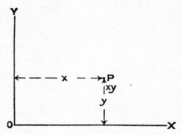

Now all careful observers of the phenomenon of the rainbow know that above the usual bright bow there is another, sometimes very faint, at other times much more distinct, spoken of as the 'secondary bow'. Descartes succeeded in explaining this bow, and he accurately traced out the paths of the rays which produce it.

FIG. 54.   Cartesian Geometry. The co-ordinates of a point with respect to two axes of reference.

We now turn to the mathematical portion of the *Discours* ; that which deals with Descartes's discovery of the principle of co-ordinate geometry. The basic feature is that a point in a plane can be completely fixed if we know its perpendicular distances from two arbitrarily chosen lines of reference OX and OY (Fig. 54). These distances, usually designated by x and y, are termed the co-ordinates of the point, and given such co-ordinates, the point is as surely fixed in the plane as is a place on the earth's surface when its latitude and longitude are given.

Again, suppose we are told nothing more definite about a point than that one co-ordinate is always twice as much as the other ; that is to say, that x is always equal to $2y$. As a statement in algebra we may put it thus :

$$x = 2y.$$

We may now try to represent such a point with regard to Descartes's two axes of reference, OX and OY. We have only the one fact to go upon, that $x = 2y$, and we find that there are any number of points, P_1, P_2, P_3, &c. (Fig. 55), for which this is true, and we quickly see that all these points lie upon a straight line passing through the origin O (the point of inter-

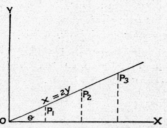

Fig. 55. Cartesian Geometry. Application to a straight line.

section of OX and OY), and having its inclination to OX such that $\tan \theta = \frac{1}{2}$.

This straight line is in fact the geometrical representation of the algebraical statement that $x = 2y$; and conversely, the equation $x = 2y$ is the algebraical representation of the geometrical fact that a line is such that every point on it has its x co-ordinate twice the length of its y co-ordinate. So we see how Descartes succeeded in welding together the hitherto separate subjects of algebra and geometry.

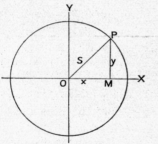

Fig. 56. Cartesian Geometry. Application to a circle.

Let us take another example. Suppose we are again not definitely told what are the co-ordinates of the point, but that the point is to be such that the sum of the squares of the two co-ordinates gives a constant answer. For example, suppose we are told that $x^2 + y^2 = 25$. Clearly any point on a circle of centre O (the origin) and radius 5 units will satisfy the required condition, since if we consider any right-angled triangle such as POM (Fig. 56), where PM is the y of the point and OM is its x co-ordinate, we must always have

$$OP^2 = OM^2 + PM^2$$
$$= x^2 + y^2$$

and if $OP = 5$, OP^2 will be 25, giving the required condition. Here again we may say that the equation $x^2 + y^2 = 25$ is the algebraical representation of a geometrical fact, namely, a circle of radius 5 units, with centre at the origin ; or we may put it that drawing such a circle is a geometrical representation of the algebraical fact that $x^2 + y^2 = 25$.

But it would be a mistake to say that analytical geometry is the mere application of algebra to geometry, or of geometry to algebra. It is the linking up of the two subjects into what becomes a completely new branch of mathematical inquiry. So we may speak of $x^2 + y^2 = 25$ as a circle, and we should by so doing be speaking just as correctly as we should if we were to call $x^2 + y^2 = 25$ an equation. It is a circle, and it conveys indirectly all the information which the word 'circle' conveys to the mathematical student. Any particular property of the circle which can be brought out by a careful geometrical construction can be just as surely brought out by direct algebraical processes without even so much as drawing a figure.

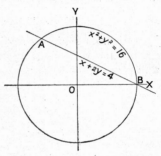

FIG. 57. Cartesian Geometry. Intersection of straight line and circle.

As an example, for the benefit of those readers who care to have one, suppose we consider the problem of the intersection of a circle and a straight line. We know that $x^2 + y^2 = 16$ is a circle ; and that $x + 2y = 4$ is a straight line. To see where they intersect, we could *draw* them, as in Fig. 57, and see from the figure where they cut. But we can dispense with a drawing. For the points A and B lie on *both* the circle and the straight line simultaneously, so that the two statements $x^2 + y^2 = 16$

and $x + 2y = 4$

are simultaneously true. Hence we can treat the problem as the solution of two simultaneous equations in algebra.

From the second equation, $x = 4 - 2y$.

Substituting this value for x in the first equation, we get :

$$(4-2y)^2+y^2 = 16$$
$$\text{i. e. } 16-16y+4y^2+y^2 = 16$$
$$\text{i. e. } \qquad 5y^2-16y = 0$$
$$\text{i. e. } \qquad y(5y-16) = 0$$

whence
$$y = 0 \text{ or } \frac{16}{5}$$

giving
$$x = 4 \text{ or } -\frac{12}{5}$$

So that the two points of intersection of the line and the circle are those whose co-ordinates are

$$(x = 4, y = 0) \text{ and } \left(x = -\frac{12}{5}, \ y = \frac{16}{5}\right).$$

There is no need for us to discuss Descartes's development of this line of thought, or his application of it to tangents. The main thing is to appreciate the enormous value of the fundamental idea as a contribution to mathematical inquiry. It is for this that he is included in these pages.

5. *Descartes's Later Life*

After the publication of the *Discours* in 1637, Descartes worked steadily on, publishing his *Méditations* in 1641 and the *Principia Philosophiae* in 1644. This latter, it will be remembered, contained his famous theory of vortices, and so enthusiastic was its reception in his own native France that in 1647 the French Court granted him a pension as a reward for his labours.

Descartes was taking his life seriously. It will be remembered that as a child of very delicate health he had contracted the habit of early thinking and late rising. The habit stuck to him. He thought out all his problems in bed, rose late, and devoted his afternoons to social functions and exercise. He was always scrupulously careful about his health, and it was his definitely expressed ambition to die of a ripe old age.

It was an ambition which did not materialize, for in 1649 he was invited by Queen Christina of Sweden to join her Court in the rôle of philosophic tutor. Christina was a somewhat shallow-minded lady who liked to be surrounded by great minds.

Descartes hesitated. He was fifty-three years of age, and he dreaded the cold climate of a Swedish winter. Moreover, Queen Christina was a very early riser, and he was faced with the prospect of giving lessons in philosophy at five in the morning ! To break the lifelong habit of late rising was naturally a most serious matter, and there is no wonder that he hesitated. However, Descartes loved adulation, and the idea of intimate proximity with royalty proved too tempting. So he went to Stockholm. It was a fatal decision. The strain proved too great for so delicate a man, and he broke down under it. He developed inflammation of the lungs, and the Court physician could do nothing for him. He died on the 11th February 1650. He was at first buried in Stockholm, but seventeen years later his body was removed to Paris, where a magnificent monument was erected to his memory in the Church of Ste. Geneviève.

Descartes was a very great man. We have said nothing here of his eminent contributions to anatomy, biology, and moral philosophy. In these, as in mathematics and physics, he left his mark.

In appearance he ' was a small man with large head, projecting brow, prominent nose, and black hair coming down to his eyebrows. His voice was feeble. Considering the range of his studies he was by no means widely read, and he despised both learning and art unless something tangible could be extracted therefrom '.[1]

There was much that was selfish in his character, and he was very jealous of his rivals. He was so far influenced by this as purposely to obscure his meanings and his language. In his *Discours* he freely confesses ' Je n'ai rien omis qu'à dessein . . . j'avois prévu que certaines gens qui se vantent de sçavoir tout n'auroient pas manqué de dire que je n'avois rien écrit qu'ils n'eussent sçu auparavant, si je me fusse rendu assez intelligible pour eux '. On the other hand, he does not always give credit to his contemporaries when credit is fairly due to them. Thus, when he wrote on the rainbow, he made no mention of Father Dominis and his work, although he must have been considerably indebted to him on the subject.

[1] Rouse Ball, *History of Mathematics.*

IX

SIR ISAAC NEWTON

1. *Science in the Seventeenth Century*

WE may now pause to take stock of the scientific position in the middle of the seventeenth century. That position, fortunately, was a very different one from that of a hundred years before. It was much more favourable to further progress. The outstanding fact was the overthrow of the Aristotelian tradition. The first warning blast of the attacking forces was sounded by the publication of Copernicus's *De revolutionibus orbium caelestium* in the year of his death 1543, and for one hundred years the fight had been carried on, at first by Kepler and his followers, and later by the experimental school of philosophy headed by Galileo on the Continent and Gilbert in England. It was an uphill fight of reason against prejudice, and although the forces of prejudice were strong, the logic of reason was stronger. The result was never more than a question of time. The world was ready for a new doctrine, and we have seen what a powerful effect was produced by Descartes's Theory of Vortices. It is curious that after the spade-work of investigation, experiment, and observation had been done by Kepler, Galileo, and Gilbert, the final overthrow of the Aristotelians should have been produced by what has since proved to be a futile speculation, having foundation in neither fact nor experiment.

FIG. 58.   SIR ISAAC NEWTON

There is no question of the reality of the deep interest which was developing in the realms of scientific inquiry at this time. Much of this development was undoubtedly due in particular to the writings of two men—Francis Bacon (1561–1626) in England, and René Descartes in France and Holland. Much controversy has raged round the question of Francis Bacon's merits as a leader of scientific thought. He was not a scientist, but he wrote on scientific method in his *Novum Organum,* and laid down a comprehensive scheme of principles which he considered should guide procedure in scientific inquiry. Apart from their intrinsic value (probably in these days very little), his writings achieved a wide publicity and commanded an attention, the effect of which must not be underestimated. There is no doubt that Francis Bacon gained for science the receptive ear of the public at large, and contributed to an interest in research which made smoother the thorny path of the student of nature.

Descartes, too, in his *Discourse on Method* gave an equally great impetus to scientific inquiry on the Continent. He taught clearly and successfully that no statement was necessarily true because some one of authority in the past had made it.

A sign of the times was the appearance during this period, for the first time in history, of various learned societies in different European centres, whose object it was to bring together men of a philosophic turn of mind for friendly discussion and argument. Thus in 1603 there was founded in Italy the Lincean Society, under the patronage of the Marchese Federigo Cesi. Galileo was himself an active member of it, and after a period of decline it was succeeded by the famous Florentine School of physicists who in 1657 banded together to form the Accademia del Cimento, with which were associated such illustrious names as Viviani and Torricelli and their disciples. In France the Royal Academy of Sciences was founded in 1666, during the reign of Louis XIV, and much about the same time the Institute of Bologna was also formed.

The formation of such institutions was first advocated by Francis Bacon in his writings, so it is not a matter for surprise that England, too, early developed its learned society. In 1645 there began to gather together a body of men in Oxford, who afterwards united again in London under a royal charter of incorporation by Charles II in 1662, to form the Royal Society for the Advancement of Learning.

Finally, mention should be made of the fact that during this period observational astronomy received its first recognition in the establishment of the great national observatories—that of Paris in 1667 and of Greenwich in 1675.

Such, then, were the conditions under which the pursuit of knowledge was fostered in the middle of the seventeenth century. It is not surprising, therefore, that the latter half of the century and the beginning of the eighteenth century proved to be an era of remarkable scientific activity, characterized by tremendous strides in mathematics and physics. This period, too, produced a galaxy of brilliant philosophers and mathematicians of the first magnitude. Boyle, Hooke, and Halley in England ; Leibnitz, Huyghens, Torricelli, Pascal, Cassini, and Guericke on the Continent, were but a few of them. Towering head and shoulders above all his contemporaries, a veritable giant among the giants, a man whose intellect and whose contributions to knowledge are incomparably greater than those of any other scientist of the past, was that prince of philosophers, Sir Isaac Newton.

2. *Newton's Early Life*

The Newtons were yeomen of Lincolnshire, with a local tradition dating back to the fifteenth century. Theirs was not a very large estate, but such as it was it had always been zealously husbanded and passed on from generation to generation. It was situated in the manor of Woolsthorpe, near Grantham, and it was here that Isaac Newton was born on Christmas Day 1642, the year of Galileo's death. His father, unfortunately, had died just before this at the very early age of thirty-six, and the responsibility for Isaac's upbringing devolved upon his mother.

He was by no means a healthy baby. His life was despaired of on more than one occasion. However, with the watchful care of his mother, he must have soon thrown off these ' symptoms of an early death ', since he lived to be eighty-five years old.

Isaac's mother did not long remain a widow. She married again, and went to live with her new husband, the Rev. Barnabas Smith, at North Witham. Isaac did not accompany her, but was looked after by his grandmother, Mrs. Ayscough, who came to Woolsthorpe.

At the age of twelve, Isaac was sent to the King's School at Grantham, staying meantime at the home of the local apothecary. At first he did not shine at school, nor had he any inclination to do so. Indeed he tells us that he was for some time the lowest boy in the lowest class but one. He was just a healthy, normal, mischief-loving boy, without a care. Like his Continental

FIG. 59. The Manor-house, Woolsthorpe ; the birthplace of Sir Isaac Newton, showing the solar dials he made when a boy.

predecessor, Galileo, however, he very soon manifested a strong inclination for the making of mechanical models—kites, wind-mills, and the like. There is a story that he once tied paper lanterns to the tail of a kite he had made, and sent it up at night with the object of deluding the people into believing that they were watching a comet ; and another, that after days of watching some workmen construct a windmill in the neighbourhood he made an excellent working model of one for himself.

An important little event in school life now happened which was something of a revelation to both Newton himself and those around him. He fought a fight against odds and won. It seems that a bigger boy kicked him. No one worth an ounce of salt takes a kicking lying down. So Newton fought the boy and thrashed him. The affair set young Newton thinking. The boy was higher up in the class than he, and he argued to himself that if he could thrash the fellow at fists he could thrash him at

FIG. 60. Grantham Free Grammar-school, restored 1857
The school of Sir Isaac Newton.

work. He set to work to do it, and did more. He rose to the top of his class !

At the age of fifteen he was withdrawn from school by his mother owing to the death of her second husband. She had now returned to Woolsthorpe, and was anxious to maintain the yeoman traditions of the Newtons. As Isaac Newton was to own his property in the near future, it was just as well, she thought, that he should start early at farming and husbandry. But there was nothing of the farmer in Isaac. He had developed the study of mechanical contrivances and all that pertained thereto into an absorbing interest. However, he kept the fact to himself. He evidently felt that if his mother were to know of it he would have to do a little more farming and far less studying. So he said nothing, but every week, when he was sent in to Grantham with an old servant on market days to do the necessary buying and selling for the farm, he managed to steal a few hours for his books and models. He had evidently got on the right side of the old servant, who was prevailed upon to go alone to Grantham, leaving young Newton to his books at some convenient point on the way.

If his mother saw nothing of his student proclivities, she at least saw he was making a poor farmer, and being puzzled as to what to do about it she turned to a brother for advice and help. This gentleman, a parson, sought out Isaac to have a chat with him. He expected to find him farming. Instead, he found him reading a book on mathematics. He was sensible enough to realize the impossibility of the position, and as a result of his subsequent talks with his sister, back went Isaac Newton to the Grantham Grammar-school, this time with the definite object of preparing himself for a university career at Cambridge, and here he pursued the usual course of classics common to the schools of those times. At the age of eighteen, in the year 1660, he left Grantham with the blessings of his head master and the good wishes of his fellow pupils, and entered Trinity College, Cambridge.

3. *At Cambridge*

Hitherto young Newton had had no opportunity of displaying his great intellect. It is very probable that he was unconscious of his own mental powers. Nevertheless his chance had now come. Lectures were of little use to him. His mind worked far more rapidly than the prescribed pace laid down by a scheme of lectures. He worked through a series of books, starting with Euclid's *Elements*, which he found very easy. Kepler's *Optics*, too, gave him no difficulties. He next tackled Descartes's *Geometry*, and this, though he confesses that he did so with difficulty, he mastered too.

From this he passed on to other books, and now he was sufficiently sure of himself to become somewhat critical in his reading, and his criticisms and comments (and frequently improvements) were to be seen in the form of marginal notes completely filling all the available blank spaces of the books he read.

The Lucasian Professor of Mathematics under whom Newton worked was Dr. Isaac Barrow. He was an eminent mathematician and a discerning man of science, and it was not long before he noticed Newton's remarkable abilities. He encouraged Newton to see him frequently and to discuss his work with him. The warm friendship that sprang up between them had far-reaching results later in the invention of the calculus—that branch of higher mathematics which has so completely revolutionized practically every branch of science.

For the first few years he devoted himself mainly to mathematics. They were fruitful years, but we will defer our record of his mathematical discoveries for the moment. At the age of 22 he took his B.A. degree, and a year later, in 1665, an outbreak of plague caused the university to be temporarily closed. So Newton retired to the quiet of his own home in Woolsthorpe, Lincolnshire, staying there till 1667.

It was during this period that he turned his thoughts to those speculations on the subject of gravity which resulted in his famous enunciation of the inverse square law of universal gravitation, and enabled him later to give a definite proof of the three laws of planetary motion discovered, but left unexplained, by Kepler.

In 1667 Isaac Newton, now a Fellow of his college, returned to Trinity and went ahead at his researches in mathematics, optics, and dynamics. There was little that his fertile brain did not tackle, and when he was still in his twenties he had achieved more than would have been considered a brilliant lifework in many another man of fame. The differential calculus, the perfection of the reflecting telescope, the beginning of spectrum analysis, the law of universal gravitation, were but a few of a host of different original investigations for which he was responsible. And he did it all quietly. His notes were voluminous, but he published little, and for a time only those with whom he came into intimate contact knew of his researches. Much of the work had only reached its early stages, and a portion of Newton's later life was to be spent in maturing and perfecting his earlier investigations.

Nevertheless his genius was fully apparent to his professor, Dr. Isaac Barrow. Barrow was a churchman as well as a mathematician. There were many problems in theology of interest to him, for which he desired more time. He fully recognized in Newton a man superior to him in mathematical and scientific ability. So in 1669 he resigned his professorship in Newton's favour. Newton was twenty-six years of age on the date of his appointment, and he held the professorship for the next twenty-five years.

Let us consider briefly a few of the more important of his contributions to knowledge, taking in turn his work in optics, in dynamics, and in mathematics.

4. *Newton's Work in Optics*

Newton's work in optics may be said to have dated from 1664, in which year he is known to have purchased a prism, ' to try the celebrated phenomenon of colours '. His work, however, could not have been of great value until 1669, for in the year previous to this his friend Dr. Barrow had published a very faulty *Theory of Colours* in the preparation of which we know him to have freely consulted Newton.

It will be remembered that Descartes had investigated the problem of determining the correct surface of a lens which would possess a proper point-focus, i. e. which would be free from the error known in optics as spherical aberration ; and he found that under certain conditions a paraboloidal surface would do. Newton attempted to follow this up practically by trying to grind lenses in the laboratory to the required shape. It was difficult, but it soon led Newton to a discovery of importance, for he saw that, however accurately the grinding was performed, he kept getting what we may vaguely term ' colour troubles ', and what students of optics will recognize by the name of ' chromatic aberration '.

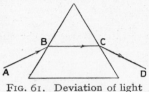

FIG. 61. Deviation of light by prism.

Newton thought this over and began to suspect a relationship of some kind which could produce different refrangibilities for different colours.

This led to his famous experiments with the prism which were the historical beginnings of the vast modern subject of spectrum analysis. It is, of course, well known that when a ray of light AB (Fig. 61) passes through a triangular prism of glass it undergoes two successive bendings, or refractions BC and CD, each being a deflection towards the thicker portion of the prism.

Newton's experiment was as follows. He arranged a small round hole H (Fig. 62) in the window shutter AB of a darkened room. A narrow beam of sunlight was admitted through the

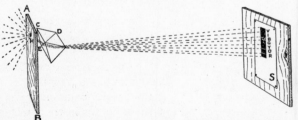

FIG. 62. Newton's experiment on the dispersion of white light.

shutter at H, and gave a spot of white light on a screen S opposite the shutter.

Newton now interposed a prism CDE as in the figure. The effect was twofold. The light was, of course, refracted or bent as in Fig. 61. But, further, the circular spot became elongated into a band of coloured light nearly five times its breadth, the succession of tints passing insensibly from one to another, and

showing different degrees of refrangibility for different colours. Newton detected seven main colour types—red, orange, yellow, green, blue, indigo, and violet, the red being bent least and the violet most.

Mark how carefully Newton tackled the problem of interpreting this experiment. Why were the rays spread out? Perhaps, thought he, because the rays nearer the vertex E have less glass to pass through and so suffer less bending. He tried sending one ray through a thin portion of the prism, and another through the thicker portion. From each he got a spectrum, and both were of the same length. That settled that question. Then, perhaps, the elongated band is produced by a flaw in the glass. So he tried other prisms, but always he obtained the spectrum band. Further, he argued that if it were due to a flaw, then the trouble would be doubled by doubling the prism, i. e. having two of the same vertical angle. He arranged these with one reversed, as in Fig. 63, and found that so far from doubling the effect of colour, they appeared to nullify each other. He got neither band nor colour effect, but a normal undistorted image. So this explanation, too, had to be rejected.

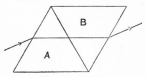

FIG. 63.   Recombination of light by double prism.

He next thought that possibly it may be due to the fact that the rays entering the hole H in Fig. 62, from different portions of the sun's disk, would be slightly inclined to each other. But calculation showed even this to be a negligible consideration. However, he had still not exhausted the possibilities. Perhaps the effect of the prism was to bend the rays into curves which would strike the screen at different degrees of obliquity, producing the effect of elongation. So he tested the length of the spectrum at different distances from the prisms. It was always in direct proportion to the distance, however, proving the rays to be rectilinear.

Note how carefully the problems were being reduced to narrower limits. Newton was forced to conclude that the question of colour must vitally affect the explanation of the whole phenomenon, and he determined to *isolate the rays of one colour only*, and experiment upon each in turn. How was he to do this? Refer back to Fig. 62. Suppose we have a hole pricked in the screen *S* at the place where one of the rays, say the green, falls on it. Then, whilst all other colours are stopped by the screen, the green ray passes on and can be experimented upon. Newton did this. He isolated each colour in turn, and made it pass through a second prism, and in each case carefully measured the refraction produced. He was careful to arrange for each colour to enter the same point of the prism at the same angle, in order to make the comparisons scrupulously fair. He was delighted to find that, *proceeding along the spectrum colours from red to violet, the refrangibility steadily increased.*

The conclusion was, therefore, that sunlight, or white light, is not homogeneous, but is 'made up' of many differently coloured rays of differing refrangibilities (or refractive indices), these being least for red rays and most for violet rays, and that as a consequence the effect of a prism will be to separate out these primary rays or colours by their different degrees of refraction. This spreading out of the rays is spoken of as the phenomenon *of dispersion of light.*

It will not be difficult for the reader to see now that an arrangement of two prisms such as is shown in Fig. 63 will cause a reuniting of the rays separated out by the first prism, and giving as a result no colours or dispersion of any kind whatever.

Nor was it difficult for Newton to perceive why lenses produce 'colour trouble' (chromatic aberration), no matter how perfect

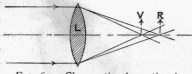

FIG. 64. Chromatic aberration in lenses.

the shape might be from the point of view of 'spherical aberration'. For to each different colour there would correspond a different point-focus, the nearest being, say, *V* (Fig. 64) for the most refrangible violet rays, and the farthest *R* for the least refrangible red rays. So that, instead of a sharp point-focus, there could only be a coloured patch *VR*.

Newton came to the conclusion that the use of the principle of refraction in optical instruments was undesirable, and he turned his attention accordingly to the construction of reflecting telescopes. Now this question had also been attempted by James Gregory. The whole matter was a question of design. For, given a good speculum or spherical mirror M (Fig. 65), the rays

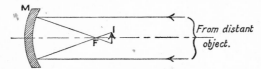

FIG. 65.   The principle of the Reflecting Telescope.

falling on it from a distant object would produce an image I near the focus F, and this could be suitably magnified by a small lens of some kind. Nothing could be simpler. But there is a real difficulty nevertheless. Where can the head of the observer be placed so as to view the image without interfering with the incident rays ?

Gregory's suggestion was one which involved cutting a small circular hole in the middle of the mirror, and telescopes of this

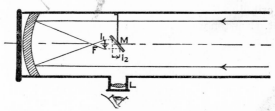

FIG. 66.   Principle of Newton's Reflecting Telescope.

kind are occasionally seen. But Newton's suggestion was somewhat simpler. The image I, having been formed, a small mirror M, supported at an angle of $45°$ to the axis, produced a further horizontal image I_2, and this could be viewed directly through a small lens L in the side of the case of the instrument, giving both increased magnification and comfort of observation.

Newton's first telescope was small—one inch in diameter and six inches long—yet it gave a magnification of forty. The concave mirror was prepared from a mixture of copper and tin, and gave a very clear image. His second instrument was better, and was presented by him to the Royal Society in 1671. They were delighted with it, and expressed their thanks by electing Newton a Fellow. As to the actual importance of Newton's work on reflecting telescopes it will suffice to point out that all the giant telescopes of the world's best observatories are made on the reflecting principle.

Yet how was Newton's work on optics received by his contemporaries? Newton communicated an account of his experiment on colour to the Royal Society in 1671, and in a letter to Oldenburgh, the secretary to the Royal Society, he described his work as ' an account of a philosophical discovery which induced me to the making of the telescope : and I doubt not but will prove much more grateful than the communication of that instrument ; being, in my judgement, the oddest, if not the most considerable detection which hath hitherto been made in the operations of nature '.

In England these communications were at first well received, but on the Continent there developed an extraordinary outburst of petty antagonism to Newton, the arguments advanced by way of criticism being frequently as ignorant as they were persistent. Newton was exceedingly sensitive to these criticisms. He never courted publicity in any shape or form, and he preferred to leave these criticisms unanswered. But Oldenburgh prevailed upon him to reply, and having vanquished his Continental ' critics ', he prepared to withdraw himself from publicity once more. But a formidable critic now appeared at home in the person of Dr. Hooke, an able Fellow of the Royal Society. Looking back on the records of those times it must be confessed that Hooke was prompted by motives of jealousy at Newton's success in problems which had baffled him. It is immaterial what exactly were Hooke's arguments and contentions. Newton answered them both with dignity and force, but it left his sensitive nature somewhat outraged. ' I find it yet against the grain to put pen to paper any more on that subject ', wrote he to Oldenburgh, whilst to the illustrious Leibnitz he expressed himself thus : ' I was so persecuted with discussions arising from the publication of my theory of light, that I blamed my own imprudence for parting with so substantial a blessing as my quiet, to run after a shadow.'

Newton's activities on the subject of optics continued unabated. He took up the subject of colours as seen on viewing a soap film, and he developed the subject of ' Newton's Rings ', as they are now called.

5. *Rival Theories of Light*

Mention must, however, be made of Newton's views as to the nature of light. It is, of course, obvious that the question, 'What is light ? ' must have presented itself to Newton as it did to many others, and he tried to supply an answer. His answer, as it turns out, was wrong. The matter is historically interesting, since round it there

CHRISTIANUS HUGENIUS
natus 14 Aprilis 1629.
denatus 8 Junii 1695

Fig. 67. CHRISTIAN HUYGHENS

centred a scientific controversy whose solution depended upon a test which was in fact only supplied after the death of both Newton and his illustrious opponent in the controversy, Huyghens.

Christian Huyghens was a Dutch scientist of this period. He was born at the Hague in 1629 and excelled both as a physicist and a mathematician. One of his best-known pieces of work was his continuation of Galileo's researches on the pendulum. The original form of the pendulum was such that to obtain isochronism —that is to say, continuously equally-timed beats—it was necessary to have small swings in a circular arc. But as a result of Huyghen's investigations into the mathematical properties

of the curve known as the cycloid he was able in 1658 to invent
the cycloidal pendulum, and this was able to keep accurate time
swinging over wide distances or amplitudes. Huyghens had also
done valuable work in astronomy with a ten-feet-long telescope
he had made in 1659, accurately describing the rings round
Saturn for the first time. He came to England in 1660 at the
invitation of the Royal Society, and his friendship with Newton
began some years later. He afterwards settled in France, and
it was in the year 1678 that he presented to the ' Académie des
Sciences ' his famous ' undulatory theory ' of light which represented his attempt to answer the question ' What is light ? '
and which became the opposition side to Newton's in the historic
controversy of their rival theories.

What was Huyghen's undulatory theory ? Curiously enough,
it was based on one of Newton's discoveries. Newton had shown
that the phenomenon of *sound* is caused by the vibration of air
particles being transmitted from the object producing the sound
to the ear receiving it, the vibrations being propagated in ' waves '
very much in the same way as ' waves ' are transmitted outward
in a pond from some point of disturbance. If the sound is
' excited ' by striking a harp string, for example, then the shorter
and tighter the string, the more rapid will be the vibrations, and
as a consequence the more shrill the note.

' Light', said Huyghens, ' is a phenomenon of vibrations like
sound, but simply on a different scale of size, the vibrations
being ever so much smaller and more rapid.' ' Yes,' was the
answer of his critics, ' but if that is so, then what is the vibrating
medium corresponding to the air in sound, since, for example,
there is no air between the sun and the earth in the millions of
miles of space, and therefore there is no medium to pass on the
vibrations of the sun's light to the earth ? ' Huyghen's answer
was of profound importance. ' There *is* a medium,' said he, ' and
it pervades all space. It is highly elastic and extremely attenu-
ated, passing between the particles of solid objects just as freely
as it occupies outer space.' This universal medium Huyghens
called the *ether*, and any source of light, e. g. the sun, sets up the
vibrations in the ether, and these vibrations are passed on with

tremendous rapidity (186,000 miles per second, as we now know). When these undulations or waves strike the eye they affect us physiologically with the sensations of vision. 'But', asked his critics, 'if the light waves are travelling in the sky, why do we have darkness?' The answer again was simple and decisive. 'You cannot hear sound unless your ear drum stops a sound-wave. The wave may pass you without touching your ear, and you hear nothing. A stick may move rapidly, and if you stop it with your head it will affect you physiologically with the sensation of *pain*; yet if it passes you by you feel nothing. Similarly with light. The wave may be there, but unless it impinges on your eye it will not affect you physiologically with the sensation of light.' The waves, in fact, produce an effect as though light travels in straight lines.

And what, on the other hand, was Newton's rival theory? He called it the 'Emission' or 'Corpuscular Theory'. According to this light is composed of streams of minute invisible particles of matter emitted from the luminous source in straight lines at very high velocity. It is the impinging of these streams of particles upon the retina of the eye which produces the sensation of light.

Round these two theories, then, there developed a storm of controversy. Both without doubt were ingenious. Both were able to account for all the ordinarily observed phenomena of reflection and refraction known at that time. Nowadays we know of other phenomena which Newton's theory could not explain, but which the undulatory theory can. But how were the rival claims of the two theories to be tested?

Now it was known that as a logical consequence of Newton's theory light must travel faster in a medium such as glass or water than it will in air. On the other hand, it follows from Huyghens's theory that the speed of light in these media must be *less* than for air. Here, then, was the test—definitely to measure these velocities in the different media. But how? Alas, the experiment was beyond the scientists of Newton's day. Both Newton and Huyghens died without the application of this crucial test, and the weight of Newton's superior reputation alone served to produce a balance of opinion in favour of the corpuscular theory and against the wave theory. Such phenomena as the interference of light were unknown then, or more justice might have been done to Huyghens, and it was not till 1850 that Jean Léon Foucault, of France, finally settled the whole controversy by his experiment which showed that light travels at a rate of 186,000 miles per second in air, and only about three-quarters of this speed in water.

6. *Newton's Researches on Gravitation*

We turn now to another branch of Newton's activities—that of dynamics. It will be remembered that in 1665, owing to an outbreak of plague, the University was closed, and Newton returned to his home at Woolsthorpe, near Grantham. Here he spent a quiet eighteen months of meditation on various problems, and it was here that he thought out that great law of universal gravitation which so profoundly changed the whole character of the science of dynamics.

The problem of gravity was not a new one. Speculations on the subject had interested almost every philosopher of note from the time of Plato. What had been called the power of gravity was familiar to all. It remained to discover the law which presumably this ' power ' obeyed. Newton, like his predecessors, found the problem of fascinating interest.[1]

It will be remembered that Kepler, after a lifework of patient analysis of Tycho Brahe's famous record of observations, had enunciated his three famous laws of planetary motion. The third of these laws, it will be recalled, was that for every planet, *the cube of the distance is proportional to the square of the periodic time* ; or, expressing this mathematically,

$$\frac{r^3}{T^2} \text{ is constant for all planets.}$$

Why should this be so ? This was what Newton asked himself.

To understand this further, let us vary Kepler's statements

---

[1] The familiar story of the falling apple, originating from Voltaire, is of such doubtful authenticity that it is purposely omitted from the text.

a little. He told us that the orbits of the planets are elliptical. It will simplify the problem, without upsetting the argument in any way, if we adhere to circles. Suppose the orbits are circular. What 'binding' force is there in a body like the sun which will keep a planet constantly moving round it in circular orbit? One finds a similar problem in the twirling of a mass in a circular path by means of a string. Referring to Fig. 68, suppose the string is held at C, then initially, taking the point A as the mass in question, its direction of motion is along the tangent AB. That is to say, unless otherwise restrained, it will 'fly off at a tangent', as the popular phrase goes. But it *is* so restrained—

by the string AC, which, by tending to pull the mass into itself, brings it in a given time to E on the circle instead of to D on the straight line. In effect, in the given time in question, it has pulled the mass inward towards the centre through a distance DE. The new direction of motion is now EF, the tangent at E, and the whole argument continually repeats itself, and the force along the string directed towards

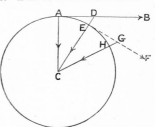

FIG. 68. Production of a Circular Orbit by a force constantly directed towards the centre.

the centre C constantly pulls the body out of its 'straight line' tendency, and keeps it moving in a circular path or orbit.

Let us now apply a little mathematics and elementary mechanics to the problem, and it will then be seen why Newton was seeking for the existence of a constant force directed towards a centre.

In his famous book, the *Principia*, Newton enunciated the three laws of motion which, as we have before pointed out,[1] were primarily due to the spade-work of Galileo's researches at Arcetri, and which constitute the basis of modern mechanics. The first of these tells us that in a world of no forces, if such a thing could be imagined, a body would do only one of two things; it would either be at rest, or, if moving at all, it would move continually

[1] Ch. vii.

in a straight line with uniform speed ; and this simply because there are no forces to make it do otherwise. A force continuously applied to a body at rest will start it moving with continually increasing speed, and a force applied to a moving body will change its motion ; that is to say, it will speed it up, or slow it down, or swerve it from its original direction. The force will in fact produce in the body an *acceleration* (or, of course, a retardation, which mathematically is merely a negative acceleration).

This was Newton's first law of motion. His second was in part nothing but a common-sense law, and said in effect that the amount of acceleration produced in a body depends upon the magnitude of the force ; a big force must have a big effect—a small force a small effect. The acceleration (or rate of change of motion) produced, then, is proportional to the impressed force. This is algebraically the $F = ma$ formula well known to all students of elementary mechanics.

His third law, that ' to every action there is an equal and opposite reaction ', does not concern us at the moment, and we therefore do no more than make bare mention of it here.

Returning to the problem of a body being whirled round a circular orbit (Fig. 68) about a given centre C, we have seen that the circular orbit is produced through the exertion of a constant force along the string directed towards the centre. As a matter of common sense, it must be obvious that the swifter the speed (let us call it v) with which the body tends to ' fly off along the tangent ', the greater must be the controlling force to give it the necessary change of speed of motion (or acceleration) inward to keep it in its circular path. Both Huyghens and Newton showed in fact that the acceleration required must be $\dfrac{v^2}{r}$ where r is the radius of the circle, and v velocity of the mass.

The investigation of this problem would be out of place here. Students of elementary mechanics will be quite familiar with it, and others will, it is hoped, be content to accept the result as here stated.

Now since the force $F = ma$, we have obviously

$$F = \frac{mv^2}{r}$$

giving us the measure of the centripetal force, as it is called, necessary to hold any given mass m moving with a speed v in a circular orbit of radius r, and *this force is always directed towards the centre of the orbit.*

We are now in a position to see a little light with regard to Kepler's third law of planetary motion. He talks of the periodic time ; he means, of course, the time for one complete revolution. If the speed is v, and the circumference $2\pi r$, then obviously we must have

$$\text{periodic time } T = \frac{2\pi r}{v} \left(\text{since time taken} = \frac{\text{distance gone}}{\text{speed}}\right)$$

whence
$$v = \frac{2\pi r}{T}$$

and hence, since
$$F = \frac{mv^2}{r}$$

we can substitute
$$\frac{2\pi r}{T} \text{ for } v,$$

and we get
$$F = \frac{m 4\pi^2 r}{T^2}$$

as an expression for the constant force required to hold a body in its circular orbit.

Now compare this with the constant expression required by Kepler's third law—namely, $\dfrac{r^3}{T^2}$.

To get a correspondence between these two expressions, we want an r^2 term to come into the numerator of the former one. The reader must be reminded that the expression $F = \dfrac{m 4\pi^2 r}{T^2}$ is con-cerned with the problem of a body whirled round a circular path at the end of a string, the force F being the inward force exerted along the string. Kepler's expression, on the other hand, is for the actual planets, where there are no strings connecting the body to the central sun. We want, in this latter case, a substitute for the force along the string. Let us assume, therefore, that in the case of the planet moving round the sun in a circular orbit (we are still regarding the orbits as circular instead of elliptical) there is a constant force directed towards the sun, exerted, so to speak, along an imaginary string. If we can take this force as being inversely proportional to the square of the radius, we shall have achieved our object of a proper correspondence between these two expressions. Let us see how it works out.

Let us suppose that, in fact, there is a law according to which a body is naturally attracted to a 'central' mass with a force which is inversely proportional to the square of the distance between them, and is directly proportional to the masses of the two bodies, M being the mass of the central or attracting body. If we express this algebraically, we have

$$F = K \frac{Mm}{r^2}, \text{ where } K \text{ is constant.}$$

But we have seen that $\qquad F = \frac{m 4\pi^2 r}{T^2}$.

Hence we may say that $\dfrac{m 4\pi^2 r}{T^2} = \dfrac{KMm}{r^2}$

which gives us $\qquad \dfrac{r^3}{T^2} = \dfrac{MK}{4\pi^2}$.

If we examine the right-hand side of this equation it will be seen that it is a constant quantity, since K is the constant factor of proportionality already mentioned, and M is the mass of the central attracting body.

We therefore have

$$\frac{r^3}{T^2} = \frac{(\text{Distance})^3}{(\text{Periodic Time})^2} = \text{Constant}$$

and *this is nothing more nor less than Kepler's Third Law.*

To sum up, what we have so far said reduces to this : that it follows from a consideration of the elementary mechanics of central orbits 'that it *would be quite easy to explain Kepler's third law of planetary motion if there could be found to exist a force of attraction towards the central body whose magnitude is inversely proportional to the square of the distance*'.

For the sake of simplicity we have confined ourselves to the case of circular orbits only. But although the mathematics is more complicated for elliptical orbits, the result is the same, so the problem is perfectly general. Whatever truth there may have been in the well-known story of the falling apple, it is extremely probable that Newton must at least have considered as significant the every-day experience of the behaviour of an object such as a freely-falling stone. Why was such an experience so fraught with significance ? It was because it enabled Newton to link up certain facts. Here was an example of a force exerted by the *earth* on the stone. So far as the planets are concerned, the force he sought was to be exerted by the *sun*. Yet in the case of Jupiter, say, an exactly similar problem presented itself in the seeking of such a force towards that planet to account for the orbits of her then-known four moons.

Was it possible, thought Newton, that in every case the force of attraction was inversely proportional to the square of the distance ? In that case would it account too for the motion of our own moon round the earth ? For surely if the earth attracts the stone it must also attract the moon ?

Here was a splendid chance of applying a test. The earth's pull or attraction falls off as the square of the distance. The moon was known to be distant sixty times the earth's radius from the earth's centre. Hence the attraction exerted by the earth on the moon must be $\left(\dfrac{1}{60 \times 60}\right)$ of the attraction it will exert on a body at its own surface (since a body on the earth's surface is $\dfrac{1}{60}$ of the distance of the moon from the earth's centre).

Now a body on the earth's surface is pulled to it (i. e. ' drops ') a distance of 16 feet (or more exactly 193 inches) in one second. Therefore the moon should ' drop ' a distance of $\left(\dfrac{16}{60 \times 60}\right)$ feet in one second. But this can be tested. We know by observations exactly how long the moon takes to go once round, and we know the distance between the earth and moon. Therefore we could draw a diagram like Fig. 68, to scale to represent the moon's motion round the earth C, and we could calculate how much arc AE (still referring to Fig. 68) could be traversed by the moon in one second. All we have to do is to calculate the ' drop ' DE, and assure ourselves that it works out to $\left(\dfrac{16}{60 \times 60}\right)$ feet.

By a tragedy of misfortune for which Newton was not to blame, his test was doomed at first to disappointment. The accuracy of the result depended upon the accuracy of the value taken as the radius of the earth. Newton could only take the accepted value of the times, and it was, alas, wrong. It was assumed to be 3,436 miles, whereas the correct value is 3,963 miles. Consequently, instead of getting the required drop for the moon of $\left(\dfrac{16}{60 \times 60}\right)$ feet in one second, he only got $\left(\dfrac{14}{60 \times 60}\right)$ feet in one second.

Newton's disappointment was keen. He had no reason to suspect his data, and so he found himself obliged to abandon the basic assumption of an inverse square law. This was in 1666.

For the next step in the story we are carried to the year 1682, when Picard, at a meeting of the Royal Society, communicated the results of his more accurate determinations of the value of the earth's radius. Newton was present, and he made a careful note of Picard's results. Immediately he began to recall his work and hopes of sixteen years ago. He hurried home and routed out his old papers and calculations on the subject. His excitement at the anticipation of complete success to his theory was too much for him. He was too agitated to finish his calculations, and he got a friend to do them for him. The result was a complete triumph. The value for the moon's ' fall ' per second was exactly $\left(\dfrac{16}{60 \times 60}\right)$ feet. At last he had discovered both the true law of universal gravitation and the true explanations of Kepler's laws of planetary motion. And all this would have been definitely achieved sixteen years before but for an inaccurate determination for which he was not responsible.

Yet despite the magnificence of this achievement, Newton said nothing about his discovery. He was now, as always, chary of publicity. He hated alike both adulation and attack. How then did his discovery ultimately receive the wide publicity which its importance demanded ? The story is an interesting one. The problems which Newton had solved so successfully were also being attempted by his contemporaries. All the chief members of the Royal Society were intensely interested. Three men in particular who were giving much time and trouble to the problems of gravitation and the solar system were Hooke, Sir Christopher Wren, and Edmund Halley, a distinguished astronomer and mathematician.

In January 1684 Wren made an offer of a present of a book to the cost of forty shillings if either of the others would bring him within two months a proof of the statement that if a planet be attracted to the sun with a force obeying the inverse square law, its path would be an ellipse. They both failed to supply the proof. But in August of the same year Halley had decided to consult Newton about it, not knowing that Newton had even thought of the problem before, but convinced nevertheless that his genius would help to find a solution.

Fig. 69.   Medal commemorating Edmund Halley.

There were few preliminaries to the conversation. Halley came straight to business. ' What will be the curve described by the planets on the supposition that gravity diminishes as the square of the distance ? ' he asked. Newton's immediate reply was ' An ellipse '. ' But how do you know ? ' retorted the amazed Halley. ' Why,' said Newton, ' I have calculated it.' He began searching for the papers containing the calculations. He could not find them immediately, but promised to send them as soon as possible. Halley hurried back to London, and in the following November received the calculations. They were communicated to the Royal Society early in 1685, and it was therefore to Edmund Halley that the world was indebted for bringing to light what must always remain one of the most important documents in the world's scientific history.   As Halley proudly put it, he was ' the Ulysses who produced this Achilles '.

The importance of Newton's work was by no means lost on the Royal Society.   They wrote to Newton and asked for permission to publish his researches.   Newton consented, and as a consequence the world has his epoch-making *Principia*, or *Mathematical Principles of Natural Philosophy*.   It is without exception the most important work in natural philosophy extant.

Halley spared neither trouble nor expense in seeing the work through the press, and he was justified.   The work on the whole was well received by those in a position to judge it.   Yet there were some detractors who did not hesitate to attack Newton. Hooke in particular was especially virulent in his attack, as he had been on a former occasion in connexion with Newton's work in optics.   Here, as before, Hooke claimed priority, declaring that Newton had derived his solution from his (Hooke's) work. This was an unjust claim, as all are now agreed.   In a second edition, however, Newton acknowledged the part Wren, Hooke, and Halley had each played in the researches on gravitation and the solar system generally.   We can well imagine, from what has previously been said, how painful the whole controversy was to Newton.   He was near suppressing the whole of the third book entirely.   ' Philosophy ', wrote he to Halley, ' is such an impertinently litigious lady that a man had as good be engaged in lawsuits as have to do with her.   I found it so formerly, and now I can no sooner come near her again, but she gives me warning.'   Halley, fortunately, succeeded in dissuading him from this step, and so the world has the whole work complete and unabridged.

And what was the result ?   Here was an entirely new philosophy presented to a world which had been slowly weaned from the Aristotelian School, and which had by now been taught to accept the Cartesian view.   Even Newton himself had been taught Descartes's Vortex Theory as a ' real live ' thing.   We have seen that the world does not abandon a theory in a hurry.   So we cannot be surprised that on the Continent Newtonian physics made but slow progress, until Voltaire stirred up his contemporaries and aroused them to face facts. In England, however, the abandonment of Descartes in favour of the Newtonian philosophy was much more rapid, as one may well suppose, and by the time Newton had died the scientific opinion of the country was solid for his teachings.

7. *Newton's Mathematical Researches*

We have, so far, considered in turn Newton's researches in optics and in mechanics. We have now to consider his contributions to pure mathematics. He began as early as the year 1665, at the age of twenty-three, with the discovery of the binomial theorem. The actual nature of it is hardly a matter for this work. We will merely remark that it was but a stepping-stone in the progress of Newton's mind : that it was merely a weapon— a mathematical weapon, which he required to help him to solve the age-old problem of finding the area of a figure bounded by a curve ; and of finding the length of a curved line.

The binomial theorem was, in fact, but a step towards the creation of that wonderfully fertile scheme of investigation which Newton called his *theory of fluxions*, and which to-day we speak of as the differential and integral calculus.

It is difficult to speak of this branch of Newton's work in terms intelligible to the non-mathematical reader, and perhaps the wisest course for such a reader would be to take it all ' as read ', and pass straight on to the next section. The word ' fluxion ' indicates a flow. According to Newton, all types of geometrical quantities could be regarded as being generated by a continuous flow or motion. Thus a line is generated by the motion of a point, a surface by the motion of a line, a solid by the motion of a surface, and so on. That being so, Newton next went on to speak of the speed or velocity of any of these moving magnitudes as the *fluxion of the magnitude generated*, e. g. the speed of a moving line is the fluxion of the surface created, the speed of the moving surface is the fluxion of the solid so produced, and so on.

As a matter of convenience, Newton employed Cartesian co-ordinates to help him in this conception. So if we take the case of a moving point P whose co-ordinates are x and y respectively referred to two axes at right angles, and whose velocity is the fluxion of the arc so created, then since the velocity can be resolved into two velocities parallel to each axis respectively, each of these resolved velocities will give the fluxion of x and y respectively.

The converse conception is also possible, and we speak of the arc as the *fluent* of the velocity of the moving point with which it is described ; and the surface is the fluent of the velocity of the moving arc with which it is described, and so on.

Now suppose that the fluxion of a curve is constant, that is to say, suppose the curve is described by the point moving along it

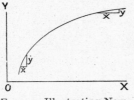

FIG. 70. Illustrating Newton's Theory of Fluxions.

with uniform velocity. Then the ratio of the fluxion of the x co-ordinate (or *abscissa*, as this co-ordinate is called) to the fluxion of the y co-ordinate (or *ordinate* as this co-ordinate is called) will be determined solely by the nature of the curve. The ratio will be small if the curve is steep, and the ratio will be big if the curve is ' flat ' (Fig. 70).

Conversely, still considering the case of a curve of constant fluxion, if we know the ratio of the fluxions of the co-ordinates at any given instant, the nature of the curve can be built up, or in other words the equation to the curve can be found. The former operation Newton called the ' Method of Fluxions '. It corresponds to the differential calculus of to-day. The latter operation was the ' inverse method of fluxions ', and forms the starting-point of the modern integral calculus.

Now a word as to Newton's notation. Suppose x is a given fluent. Then he denoted its fluxion by $\dot{x}$. Further, if $\dot{x}$ is in its turn a variable or fluent quantity, then its fluxion was denoted by $\ddot{x}$; so that $\ddot{x}$ was a fluxion of a fluxion, or, as Newton expressed it, a fluxion of the second order, or more shortly, a second fluxion. Obviously, if x is such that it varies *directly* with the time, then $\dot{x}$ is a constant, and therefore $\ddot{x} = o$.

Conversely, since x can itself be considered a fluxion of another quantity which would be its fluent, Newton denoted this fluent by x' in some books and by $[x]$ in others ; and from these in their turn he got the second fluents x'' or $[[x]]$, and so on.

Finally, Newton spoke of the infinitely small increases in the magnitude of the variable in indefinitely small intervals of time as the ' moments ' of the fluent. Newton denoted the small interval of time by o. Hence if x be the fluent, since $\dot{x}$ is the fluxion, the increase in the value of the fluent in time o must be the product $\dot{x}o$, and this quantity is the ' moment ' of x. That is to say, after an indefinitely small interval of time x has assumed the value $x + \dot{x}o$.

This, in brief, and, it is feared, in somewhat vague terms, is the outline of the fundamental ideas underlying Newton's theory of fluxions. It was not entirely a result of Newton's unaided genius. Mention has already been made of his tutor and professor at Cambridge, Dr. Isaac Barrow. To him history must apportion some of the credit for Newton's theory, for he had himself been interested in this question and there is no doubt but that Newton derived many of his notions from conversations and discussions with Barrow.

Students of the differential calculus will have noticed that the notation Newton used in his fluxional calculus is not that which is used to-day. The notation of the calculus of to-day is the invention of Gottfried Wilhelm Leibnitz, and indeed the mathematical history of this period is almost entirely a history of a long and painful controversy between these two great men on the subject of their rival claims to the invention of the calculus.

8. *The Battle of the Calculus*

As usual, the trouble was probably largely due to Newton's reticence and hesitation to publish his papers. We know that he used his theory of fluxions in 1666. We also know that a manuscript circulation of the theory existed amongst friends and pupils in 1669. Yet no full publication of the theory occurred till 1693. Compare these facts with those of Leibnitz's version of the calculus. He used it in his note books in 1675, nine years after Newton first used his theory of fluxions. He wrote to Newton about it in 1677, and he first published it in 1684, *nine years before Newton's theory was published.*

Who then really invented the calculus ? There appears to be no doubt but that Newton was the first with his theory of fluxions. The question then becomes, did Leibnitz invent it independently of Newton, or did he in fact get the idea from Newton ? The answer is largely a question of Leibnitz's good faith. Was this open to doubt ? Let us try to examine the facts.

In 1673 Leibnitz visited England and met Oldenburgh, the secretary to the Royal Society. At this time he knew little of mathematics, but when, shortly after, he became interested in the subject, his remarkable mental talents soon enabled him to grasp all that was then known on the subject. On leaving England he maintained a friendly correspondence with Oldenburgh, and in 1676 the latter forwarded to Leibnitz an account of Newton's theory

FIG. 71. GOTTFRIED WILHELM LEIBNITZ

of fluxions, concealed under an anagram. A year later, in 1677, Leibnitz replied to Oldenburgh with ' a short account of an equally general method which he had invented, which he called the differential calculus '. This Leibnitz definitely published in 1684 in his journal, the *Acta Eruditorum.*

The position was now that whilst Leibnitz's calculus was published and was spreading rapidly on the Continent, Newton's ' fluxions ' was unpublished and unknown except to a few friends. Indeed, it is somewhat ironical that the first book to appear in England connected with the subject was a treatise by Craig, who definitely acknowledged Leibnitz as his source.

At first there was little dispute between the two rivals. Each appeared to agree that the two systems were honestly invented independently of each other. But external circumstances gradually drove them into controversy. The beginning of this was seen in the growing rivalry in this period between the English and the Continental mathematicians. For this there was no definite foundation ; yet it was there. Leibnitz's differential calculus had spread so rapidly abroad that mathematicians here who knew Newton felt that a great injustice was being done to their premier philosopher.

Of the later developments in this unfortunate controversy we will say very little. Before the matter was finally dropped, there were even open accusations against Newton on the part of Continental mathematicians to the effect that he had derived his own ideas from Leibnitz. The Royal Society, at the request of Leibnitz, held an inquiry into the whole question. From this Newton's reputation emerged unblemished.

One further remark we will make. The world can never know the real facts, for the vital witnesses, the only two who really knew the whole truth, the two men who in 1676 had passed on Newton's papers to Leibnitz, were John Collins and Oldenburgh ; the former died in 1683, the latter in 1684, whilst Leibnitz's theory of the differential calculus was published immediately after.

And what was the result after all ? The personal feeling which had been aroused by these serious events was so strong that in England only the theory of fluxions was taught, whilst on the Continent the differential calculus made rapid progress. The latter, of course, proved in fact to be much the better theory in its many applications to the problems of physics, mechanics, and astronomy, and so we find that for some time after Newton's death, whilst great strides were made in these subjects on the Continent, in England there was little more than a marking of time.

9. *Newton's Later Life*

In 1669 Newton had succeeded Dr. Isaac Barrow to the Lucasian Professorship of Mathematics at Cambridge University. We may judge the high esteem in which he was held by his countrymen from the fact that when, owing to the lapsing of his fellowship, in 1675 he found himself faced with financial anxieties, he was granted a special patent by the Crown authorizing him to retain the fellowship for as long as he held the professorial chair.

So the years went on, Newton's time being fully taken up with lectures, research, and the controversies arising therefrom, and occasionally with a variation of the routine by theological studies. His work was by no means confined to the subjects which we have already discussed. He was greatly interested in chemistry, in chronological astronomy, and in thermometry. He was the first to prove that change of physical state, i. e. freezing and boiling, took place at a constant temperature. He was also interested in geology, in magnetism, and electricity, and indeed in almost every branch of natural philosophy.

By 1687 Newton had completed the three books which constitute his great masterpiece, the *Principia*, and in that year there developed an interesting conflict between Crown and University in which Newton became involved. King James II had issued an order to the authorities of the University of Cambridge that one Father Francis, a Benedictine monk, should be admitted to the degree of Master of Arts without taking the oaths of allegiance and supremacy. The university regarded this as an infringement of their rights and privileges, and they refused to comply with the King's command. The Vice-Chancellor was ordered to London to answer the charge of contempt for the authority of the Crown, and he took with him a delegation of nine to uphold the rights of the university in the High Courts. One of these was Newton, and he played a prominent part in the subsequent proceedings, with such success that the Crown gave way. By way of reward, Newton was in 1688 elected to parliament as a member for the university, though by a narrow majority. This parliament was dissolved in 1689, and he then returned to Cambridge once more to pursue his professorial duties.

The strain of work, at all times heavy, now began to tell on him, and at the age of fifty, in 1692, he had a serious breakdown. Usually quiet, shy, and reserved, he began to develop an irritability and a forgetfulness which a bad bout of insomnia only served to accentuate. One morning he went to early service leaving a lighted candle on his desk. On his return he found that there had been a fire as a result of the upsetting of the candle, caused, it is asserted, by his little dog ' Diamond '. But whatever the cause, several valuable papers which were the results of considerable labour on his part were totally destroyed, and Newton was much affected thereby. ' I am extremely troubled at the embroilment I am in ', wrote he to Mr. Pepys, ' and have neither ate nor slept well this twelvemonth, nor have I my former consistency of mind.' A period of melancholy followed. Some assert his mind was affected, but this is highly improbable. There is no doubt that his normal powers of concentration were temporarily absent, but beyond this there was nothing other than the irritability and nervous depression of a temporary breakdown in health.

He soon regained his former health and elasticity of mind, and in 1694 we find him engaged in a discussion with Flamsteed, England's first astronomer royal, on certain problems connected with the moon's motion.

In the same year, his former parliamentary friend, Mr. Montague, afterwards Lord Halifax, became Chancellor of the Exchequer, and in the course of his duties at this post he became interested in the problem of the improvement of the coinage, at that time in a debased condition. In this connexion Mr. Montague in 1695 offered Newton the position of Warden of the Mint. As the appointment carried with it a salary of some hundreds of pounds a year, and the duties were such as not to interfere with his university professorship, Newton accepted the offer. His scientific knowledge enabled him to carry through the task of recoinage with great skill, and as a reward for his services he was in 1697 promoted to the position of Master of the Mint with a considerably increased salary, and shortly after this he received the signal honour from France, in 1699, of having his name enrolled as the first foreign Associate of the Academy of Sciences at Paris.

Newton was a conscientious man, and he soon realized that he had now undertaken more duties than he could properly carry out. We must remember that in addition to his professorship at Cambridge and his Mastership of the Mint, he was at this time embroiled in a bitter controversy respecting his theory of fluxions. And so we find that in 1703 Newton resigned his chair at Cambridge, thus terminating an honourable connexion with Trinity College which had lasted since 1660, in which year he had first become an undergraduate.

With this step, too, the main work of his life may be said to have ended. The brilliant researches into so many branches of scientific activity which had characterized the past twenty-five years of his career were replaced by the steady labours attendant upon his duties at the Mint, supplemented by an active interest in the scientific work of his contemporaries, and, as we have already seen, an active defence of his own work in the past against the attacks of his Continental traducers.

In 1703, the year in which he vacated his professorship, he was elected President of the Royal Society, and in 1705 he received the honour of knighthood from Queen Anne. His university, too, had once more elected him as its representative in parliament, and what with the Mint, the Parliament, and the Court (at which he was now a great favourite), how different was the general routine of his life as compared with the days of his lectures, his experiments, and his calculations !

Yet he still remained a power of the first magnitude in the world of science and mathematics. At this time there had developed a system of international rivalry in mathematics which took a very curious form. It consisted in the bandying about of challenges. A man would develop a difficult problem the solution of which would often involve some really original work, and he would challenge the world to solve it. Presumably the challenger himself would have a solution ready, and his object was to assert his own superiority over his contemporaries. All the great mathematicians of the day took part in these challenges : the two Bernouillis, Huyghens, Leibnitz, de l'Hôpital, and Newton.

Newton was never beaten. For example, in 1697 John Bernouilli proposed the problem of finding the nature of the line other than a vertical straight line, along which a body must descend from one point to another in the minimum of time. Leibnitz spent six months in finding a solution and then triumphantly suggested sending the problem to Newton. Newton gave a complete solution within twenty-four hours. He published it anonymously, but Bernouilli at once recognized his hand, exclaiming ' Ex ungue leonem!' (' Even as the lion is known by his paw.') On another occasion, in 1716, Leibnitz proposed another problem which Newton received one afternoon after a fatiguing day's work. Nevertheless he solved the problem within five hours.

Throughout his old age, as with his earlier years, we find in this great man the same shyness, modesty, and sensitiveness of nature. He seldom talked of personalities, of himself or of others. Yet with it all he was ' candid and affable, and always put himself on a level with his company '. In appearance he was of medium height, inclined to stoutness in later life, square-jawed, and sharp-featured. His hair was grey from the age of thirty, and speedily became silvery white, lending him a venerable appearance. He had no recreation and took no exercise. Hard work and deep meditation for anything up to eighteen hours per day were his usual portion.

The stories of his absent-mindedness during the period of his absorption in his problems are legion. Thus he was riding home once and dismounted to walk his horse up a steep hill. When he reached the top he emerged from a reverie to find that the horse had slipped the bridle and gone away, leaving the bridle in his hands. On another occasion he left his guests to get some more wine, but forgot all about them and was found hard at work in his study. Yet another story tells of how a friend, Dr. Stukeley, called on him. Newton was out but his table was laid for dinner. Dr. Stukeley lifted the cover and ate the dinner, and then replaced the cover. When Newton appeared later he greeted Stukeley, and sat down and lifted the cover. ' Dear me,' said he, ' I thought I had not dined, but I see I have.' So the years went by. He was always occupied with mental employment, and usually enjoyed an even state of health, until he was about eighty years of age. He began to suffer from gout and other ailments, in the intervals between which his mind remained unclouded. Much of his time was now given up to study of divinity. On the 28th of February 1727 he rather unwisely attended a meeting of the Royal Society, from the fatigue of which he never recovered. He became insensible on the 18th of March and passed peacefully away on the 20th, in the eighty-fifth year of his age.

The nation paid his memory all honour. For a week his body lay in state, and on the 28th of March he was interred in Westminster Abbey, and here a handsome monument was afterwards erected to his memory.

Eulogies on his life and character exist by the score. One of the most interesting is that attributed to Leibnitz. On being asked by the Queen of Prussia what he thought of Newton, his answer was, ' Taking mathematicians from the beginning of the world to the time when Newton lived, what he had done was much the better half '. The following eulogy from Playfair's *Dissertation* is also worthy of mention :

' To his important inventions in pure mathematics Newton added the greatest discoveries in the philosophy of nature ; and, in passing through his hands, mechanics, optics, and astronomy were not merely improved but renovated. No one ever left knowledge in a state so different from that in which he found it. Men were instructed not only in new truths, but in new methods of discovering truth : they were made acquainted with the great principle which connects together the most distant regions of space, as well as the most remote periods of duration ; and which was to lead to future discoveries, far beyond what the wisest or most sanguine could anticipate.'

For, comparing scientific knowledge as he left it with the state in which he found it, his work was in the real sense of the term a revelation. His own view of it all is characteristically modest, and fully worthy of record, and with it we conclude his biography. ' I know not ', wrote he shortly before his death, ' what the world may think of my labours, but to myself it seems that I have been but as a child playing on the sea-shore ; now finding some prettier pebble or more beautiful shell than my companions, while the unbounded ocean of truth lay undiscovered before me.'

X

ROBERT BOYLE

1. *Early Life*

IN comparison with the intellectual giant whose life and work
we have just studied, the achievements of the more normal type
of scientific pioneer must inevitably appear at a serious dis-
advantage. Nevertheless full
tribute must be paid to the
brilliant band of contem-
poraries who lived and worked
in Newton's days. This was
a period so rich in scientific
genius that it would be unjust
to study the work of any one
man without clearly pointing
out that he is chosen, not for
any outstanding merit above
his colleagues—Newton being,
of course, a notable exception
—but rather as a typical
representative of the genius
of his days.

FIG. 72.   THE HON. ROBERT
BOYLE

With this understanding we
come to a brief study of the life of the Hon. Robert Boyle,
' saint and scientist '. He belongs to the earlier half of Newton's
days, but apart from the famous ' Boyle's Law ', which has
brought him the notice of all schoolboys, his chief mission was
to teach, by the strong force of his lifelong example, the value
of experiment in research. That example was indeed necessary.
The original pioneers, Galileo and Gilbert, had been followed by
the Cartesian school of thinkers, who preferred synthesis and
theory to analysis and experiment. Francis Bacon, Lord Verulam,
had pleaded for an experimental basis for research, though not
himself a scientist. But what he preached Robert Boyle practised, and he did so with a patience and a persistence which,

accompanied as it was by many successful contributions to scientific knowledge, fully entitle him to be reckoned in the forefront of the world's great philosophers.

Robert Boyle was an Irishman, and was born at Lismore in Ulster on the 25th of January 1627. He was the seventh son of Richard Boyle, Earl of Cork, a man who was able to trace his descent back to Saxon times. According to the Domesday Book, the family of Biuvile (as the name was then written) held land in Herefordshire. The Boyle family were not, however, possessed of much wealth when Richard Boyle went to Ireland. Indeed, he tells us that when he arrived at Dublin in 1588 his total fortune was twenty-seven pounds three shillings, a diamond ring, a gold bracelet, personal clothing, a rapier, and a dagger. He made good, however, and was able to buy from Sir Walter Raleigh all his lands in Munster. He was created Earl of Cork in 1620.

Robert's mother, Catherine, only daughter of Sir Geoffrey Fenton, the Irish Secretary of those days, died when he was but three years old. His upbringing was therefore in the hands of his father. The earl took his responsibility very seriously. He had his ' views' on the subject of training a child. He was genuinely fond of Robert, but he was no ' mollycoddler', and with no wife to say him nay, he was able to carry out his theories with probably much greater freedom than he might have done had Robert's mother been still alive. ' He had ', says one biographer, ' so great an aversion to the ill-judged fondness of some parents, who will scarce let the sun shine, or the wind blow upon their children, that he committed him to the care of a nurse in the country with orders to bring him up hardy.' The simple life and the healthy air no doubt benefited Robert greatly, but there was one unforeseen result which a different theory of education might have avoided. Among the country children with whom Robert used to play were some who stuttered. Early childhood is an age of imitation, and it was not long before young Boyle stuttered too. The imitations first made in jest soon became an unbreakable habit, and Boyle stuttered for the remainder of his life.

When eight years old, he was sent to England to be educated

with his brother at Eton under Sir Henry Wotton, an old friend
of his father's. Here Robert learned French and Latin rapidly,
and showed signs of coming scholarship of a high order. He was
the victim of a certain amount of favouritism, however, in the
sense that his master would often ' bestow upon him such balls
and tops and other implements of idleness as he had taken away
from others that had unduly used them '. He was unusually
introspective for a child. He studied himself and his mental
tendencies to a surprising degree, and he tells us that when he
found himself developing irregular mental habits he would
endeavour to cure himself by settling down to such humdrum
tasks as problems in square and cube roots. Certainly as a result
he became a clear thinker. On one occasion the wall of his bed-
room fell in, and only the curtains of his bed saved him from
serious damage. The dust raised by the débris was, however,
so very thick that he would have been stifled but for the fact
that his quick brain prompted him to wrap his head in the sheet
and allow the air to strain through it.

After four years at Eton, Robert was withdrawn from school
by his father, and he spent the next few years with a private
tutor at Stalbridge. He now began writing verse, studying the
Scriptures, and recording the memoirs of his school-days.
This was surely remarkable in a lad of twelve years, and
inclines one to look for a tendency to scientific precociousness in
him, but there was no sign of this. He was evidently of a somewhat emotional disposition. He began to show an earnest desire
to study the Scriptures in their original languages. For this
purpose he was sent abroad in 1638, accompanied by an older
brother. Both were placed under the charge of M. Marcombe,
a French tutor, and they used their time abroad under his wise
guidance to the best advantage. They first went to Leyden, in
Holland, for a short course at the university ; thence into France,
staying for a while at Lyons, and later into Switzerland, where
for a time they settled at Geneva.

It was here that Robert Boyle suffered the great emotional
experience which, as he freely confesses, strongly inclined him
towards an earnestly religious life for the remainder of his days.

He was badly frightened by an unusually severe thunderstorm in the middle of the night. To use his own words, written in the third person,

' For at a time which (being in the very heat of summer) promised nothing less, about the dead of night that adds most terror to such accidents, [he] was suddenly waked in a fright with such loud claps of thunder (which are oftentimes very terrible in these hot climes and seasons), that he thought the earth would owe an ague to the air, and every clap was both preceded and attended with flashes of lightning, so frequent and so dazzling that he began to imagine them the sallies of that fire that must consume the world. The long continuance of that dismal tempest where the winds were so loud as almost drowned the noise of the very thunder, and the showers so hideous as almost quenched the lightning ere it could reach his eyes, confirmed him in his apprehensions of the day of judgement being at hand. Whereupon the consideration of his unpreparedness to welcome it, and the hideousness of being surprised by it in an unfit condition, made him resolve and vow that, if his fear were that night disappointed, all his further additions to his life should be more religiously and watchfully employed. The morning came, and a serene, cloudless sky returned, when he ratified his determinations so solemnly, that from that day he dated his conversion.'

The two Boyles left Geneva later for Italy, and amongst other places they visited Florence. Here Robert made a study of Galileo's writings, and they impressed him profoundly, and doubtless his later love of experimental science must have been largely inspired by this visit.

2. *The Royal Society*

In 1644 the two returned home. Their father had just died, and Robert found himself the inheritor of the Stalbridge estates. The country was in a turmoil owing to the war between the Royalists and Parliament ; but in this conflict Boyle took no part. He was essentially a student, and had no interest in politics. Whatever the ruling authority, he was prepared to abide peacefully by the laws of the land and to do his duty as a citizen and a Christian.

There were others, too, who preferred study and philosophic

discussion to partisanship and strife, and these people gravitated instinctively towards each other. They constituted themselves into an ' invisible college ', as they called themselves, and their gatherings were important as being the foundation of what became ultimately the Royal Society for the Advancement of Learning.

Boyle derived much pleasure from these gatherings, and indeed he found himself in a goodly company. The original idea of the formation of this philosophical debating society appears to have come from Dr. Theodore Hooke, a German scientist who had settled in England, and who must not be confused with Robert Hooke who was so persistent an opponent of Sir Isaac Newton. These *virtuosi*, as Boyle called them, included such men as Seth Ward, afterwards Bishop of Salisbury, Dr. Goddard, Dr. Wallis, afterwards the Savilian Professor at Oxford, Dr. Wilkins, Warden of Wadham College, Oxford, and later the Master of Trinity, Cambridge, Dr. (afterwards Sir William) Petty, Dr. Ralph Bathurst, and Christopher Wren. They met originally in London,[1] their meetings dating from 1645. Their ' venue ' was varied according to circumstances. When subjects connected with the study of optics were under discussion, they would meet at Dr. Goddard's lodgings, because that eminent philosopher kept an assistant at work there, grinding lenses and constructing optical instruments. At other times they would meet at Gresham College. The range of the subjects discussed was very wide, and the only topics that were forbidden were politics and religion. It is well that we should ponder over the striking contrast of these gatherings in the peaceful atmosphere of science to the surrounding conditions of strife, bloodshed, and political dissension.

For some years the gatherings continued in London. Boyle attended whenever he could, but he was something of a wanderer at this period, and much of his time was spent both on his Irish estates and at Stalbridge. When in London he lived with a sister, Lady Ranelagh, to whom he was devotedly attached. Boyle

---

[1] Informal gatherings probably began at Oxford, but these were not on the organized scale of those which were held in London, and which probably mark the true beginnings of the ' invisible college '.

was a life-long celibate, though when he was twenty he courted the beautiful daughter of Cary, Earl of Monmouth. Although he did not marry the lady, she was nevertheless the source of much literary inspiration in him, and to her influence is attributed a work Boyle wrote called *Seraphic Love*. He also wrote a *Free Discourse against Swearing* much about this time.

On his return from Ireland in 1654, Robert Boyle definitely settled in Oxford, and now began to take up scientific investigation in deep earnest. Being a comparatively wealthy man, he had no difficulty in doing this. He equipped a laboratory in his lodgings, and engaged Robert Hooke as his assistant, and these two collaborated in many investigations of first-class importance.

By this time, too, a number of the original members of the ' invisible college ' had removed to Oxford. In order to maintain proper continuity of discussions, and to avoid disbanding the ' college ', it was arranged for meetings to be held both at London and Oxford. A proper intercourse was thus maintained between the two ' branches ' so as to keep in touch with the problems upon which each was engaged.

At Oxford, as in London, the ' venue ' was varied to suit the circumstances of the occasion. Thus Dr. Petty's lodgings were at the house of an apothecary, and discussions which involved the handling or inspection of drugs were, therefore, most conveniently held there. But Boyle's lodgings and laboratory came in for the larger share of the meetings at Oxford. The importance of this unofficial organization soon became evident to everybody interested in philosophy, and those in authority began to realize that a great national service would be done by extending to this band of *virtuosi* the official recognition of the state. The return to power of King Charles II, himself a dilettante student of science, offered the opportunity, and in 1660, ' the invisible college ' was finally incorporated by Royal Charter into the *Royal Society*, and its members became Fellows. The Honourable Robert Boyle was a member of the Council from the outset, and so important has this institution become in the scientific scheme of this country that a Fellowship of the Royal Society is nowadays regarded as the greatest scientific distinction which a man can receive.

3. *Researches on the Atmosphere prior to Boyle*

The study of the physics of the atmosphere is one with which must be honourably associated the names of Blaise Pascal (1623–62) in France, Evangelista Torricelli (1608–47) and Vincenzo Viviani (1622–1703), both pupils of the great Galileo, in Italy, Otto von Guericke (1602–80) in Germany, and Robert Boyle in England. What was the position when Boyle began to take the matter up for experimental investigation ?

Prior to Galileo, very little was known about the atmosphere, and from the days when Aristotle taught that there could be no such thing as a vacuum, the general belief as expounded by philosophers in general, even up to the time of Descartes, was in the dictum that ' nature abhors a vacuum '. The ' horror vacui ' was an established institution, as though nature held its own views on the subject, and had its own feelings in the matter.

The first doubts—and they were but vague—were held by Galileo when he was told that a suction-pump having a very long suction-pipe was unable to raise a greater ' head ' of water than about thirty-three feet. We know now that this was simply because such a head of water was a measure of the atmospheric pressure, but Galileo, not knowing this, merely wondered if this did not indicate a measurable limit to the force of the ' horror vacui '. We may also say of Galileo that he knew that the air has weight. This he showed by weighing a glass vessel filled with air, and then forcing more air in under pressure and weighing again.

Galileo's friend and pupil, Torricelli, took the next important step in this subject. Accepting the fact that the ' head ' of about thirty-three feet of water was a measure of the resistance of a vacuum, he argued that it could be better measured with a heavier liquid. He chose mercury and expected to get a column about one-fourteenth of the height of the water column. The historic experiment, always associated with his name, was actually performed in 1643 by Viviani, pupil of both Galileo and Torricelli, and was a thorough success. It was virtually the first barometer in history. The full significance of this experiment was undoubtedly not lost upon Torricelli. Although he never actually published his account, he wrote of it in detail to his friend Ricci, in Rome, in the course of which he declared, ' the aim of my investigation was not simply to produce a vacuum, but to make an instrument which shows the mutations of the air, now heavier and dense, and now lighter and thin '. He even realized the expansion effect of the temperature as a disturbing factor in his results, though it was not until 1704 that any proper temperature corrections were applied to barometric readings.

The next great step was taken by Pascal. This young genius —who established his fame as a mathematician when but sixteen years old and died at thirty-nine—heard of the Torricelli experiment indirectly from Father Mersenne (of whom we have already heard in Chap. VIII as the intermediary between the great mathematicians of those days), who had himself received an account of the experiment from Ricci. Not all the details reached Pascal, who therefore had to think out the lessons of the experiment independently. He records as his conclusion ' that the vacuum is not impossible in nature, and that she does not shun it with so great a horror as many imagine '.

Pascal's next step was of profound importance. If, he argued, Torricelli's mercury column was held up by the pressure of the air only, then surely at a high altitude there is less air and, therefore, less pressure, and the mercury column would be shorter. So he measured it at the top of a church steeple in Paris. The difference was insufficient to be conclusive. He therefore asked a brother-in-law in Auvergne to try this experiment by ascending the mountain known as the Puy-de-Dôme. One can imagine the delight of the experimenter in finding that at the completion of the ascent the mercury column had fallen three inches.

So ended the doctrine of the ' horror vacui ' in France and Italy. Meanwhile in Germany Otto von Guericke was conducting his experimental campaign to the same end. Some of his experiments were both ingenious and theatrical, and were connected with a study of ' suction '. He filled a wine cask with water, tightly closed up the cask, and then tried to remove some of the contents by means of a brass pump. But he only succeeded in bursting the connexions between cask and pump. On strengthening these connexions and trying again, it required three strong men pulling at the piston to draw some water out, to the accompaniment of the hissing noise of air forcing its way in through small leaks to replace the water. He next replaced the leaky cask by a copper sphere, and although water was drawn out at first, the effect of the air pressure outside was such as to cause the sphere suddenly to collapse ' with a loud clap and to the terror of all '.

The result of Guericke's experiments was his invention of the air pump. It was a crude affair whose chief merit lay in the fact that it was the forerunner of better things, but nevertheless it did enable him to carry out experiments with varied pressures. For example, he found that ' a clock in a vacuum cannot be heard to strike ; and a flame dies out in it ; a bird opens its bill wide, struggles for air, and dies ; fishes perish ; grapes can be preserved six months *in vacuo*, and so on.' Then there was his famous experiment of the Magdeburg hemispheres, 1·2 feet in diameter. These were held together by the atmospheric pressure on exhausting the interior, and in an impressive experiment before the Emperor Ferdinand III and the Reichstag in 1654, the hemispheres were pulled apart only when teams of four pairs of horses were hitched to each.

FIG. 73. Boyle's pneumatic engine or air-pump.

Guericke's contributions to scientific investigations were many and varied, and included a ' weather glass ' for predicting the weather and an electrical machine based on the excitation of a rotating ball of sulphur ; whilst in astronomy he interested himself successfully in the periodicity and orbits of comets. Guericke's researches were published in *Experimenta Magdeburgica* in 1672. He died in 1686.

4. *Boyle's Researches on the Atmosphere*

Guericke's air-pump and experiments were first described in a book by Kaspar Schott, called *Mechanica hydraulico-pneumatica*, published in 1657. It was through this work that Robert Boyle learnt these researches, and they stimulated him into taking up the subject for himself. At this time he was living at Oxford, where he had set up a laboratory with Robert Hooke as his chief assistant.

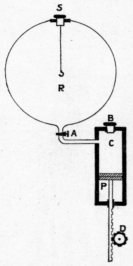

FIG. 74. Diagram illustrating the principle of Boyle's air-pump.

At the outset Boyle realized that for efficient work, something less crude and more workmanlike than Guericke's air-pump would have to be devised. This then was his first problem—the invention of an efficient pump which would enable him to experiment freely at pressures both greater and less than that of the atmosphere. The instrument which was produced can, however, hardly be said to be Boyle's, since Guericke supplied the original idea, and Hooke supplied the mechanical skill. Both Boyle and Hooke freely collaborated to produce the result, and accordingly they share the honours.

The principle of the instrument is shown diagrammatically in Fig. 74. In the light of modern air-pump practice it seems, of course, very crude. Nevertheless, it was a real advance on the pumps of those days, and, as we shall see shortly, it was the means of achieving much. The glass receiver R was spherical in shape and of about three gallons capacity. It was closed at the top by a brass plate fitting into a hole in which was a brass stopper S. Dangling from S was a string and hook from which could be suspended any article which it was required to subject to varying pressure. The receiver R was made to communicate with the vertical pump-barrel C by means of a pipe and stop-cock A. There was a hole at the top of the barrel C which could be used as an exhaust or kept closed by means of a brass plug B, as desired. The piston P was made of wood, and was surrounded by well-greased leather. It was solid and contained no valves, such things being then unknown. The piston was actuated by a rack and pinion arrangement D on the piston rod, the pinion being worked by hand.

Suppose we wish to exhaust R. The procedure is as follows. Open the stop-cock A, keeping B shut. Draw P down. The air originally only in R now also fills C. Hence the pressure in R is somewhat reduced. Now close A and open B, and move P up. The air in C is driven out through B, and we are now able to repeat as before, each cycle of operations leaving the pressure in R more and more diminished.

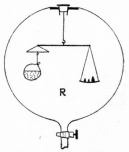

FIG. 75. Boyle's determination of the weight of the air.

Suppose, on the other hand, it is required to increase the pressure in R. The procedure described must be reversed. Keeping A open and B closed, and starting with P at the bottom, move P up, so driving the air from C into R. Close A and open B, and move P down. More air is thereby drawn into C from outside. Close B, reopen A, and repeat as before, and it will be seen that each such cycle of operations leaves the air in R at increased pressure.

This then was the apparatus with which Boyle equipped himself in order to carry out his researches. What did he do? One of his first experiments was to measure the weight of a given sample of air. His predecessors had contented themselves rather with showing that the air *has* weight than with measuring what that weight was. Boyle suspended a balance in the receiver R. From the left pan dangled a bladder half-filled with water, and in the right pan were weights to produce exact balance. On exhausting the receiver the bladder and its contents of air and water were now heavier. By a series of trials, the weights on the right hand side were now adjusted so that exact balance was obtained not before introducing into R, but after R was evacuated. The difference between the two readings was then a measure of the weight of the air in the bladder.

Boyle was able to demonstrate the degree of rarefaction which his pump could produce by introducing into R a barometer tube and reservoir (Fig. 76), and cementing the joint at A. By exhausting R he succeeded in getting down to less than one inch

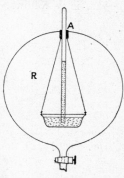

of mercury. Boyle realized how this, of which he speaks in his work *The Spring of the Air* as the nineteenth experiment, disproved the theory of the ' horror vacui '. For considering the evacuated space above the liquid in the barometer tube, he writes :

' And as for the care of the public good of the universe ascribed to dead and stupid bodies, we shall only demand why, in our nineteenth experiment, upon the exsuction of the ambient air, the water deserted the upper half of the glass tube, and did not ascend to fill it up till the air was let in upon it. Whereas, by its easy and sudden rejoining that upper part of the

FIG. 76. Barometer readings at reduced pressure.

tube, it appeared both that there was then much space devoid of air, and that the water might, with small or no resistance, have ascended into it, if it could have done so without the expulsion of the re-admitted air ; which, it seems, was necessary to mind the water of its former neglected duty to the universe.'

After which sarcasm he proceeded to the true explanation in terms of the pressure of the air in R.

Another of his experiments was on the subject of suction. Having exhausted R as far as possible, he closed the stop-cock S and removed the receiver from the pump. Immediately below the pipe was placed a brass valve V (Fig. 77) to which was attached a small scale pan P. On suddenly opening S the attempted inrush of air into R created an upward thrust on the under surface of V, forcing it up against the inlet pipe below R, and automatically closing it. The force of suction here brought into play could now be measured by putting weights in the pan P until the valve was just forced away again. This Boyle refers to in *The Spring in the Air* as his thirty-second experiment. He wrote as follows :

' For, in the next place, our experiments seem to teach that the supposed aversation of Nature to a vacuum is but accidental, or in consequence, partly of the weight and fluidity, or at least the fluxility of the bodies here below ; and partly, and perhaps principally, of the air, whose restless endeavour to expand itself every way makes it either rush in itself or compel the interposed bodies into all spaces where it finds no greater resistance than it can surmount. And that in those motions which are made "ob fugam vacui" (as the common phrase is) bodies act without such generosity and consideration as is wont to be ascribed to them, is apparent enough in our thirty-second experiment, where the torrent of air, that seemed to strive to get into the emptied receiver, did plainly prevent its own design, by so impelling the valve as to make it shut the only orifice the air was to get in at. And if afterwards either Nature or the internal air had a design the external air should be attracted, they seemed to prosecute it very universely by contriving to suck the valve so strongly, when they found that by that suction the valve itself could not be drawn in ; whereas, by forbearing to suck, the valve would, by its own weight, have fallen down and suffered the excluding air to return freely and to fill the exhausted vessel.'

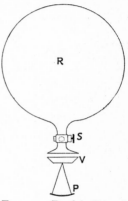

FIG. 77. Boyle's Experiment on Suction.

There were many other experiments, not all connected with hydrostatics, as for example, the suspending in the receiver of a watch to show that sound will not travel in a vacuum, but requires a medium for its propagation. The above, however, are probably the most important of his first series of experiments.

5. *Discovery of Boyle's Law*

In 1660 Boyle published his results in a work called *New Experiments . . . touching the Spring of the Air*. He illustrated the pressure exerted by the air by calling to his aid a sort of analogy in which he pictured the air particles as behaving as though each was like a spherical spring. The effect of pressure was to compress the spring and so to diminish the volume.

The book was on the whole a sound record of experimental work. Nevertheless, it met with a certain amount of opposition, particularly from Franciscus Linus, a Jesuit father of Liège. Linus offered, by way of objection to Boyle's simple contentions, the view that the air was of itself incapable of performing ' such great matters as the counterpoising of a mercurial cylinder of 29 inches ; he claimed to have found that the mercury hangs by invisible threads (*funiculi*) from the upper end of the tube, and *to have felt them when he closed the upper end of the tube with his finger*'. In these days one is tempted to wonder that Boyle should have troubled to reply to such utter nonsense, yet he did, and on the whole it is well he did so. For as a consequence of the further experiments which he now undertook by way of reply to Linus, he discovered that great truth which we all speak of to-day as Boyle's Law.

' We shall now endeavour ', wrote he,[1] ' to manifest by experiments purposely made, that the spring of the air is capable of doing far more than it is necessary for us to ascribe to it, to solve the phenomena of the Torricellian experiment. . . . We took then a long glass tube, which by a dexterous hand and the help of a lamp was in such a manner crooked at the bottom, that the part turned up was almost parallel to the rest of the tube and, the orifice of this shorter leg . . . being hermetically sealed, the length of it was divided into inches (each of which was divided into eight parts) by a straight list of paper, which, containing those divisions, was carefully pasted all along it.'

A similar scale was pasted on the other limb, and mercury was then introduced ' to fill the arch or bended part of the siphon ', so that the level was the same on each side (Fig. 78 (*a*)). ' This

[1] Boyle's *Defence against Linus*.

done, we began pouring quicksilver into the longer leg . . . till the air in the shorter leg was by condensation reduced to take up but half of the space it possessed . . . we cast our eyes upon the longer leg of the glass . . . and we observed not without delight and satisfaction, that the quicksilver in that longer part of the tube was 29 inches higher than the other.' He had in fact by applying a pressure of two atmospheres obtained half the original volume (Fig. 78 (b)).

By this means Boyle obtained a series of readings showing the relation between pressure and volume for pressures in excess of that of the atmosphere. It now remained for him to obtain a further series for pressures less than that of the atmosphere. For this his first tube was of no use. He now employed a long tube A (Fig. 79), about 6 feet long, closed at the lower end, and filled with mercury. Into this was introduced a warmed long narrow open tube B, sealed at the top C with wax. On cooling, the level of the mercury rose in B above that of A, the differ-ence in heights giving the excess of atmospheric pressure over that of

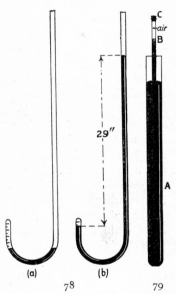

FIGS. 78 and 79. Experiments on Boyle's Law.

the imprisoned air. By pushing the tube B farther in or out of A, a range of such pressures was obtained, and the corresponding volumes as measured by the length of the air column were read.

By such methods Boyle was able to range his pressure readings from as little as $1\frac{1}{4}$ inches of mercury to $117\frac{9}{16}$ inches, and he drew up a table of comparisons of his observed pressures with the theoretical values he should have obtained 'according to the hypothesis that supposes the pressures and expansions to be in reciprocal proportion '.

His results, having regard to the difficulties with which he had to contend, particularly in the second series of readings, were excellent, and thoroughly established the law with which his name is so familiarly associated.

In France, however, the law is not so known. Fourteen years after Boyle's famous experiment, Edmé Mariotte, a French scientist of repute, published a book, *Sur la nature de l'air*, in which he described his own independent discovery of the law ' that air condenses in proportion to the weight by which it is loaded '. It seems indeed curious that Mariotte should have been unaware of Boyle's researches, yet so it was, and in all French schools to-day they speak of Mariotte's Law just as we do of Boyle's Law.

6. *Further Scientific Work*

It must not be supposed that Boyle's scientific interests lay solely in the direction of the physics of the atmosphere, for although it is with this subject that his fame is intimately bound up, yet he has left behind him a solid record of work and speculation in other branches of science.

The subject of heat, for example, engaged Boyle's attention considerably. Much of this work is recorded in his *New Experiments and Observations touching Cold*, published in 1665. He had, for example, used his pump fairly successfully in an investigation of the influence of pressure on the boiling-point, by introducing into the receiver some water whose temperature was somewhat lower than the normal boiling-point. On reducing the pressure in the receiver he was able to reach a point at which the liquid started to boil, so showing that reduction in pressure lowered the boiling-point.

Another of his experiments in heat was to determine the relative volumes of ice and water. He used for this purpose what was then spoken of as a ' philosophical egg ', i. e. a tube terminating with a bulb, the stem of which was graduated in terms of the volume of the bulb. Into this he poured water and then immersed the bulb in a freezing mixture (allowing the stem to project above the freezing mixture in order to avoid bursting by allowing for expansion—a shrewd appreciation of the difficulties of the experiment). He then measured the final position in the stem after freezing had taken place. The result—uncorrected for changes in the glass—gave an expansion of about 11 per cent. —rather a high value.

In these days it has become universally recognized that heat is but a mode of motion. It is, however, a little startling to realize that Robert Boyle and some of his contemporaries were themselves exponents of this view 250 years ago, though their ideas were somewhat vague and their experiments more so. Nevertheless, Boyle for one was surprisingly accurate in many of his conclusions. The small particles constituting bodies, he tells us, are in rapid, haphazard motion in all directions, and this motion is called heat. Cold is produced by a ' less vehement agitation ' of the particles, and any means which could be devised to increase this agitation would be found to produce heat. To illustrate this view, he arranged for two spherical pieces of brass so made that the concavity of the one could be placed in intimate contact by means of springs with the convexity of the other. They were made to rotate in opposite directions in the evacuated receiver of his pump. The vacuum was used so as to meet the objection that the resistance to the air might be the cause of the subsequent heat. He tells us that the heat produced was so intense that he was unable to touch either of the brasses. A further illustration of his as to the heat produced by arrested motion was a hammer driving in a nail.

In dynamics it is interesting to record that Boyle verified Galileo's famous ' Leaning Tower ' experiment by eliminating the resistance of the atmosphere. He exhausted the receiver of his pump, having first introduced therein a leaden bullet and a piece of paper. The stop-cock was then closed and the receiver (in the shape of a long tube) was detached and quickly inverted. Both bodies were seen to arrive simultaneously at the bottom of the tube.

Mention must also be made of Boyle's work in magnetism and electricity. He was the first to show that magnetic forces act through a vacuum by introducing both magnet and attracted object into the evacuated vessel. He did a similar experiment with regard to electrical attraction. He also records somewhat amusingly how dry hair is easily electrified by friction. ' That false locks of hair brought to a certain degree of dryness, will be attracted by the flesh of some persons, I had proof in two beautiful ladies who wore them ; for at some times, I observed that they could not keep them from flying to their cheeks, and from striking these, tho' neither of them had occasion for or did use paint.' He goes on to tell us of how one of the ladies ' gave me leave to satisfy myself farther ; and desiring her to hold her warm hand at a convenient distance from one of these locks taken off and placed in the free air, as soon as she did this, the lower end of the lock, which was free, applied itself presently to her hand '.

7. *Boyle's Later Life*

Because of the evenness of his thoughts and his ideals the remaining biographical details of Boyle's life are soon told. Up to the time of his death he may be said to have devoted himself entirely to science and religion, and beyond these he had no ambitions. But the sense in which he lived a religious life must not be misunderstood. In 1600 the Earl of Clarendon tried to persuade Boyle to take holy orders, pleading that the interests of the Church called for this step. Such a plea would naturally weigh strongly with Boyle ; nevertheless he refused.

' He reflected that, in the situation of life he was in, whatever he wrote in support of religion would have as great weight as if he was in the character of a clergyman. That he needed no accession with respect to fortune, nor indeed any appetite for greater, but, above all, according to his wonted modesty, he frankly declared, that he had not felt any motion or tendency of mind which he could safely esteem a call from the Holy Ghost ; and so not venturing to take Holy Orders lest he should be found to have lied into it.'

Nevertheless, as a layman, Boyle lived a deeply religious life. He set up for himself a high moral standard, and he lived up to it. Blessed with private means, he distributed his charity wisely. The present-day Society for the Propagation of the Gospel in

Foreign Parts is an organization which developed from an earlier one, of which Boyle was president, and amongst the charities which interested him might be mentioned the care of widows and orphans, his distribution of about £1,000 per annum for the augmenting of the salaries of poorly paid clergy, and the founding and endowing of an annual lecture ' in honour and defence of the Christian religion '. Yet there were clergymen who did not hesitate to declare ' that Robert Boyle's researches were destroying religion and his experiments were undermining the universities '. Boyle's own life stands as a sufficiently emphatic answer to such an absurd charge.

He declined all honours. In 1665 he was invited to become Provost of Eton but declined. Always a favourite with royalty, he was on several occasions offered a peerage, but although four of his brothers were peers,[1] he persistently refused. He even declined the high honour which he was offered on the 30th of November 1680, of becoming President of the Royal Society, though in this case his refusal was his religious objection to taking the oath prescribed for the President by the Society's charter of incorporation.

In appearance Boyle was ' tall but slender, and his countenance pale and emaciated ; his constitution tender and delicate, and was therefore very careful to observe and regulate himself, according to the changes of the weather by his thermometer '. We are also told that ' his health in the latter part of his life was tender, and frequently interrupted, yet by observing an exact regimen of diet, and never indulging in excess, he attained to the sixty-fourth year of his age, and retained his sight to the last '. His eyesight, however, gave him frequent trouble.

We have already pointed out how greatly attached he was to his sister, Lady Ranelagh, and it is touching to note that they died almost together, she on the 23rd of December 1691, and he on 30th December, a week later. Both bodies were interred in the chancel of St. Martin's-in-the-Fields, in London.

The name of Robert Boyle will live in the annals of science, firstly, because he opened up by his stimulating researches

---

[1] It is amusing to note that Boyle has been referred to as ' the father of modern chemistry, and brother of the Earl of Cork ' !

in aerostatics a scientific land of promise of which even these days of aerodynamics and aerial locomotion have not exhausted the possibilities, and secondly, because by the force of his own precepts and life-long example, he brought about a welcome reaction from the synthetical school of Descartes back to the experimental school of Galileo and Gilbert. Practical investigation meant everything to Boyle. 'In my laboratory', wrote he, 'I find that water of Lethe which causes that I forget everything but the joy of making experiments.' He is reported to have said that he feared death only because after it he would know all things, and no longer have the delight of making discoveries.

We may fittingly conclude this chapter by a quotation from his book, *The Christian Virtuoso*, which reads : 'The book of Nature is a fine and large piece of tapestry rolled up, which we are not able to see all at once, but must be content to wait for the discovery of its beauty and symmetry, little by little, as it gradually comes to be more unfolded or displayed.'

FIG. 80.   A chemical laboratory in 1747.

XI

ANDRÉ AMPÈRE AND MAGNETIC ELECTRICITY

1. *Science after Newton*

THE remaining men of science whose lives we are to study belong essentially to the modern school ; the science which they helped to develop is the science taught to-day ; and the history of this last period of our work is one of steady construction and expansion along the solid paths of knowledge, pursued by great men of all nations, collaborating in friendly rivalry with a unity of purpose the aim of which was the pursuit of truth.

Newton's theory of fluxions was not so pliable as was the rival theory in its general applications to the problems beyond those which Newton had himself worked out in his *Principia*, and consequently, whilst a rich harvest of mathematical discovery was being reaped on the Continent, the mathematical and mechanical sciences lay stagnant in England for many years. Yet the

FIG. 81. ANDRÉ MARIE AMPÈRE

country was not lacking in mathematical talent. Gregory Sanderson, Waring, Emerson, T. Simpson, R. Simson, and others did excellent work, but it was in the department of pure mathematics alone ; whilst, on the Continent, Lagrange, Laplace, D'Alembert, Legendre, Lacroix, Cauchy, and a host of others were achieving fame in the newer fields of the calculus and of its applications to dynamics and astronomy.

In physical optics the period of stagnation following the brilliant record of Newton and his illustrious rival Huyghens was particularly marked, and hardly a fact of importance was elicited or a theory advanced until the beginning of the nineteenth century, when appeared Thomas Young's brilliant researches on the subject of the interference of light. These inaugurated

N

a wonderful recrudescence of research by Malus, Arago, and Biot in France, and Wollaston, Brewster, and Herschell in England, on the subject of polarized light. As a consequence, Huyghen's wave theory at last came into its own, and a line of investigation was opened up which has deeply affected all other branches of physical science.

The long barren interval had produced a rashness of speculation which, without the secure foundation of laboratory data, had brought into being such futile theories as the 'caloric' theory of heat, the 'phlogiston' theory of combustion, the 'effluvia' theory of magnets, and so on. All this was now swept aside. Chemistry was caught in the forward wave with physical science. Combustion came to be properly understood, the laws of conservation of mass and energy were established, the emission theory of light was replaced by the wave theory, and a wonderful advance was achieved in the study of electricity and magnetism which not only welded these two inseparably, but also linked up the study of electro-magnetism with that of light and radiant energy.

Let us then turn to a brief summary of the advances in the subject of electricity and magnetism, and see how it came about that this study occupies its place to-day as the binding factor of physics in general.

2. *Electrostatics prior to Ampère*

So far as the study of electricity and magnetism is concerned, the eighteenth century was one of progress only in the development of electrostatics. Current electricity was completely unknown, and prior to this period, very little more had been established than the bare facts of electrification by friction. Eighteenth-century research may be said to have started with Stephen Gray, an Englishman, and Charles François de Cisternay du Fay, a Frenchman. Gray established that different substances possessed the property of electrical conductivity to varying degrees, not through any physical differences such as colour, hardness, &c., but merely through the differences in material, so that, for example, metal wire conducts well, whilst silk does not. So he developed a grouping of conductors and non-conductors (insulators). It is also interesting to note that Gray showed the human body to be a conductor, and he electrified a boy after suspending him by means of silk strings.

Du Fay went farther. It will be remembered that Gilbert had classified substances as electrics and non-electrics, the former being capable of electrification, and the latter incapable of electrification by friction. Du Fay showed this to be an erroneous view, since all bodies could be electrified. Those which *apparently* were ' non-electrics ' were merely such good conductors that they were losing the charge to surrounding conductors as fast as they were receiving it. The problem in such cases was therefore merely one of sufficient insulation. Du Fay also succeeded in establishing that there were two kinds of electricity, and he spoke of them as ' vitreous ' and ' resinous ' electricity respectively.

The discovery of the Leyden jar in 1746 by Pieter van Musschenbroek, a renowned Dutch physicist, was the next important step. It was an accidental discovery, arising from an attempt to electrify water in a bottle. Musschenbroek confessed to his friend Réaumur (of thermometric fame) ' that he would not take another shock for the kingdom of France '. Per contra, Priestley tells us that Professor Bose, of Wittenberg, was prepared to die by the electric shock, in order that the account of his death ' might furnish an article for the memoirs of the French Academy of Sciences '.

Human nature being what it is, it is not surprising that the violence of discharge of the Leyden jar attracted much public attention. This was exploited to the full by itinerant ' performers ', and when the discharge was combined with the human body as a conductor of electricity, the exhibitions took an even more elaborate turn. Nollet, ' in the King's presence, passed the discharge through 180 guards. Later the Carthusian monks at the Convent in Paris were formed into a line 900 feet long, by means of iron wires between every two persons, and the whole company, upon the discharge of the jar, gave a sudden spring at the same instant. This behaviour of the austere monks must have been ludicrous in the extreme.'

The illustrious American, Benjamin Franklin (1706–90), is intimately associated with the progress in electrostatics which now followed. He first drew attention in 1747 to the 'wonderful effect of pointed bodies, both in drawing off and throwing off the electrical fire'. In the same communication he enunciated his now famous 'one-fluid' theory of electricity (Du Fay had hitherto taught a two-fluid theory). According to this all bodies normally possess electricity and only exhibit electrical phenomena when they acquire more than the normal amount (in which case they exhibit 'plus' or 'positive' electricity) or lose some to other bodies (in which case they exhibit 'minus' or 'negative' electricity). This theory, which very simply explains all the ordinary elementary phenomena of static electricity, gained early acceptance, and successfully held the field until very recent times.

Benjamin Franklin next turned his attention to the subject of atmospheric electricity, with brilliant success. Thunderstorms had hitherto been regarded as due to the explosions of gases in the upper atmosphere, but Franklin had recorded a number

FIG. 82. BENJAMIN FRANKLIN

of important resemblances between the phenomena of lightning and those of the electrical discharge as he knew it from the Leyden jar. These he set down in his note-book on the 7th of November 1749 as follows : ' Electrical fluid agrees with lightning in these particulars : (1) giving light ; (2) colour of the light ; (3) crooked direction ; (4) swift motion ; (5) being conducted by metals ; (6) crack or noise in exploding ; (7) subsisting in water or ice ; (8) rending bodies it passes through ; (9) destroying animals ; (10) melting metals ; (11) firing inflammable substances ; (12) sulphurous smell.' He determined to apply the property of points in ' drawing off the electric fluid ' to see if he could ' draw down ' the lightning, using a metal wire attached to a kite for the purpose. His experiment, one of the most famous in the history of science, was a complete success, and led almost immediately to the installation of lightning conductors on all large buildings.

As a consequence of the various qualitative researches to which we have here referred, the way was now paved for giving the subject a proper quantitative footing. Excellent work in this field was done by Henry Cavendish (1731–1810) in England, and Charles Augustin Coulomb (1736–1806) in France, the former of whom carried out quantitative investigations on the subject of the capacity of condensers, and even to some extent anticipated Ohm's Law : whilst Coulomb, as a result of investigations on the torsional properties of hairs and wires, constructed a torsion balance in 1777 and with it proved a number of fundamental theories in electrostatics and in magnetism. In particular he showed that Newton's law of inverse squares was as true for electric and magnetic attractions and repulsions as it was for gravitation.

3. *Current Electricity prior to Ampère*

Let us turn now to the subject of current electricity, which saw its beginnings towards the end of the eighteenth century. Curiously enough, we owe the inception of this subject to the researches of Luigi Galvani (1737–98), an Italian physician and anatomist, on a totally different problem—that of the ability of certain species of fish to give electric shocks, and from thence to the study of animal electricity in general. The phenomenon of the twitching and kicking exhibited by the leg of a dead frog on being subjected to an electrical discharge was attributed by Galvani as being due to a source of electricity in the nerve of the leg. That the convulsions were not due to outside sources of electricity he deduced from the fact that, for example, on suspending the leg by copper hooks on the balcony of his house, each time the wind blew the leg into contact with the iron of the balcony rail, the twitching was observed, although there was neither lightning nor electrical machine to supply the charge.

Nevertheless, Alessandro Volta (1745–1827), a fellow country-man, and Professor of Natural Philosophy at the University of Pavia, challenged Galvani's conclusions, and the ensuing con-troversy held the attention of the whole of the scientific world. Although it was as a biologist that Volta was known, he had yet closely interested himself in electrical science, and had invented the electrophorus in 1775. Volta suspected that the use of dissimilar metals, such as the iron and copper, in moistened contact, was the vital factor in producing the electricity, and that the nerve had no electricity of its own. He instanced such phenomena as the metallic taste experienced when holding a silver and a gold coin against the tongue, the coins being in contact at one end, or joined by a wire. The reader can try it by placing a strip of copper above the tongue and a strip of zinc below, and then allowing the ends to touch.

Volta next discovered that acidulated water gives even better results than moisture, and the evolution of what we speak of to-day as the Voltaic cell was the logical outcome. In a letter to the President of the Royal Society in 1800 he described both his well-known voltaic pile and his ' crown of cups '—a series of cups containing brine or dilute acid, into each of which were dipped strips of zinc and copper, joined ' in series '.

Such then were the beginnings of the study of current elec-tricity. Of how this subject was developed quantitatively by Simon Ohm and others, and of how from it there grew up the study of electro-chemistry, we shall have occasion to speak later. But we now pass on to another development in the direction of electro-magnetism of the greatest importance.

The honours of the initial discovery of the hitherto unsus-pected relationship between electricity and magnetism go to a Danish scientist, Hans Christian Oersted (1777–1857), a pro-fessor in the University of Copenhagen, and he performed his classic experiment which founded the science of electro-magnetism in 1819. There happened to be on his lecture-bench a magnetic needle supported horizontally. Oersted was experimenting with a galvanic battery at the time, and by a happy chance he drew the magnetic needle towards the battery so that the wire and the needle were parallel. He was amazed to see the needle, hitherto peacefully pointing magnetic north and south, swing round and set itself almost at right angles to its original direction. He next reversed the direction of the current, and the needle was again deflected, this time in the opposite direction. It was a wonderful and a conclusive discovery. In some way or other, electricity and magnetism were intimately related to each other.

The experiment was described by Oersted a year later, and at once all Europe was ringing with its significance. A new field of research was opened up. Oersted himself did not contribute anything further. He had pointed the way, but of the men who noted the road

FIG. 83. HANS CHRISTIAN OERSTED

and followed it, none did so with more brilliant success and honour than he to whose biography we now proceed—André Marie Ampère.

4. *André Marie Ampère*

This wonderful Frenchman was born at Lyons on the 22nd of January 1775. His childhood was as remarkable as was his later manhood. His father, Jacques Ampère, was a successful merchant who retired, shortly after the birth of his only son, to the privacy of a small estate he possessed in the village of Polémieux.

Little André was a born mathematician, and practically a self-taught one, for there was no school at Polémieux. He took to arithmetic as a duck to water, and he would sit for hours playing and calculating with pebbles or kidney beans. We are told that during a severe illness his mother took his pebbles from him to prevent his exciting his brain with calculations. She happened to leave him for a little while, and on her return found that he had broken up a biscuit into little pieces, and was working with these in the place of pebbles.

André's education was undertaken by his father, who first taught him to read his own language and then proceeded to give him lessons in Latin. But André was hungering for mathematics ; Latin seemed purposeless to him, and he obviously disliked the lessons. So his father abandoned them and permitted André to devote his time to algebra and geometry.

In due course he had mastered the contents of such mathematical books as were in his father's library, and he sought more worlds to conquer. At Lyons there lived a friend of his father, the Abbé Dubarron, and to him the two went. Little André Ampère was but twelve years of age, yet he knew what he wanted. He modestly asked for the loan of the mathematical works of Euler and Bernoulli, two renowned mathematicians ! One can imagine the Abbé's amazement. ' But my little fellow,' he explained, ' do you know that these books deal with the differential calculus ? ' It sounded dreadful enough to the lad, but he stood his ground. ' Well, no doubt I can learn all about it,' he answered. ' Yes, my son,' said the Abbé, ' but they are written in Latin ! ' This was a poser for the boy who had given up the subject in dislike, but there was now a purpose in the study which before did not exist. ' Then I must learn that too,' he answered.

Such steadfastness of purpose greatly impressed Dubarron, who resolved to help the lad. So whilst his father again turned to teach him Latin, the Abbé took up the calculus with him, and within a few months he was ready to read the coveted books.

By the time Ampère was eighteen, he was at the height of his mathematical knowledge, and as a culminating feat he had not only read through Laplace's *Mécanique céleste* and Lagrange's *Mécanique analytique*, but had also worked out all the difficult problems in the former. His reading, however, had not been confined to mathematics. He read every book that came within reach, whatever the subject. Small wonder, therefore, that the severe tax on his brain strained his health to the breaking-point. The grief occasioned by the death of his father, who was guillotined about this time, caused his complete breakdown.

Yet Ampère was young and full of vitality. Given the necessary stimulus, the resilience of youth was bound to assert itself. The stimulus appeared in the shape of a botanical work by Jean Jacques Rousseau which chanced to fall into his hands. The charm of the style, and the theme, so appropriate to the beautiful surroundings of Polémieux, began to awake that chord of sympathy for which his mind was waiting. He worked through the book, he hunted for specimens, and gradually his mental powers returned.

Another aid to his return to normality was supplied by a book of Latin poems which fell into his hands about this time. The poems pleased him, and he turned to others. Horace in particular appealed to him very strongly, and he developed no mean ability in the composition of Latin verse himself, and pages of his note-books were filled with them.

At last restored to health, Ampère again threw himself wholeheartedly into his life of study. Outdoor exercise was provided by botanical hunts, and in the course of one of these expeditions, when he was twenty-one years of age, he chanced to meet a lady named Julie Carron, daughter of a resident in St. Germain, a neighbouring village. With André it was a case of love at first sight. The story is recorded in his diary under the title of *Amorum*, and has been published, with his early correspondence, by Madame Cheveux, an English translation of the work appearing in 1873. In spite of the fact that his wooing was at times a little mathematical, as when he tried to teach Julie how to calculate the height of his village steeple, it met with success, and he tells us that on the 3rd of July 1797 she consented to become his wife.

This naturally brought into immediate prominence the problem of his future. The question of an income wherewith to maintain a home of his own had not hitherto troubled him. A family council was held, at which his prospective parents-in-law urged him to become a silk-mercer. But this hardly seemed to fit in with his taste for mathematics and science, and Ampère decided rather to take up teaching. He began giving private lessons at Lyons, lodging there with a relative of Julie, and was married on the 2nd of August 1799. Although not earning a large income, they were very happy. In the August of the following year his wife bore him a son, Jean Jacques Antoine, and he now began to feel the necessity for doing something more lucrative than these lessons. The persistent ill-health of his wife only accentuated this necessity, and in December 1801 he succeeded in obtaining the chair of physics and chemistry in the Central School of the Department of Aisne. This, however, was but a stepping-stone, and none too satisfactory a one at that, since his wife was too unwell to join him.

In 1802 appeared a book called *Considérations sur la Théorie mathématique du Jeu*, the object of which was to show that in the long run a persistent gambler must lose his money. Ampère's object in writing this treatise was to gain publicity, and in this he succeeded. Delambre, the famous mathematician, was impressed by the obvious talent behind the book, and through his influence Ampère was in 1803 offered an appointment as professor of physics and chemistry in a newly formed school in his own town of Lyons.

Overjoyed at the prospect of reunion with his beloved wife and child, Ampère eagerly accepted. But alas, his happiness was short-lived. His ailing wife grew worse, and on the 7th of June 1804 all hope was abandoned of saving her. ' This day has decided the rest of my life,' was his pathetic entry in his diary. Six days later Julie was dead.

The blow to Ampère was overwhelming, and once again he was a broken man. Life at Lyons became hateful to him. He determined to leave it, and in 1805 he accepted an appointment at the Polytechnic School of Paris. Here for some time he was profoundly unhappy. Painful as his experiences of Lyons had been, time had mellowed the acuteness of his sorrows, and he bitterly regretted having left the place. His was a very peculiar frame of mind at this period. Here is his own description of it in one of his letters :

' My life is a circle, with nothing to break its uniformity. . . . I have but one pleasure, a very hollow, very artificial one, and which I rarely enjoy, and that is to discuss metaphysical questions with those who are engaged in this science at Paris, and who show me more kindness than the mathematicians. But my position obliges me to work at the pleasure of the latter, a circumstance which does not contribute to my diversion, for I have no longer any relish for mathematics. . . . It is seldom, except on Sunday, that I can see the metaphysicians, such as . . . M. de Tracy, with whom I dine occasionally at Auteuil, where he resides. It is almost the only place in Paris where the country reminds me of the banks of the Rhône.'

As the months went by, however, Ampère became less moody, and more reconciled to his lot, and in July 1806 he married for a second time. Things now went more smoothly. In 1808 he was appointed Inspector-General to the University, and in 1809 he became Professor of Analytical Calculus and Mechanics at the Polytechnic School of Paris, a post which he held till his death, and here it was that his famous researches in electro-magnetism were pursued.

5. *Ampère's Researches*

To the Institute of France there came on Monday, the 11th of September 1820, a member who had just returned from Geneva. He brought with him an account of Oersted's great discovery, and amongst the excited and interested auditors was André Ampère. Ampère was profoundly impressed by the importance of Oersted's experiment. He foresaw immense possibilities. He went back to his laboratory, and repeated the experiment for himself not only in its original simple form, but with every conceivable variation.

Seven days later he appeared before the assembled Institute, and gave a report of his week's labours, and showed how he had amplified Oersted's work. He showed that if a current flow along a wire from south to north, and a magnet be held *under* the wire (Fig. 84 (*a*)), the northern point of the needle is deflected westward, but if the magnet be held *over* the wire, then it is

(Fig. 84 (*b*)) deflected towards the east. He then proceeded to generalize still further, by showing in what way a magnetic needle is deflected by an electric current, no matter what the direction of the current may be. He pictured a swimmer— a little mannikin, which came to be referred to as ' bonhomme d'Ampère '—swimming with the current so as to face the needle ; that is to say, if the needle is above the wire, the mannikin swims on his back, and if the needle is to the right of the wire, the mannikin swims on his left side, and so on. Then in every case the north pole of the needle is deflected to the left of the mannikin, and the south pole to the right. This is nowadays spoken of as Ampère's Rule. It may be re-stated thus : Imagine yourself so placed that the current enters by your feet and leaves by your mouth ; then the north pole of the magnet will always be deflected to your left side.

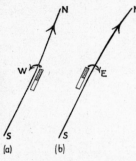

FIG. 84. Ampère's Experiments. (*a*) Magnet under current — deflexion west ; (*b*) Magnet over current— deflexion east.

Ampère's next step was of the greatest importance. He argued that since an electric current exerted on the magnet an attraction across itself, as it were, and since he could have got the same effect if he had used *another* magnet instead of using a wire carrying a current, he might reasonably expect to get a similar effect by using another wire carrying a current instead of the first magnet. In other words, he was naturally led to the problem of the *influence of two parallel electric currents on each other*. Ampère argued that two such currents ought to attract or repel each other just as surely as would two magnetic poles. He proceeded to put it to the test of experiment. He arranged two wires side by side in such a way as to permit of their being able to move freely, and he then sent an electric current in the same direction through each. The wires at once moved towards each other. He now reversed one current, and the wires at once moved away from each other.

The paper in which these experiments were described was entitled *Un Mémoire sur l'action mutuelle de deux courants électriques.* Ampère's conclusions were at once attacked. His critics asserted that what Ampère was showing them was not a magnetic phenomenon at all, but purely electrical, and that it was nothing more nor less than a case of simple electrical attractions and repulsions. But there was a conclusive answer to this, for where like electrical charges repel each other, and unlike charges attract, yet in the case of parallel currents, like currents (i.e. currents going in the same direction) *attract* each other, whilst unlike currents repel. There are always those who begrudge honour to those to whom it is due, and even when it became evident that Ampère's conclusions were unassailable, there were still those who tried to belittle him. There is a story that one of these critics, in the presence of the famous Arago, declared that since it was known that two currents acted upon one and the same magnet, it was evident, to begin with, that they would act upon each other. Upon hearing this, Arago drew two keys out of his pocket and replied, ' Each of these keys attracts a magnet, do you believe that they, therefore, also attract each other ? '

Ampère carried his researches further, and succeeded in showing that if the current strength of two such wires are C and C', respectively, and if d is the distance between them, then the force of attraction or repulsion between them $F = \dfrac{CC'}{d^2}$, a result which prompted Clerk Maxwell to speak of Ampère as the Newton of electricity.

Ampère's next experiment constituted yet another great advance on the same road. It was obvious to him that there was a magnetic ' field ' surrounding every electric current. Indeed Schweigger had already invented the galvanometer, based on the fact that in the case of a circular coil of wire, the resultant magnetic force at the centre of the coil was at right angles to the plane of the coil (Fig. 85). Schweigger saw that if instead of one turn he had many turns of wire, the magnetic effect at the centre would be correspondingly multiplied. Consequently, if the coil be in the plane of the magnetic meridian, and a magnetic needle be placed at the centre, then, on passing a current round the coil the resulting magnetic force at the centre was at right angles to this plane. Consequently there were now *two* forces acting simultaneously on the magnetic needle, (1) the force H (Fig. 86), due to the natural tendency of the magnet to point north, and (2) the force F at right angles to it, due to the magnetic effect of the current in the coil. As a result the needle was found to swing into the position of the resultant R of these two forces, and since F depends for its magnitude upon the strength of the current C in the coil, the angle θ through which the needle swung was a measure of the current strength employed. This is the basis of the whole theory of galvanometry.

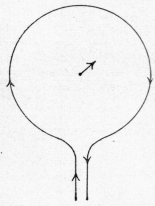

FIG. 85. Magnetic effect at centre of coil.

Ampère also utilized the idea of multiplying the magnetic effect at the centre of a coil carrying a current by having a large number of turns, but instead of arranging them into a coil as for a galvanometer, he arranged them into a solenoid or long coil, as in Fig. 87. At the centre of

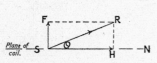

FIG. 86. Theory of Galvanometer.

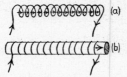

FIG. 87. Theory of the Solenoid.

each turn is a magnetic force at right angles to the turn (Fig. 87 (*a*)) and therefore along the middle of the coil, and these collectively make up a big magnetic force right along the length of the axis of the coil, as in Fig. 87 (*b*)). Consequently such a coil behaves magnetically like a bar magnet, and if freely suspended would set itself facing magnetic north and south. Ampère found that the closer together the coils, the stronger was this magnetic force along the axis of the coils, and he argued that since a bar of steel or iron always became magnetized in a magnetic field, it should also be possible to magnetize it by winding a coil round it, and passing a current through the coil. He tried this with great success. Steel of course is very retentive of magnetization, and by this means he made bar magnets which could last a long time. But soft iron is different, for it loses its magnetism immediately on removal from the magnetic field in which it is placed, and hence a soft iron bar placed in a solenoid becomes strongly magnetized as soon as the current begins, and becomes immediately demagnetized on stopping the current. So we get the *electro-magnet*, as Ampère called it, and arising from it have been many practical inventions of first-class importance.

To Ampère also belongs the honour of the first suggestions of the electric telegraph, although in the light of modern telegraphy his suggestion was very crude. His idea was to have twenty-six wires, one for each letter of the alphabet, and presumably others for the numerals. Under each was then placed a magnetic needle at the receiving end. At the sending end a current was to be sent through each wire required according to the spelling of the message, and the kicks in the corresponding magnetic needle would enable the message to be read.

Finally, considerable thought over the whole range of electro-magnetic phenomena which his industry and those of Arago and others had succeeded in bringing to light led Ampère into the realms of speculation. His theory was not so much an attempt to explain electrical phenomena by magnetism as it was the explanation of magnetic phenomena by electricity. He considered each particle in a magnet as being encircled by an equatorial current whose effect was to produce magnetic poles, and he deduced that the fact that the earth was a giant magnet was evidence of electric currents encircling the earth from east to west. According to Ampère, the process of magnetizing a bar is essentially that of causing all the molecular electric currents to flow in one direction. The theory was undoubtedly ingenious, but is of historical interest only.

6. *Ampère's Later Life*

There is very little further of incident in the life of André Ampère. He was associated with the Polytechnic School as a teacher and with the University of Paris as inspector till the time of his death, and on the whole he found his duties both irksome and cramping to his intellect. The endless routine of teaching hampered his research, and he felt this keenly. Yet it was unavoidable, for he was dependent upon his salary. Almost to the last he had to supplement his income by the giving of private lessons to those who cared to pay for them.

Yet with it all he was remarkably indifferent to fame. Thus he wrote and published a treatise on the differential and integral calculus not only without attaching to it his name, but without even a title.

As Ampère reached his fifties he developed a chronic affection of the chest, but his periodic tours to the Mediterranean in connexion with his inspectorship usually helped to restore his health. In May 1836, however, he was seized with illness during the journey to Marseilles, and in spite of every attention, he died on the 10th of June 1836, in his sixty-second year.

Throughout his life Ampère was a deeply religious Christian ; though, like most philosophers, he had his periods of doubt and scepticism. ' Doubt ', wrote he to a friend on one such occasion, ' is the greatest torment man can endure on earth.' Ampère was possessed of many of those eccentricities often regarded as characteristic of genius. His upbringing had kept him from the contact of the world. He had never been to school or college, and the conventional standards of the outside world were foreign to him. As a consequence he developed what appeared to be many absurdities of both dress and manners, and only those privileged to come into intimate contact with him knew what a warm-hearted, sincere man he was—of high ideals, a devoted husband and father, and the truest of friends.

He was very excitable, and his son tells rather amusingly of an occasion at Avignon when he was presented with a small bill in connexion with the payment of a relay of post-horses. Something in the totalling of the bill upset him. He lost his patience and his temper to such an extent that he became quite incoherent, and when eventually he paid up, the postilion disdainfully remarked, ' There's a " dog " that is not clever ! Where did he learn to count ? '

Like so many other great men and deep thinkers, Ampère was occasionally very absent-minded, and there are many amusing anecdotes in illustration of this. Thus when he became absorbed in demonstrations in the lecture-room, he would sometimes, when heated, take out his pocket-handkerchief, wipe the black-board with it, and then mop his forehead with the duster. Another story tells how, whilst proceeding to the school he was crossing a bridge over the Seine when he caught sight of a coloured pebble. He picked it up and began examining it carefully. Suddenly he realized that he was late. He pulled out his watch, looked at it, threw it into the river, thrust the stone in his pocket, and hurried away to his class.

Such, then, was the founder of Electro-magnetism, and when in 1881 there assembled in Paris an International Congress of Electricians for the purpose of the adoption of universal units for the fundamental quantities of electricity and magnetism due homage was paid to his memory and to the influence his researches had exerted on its labours, by naming after him the practical unit of current—the *ampère*.

So his memory lives. It lives in the elementary text-books on electricity and magnetism ; and it lives in the great electrical inventions which have revolutionized modern comfort in almost every branch of industrial activity ; it lives wherever, in fact, the sciences of electricity and magnetism have been welded together for the service of mankind.

XII

SIR HUMPHRY DAVY

1. *Early Days*

CONTEMPORARY with the great pioneer of electro-magnetism whose life we have just considered lived Sir Humphry Davy, a man whose researches at this period on the relationship between electricity and chemistry stand out as prominently as did Ampère's in his particular sphere of scientific activity. Davy's versatile genius found so many brilliant outlets in the various branches of physics, that, although essentially a chemist, we are bound to include him amongst the eminent band of physicists and mathematicians of which this book constitutes a record.

Humphry Davy was born at Penzance, in Cornwall, on the 17th of December 1778, of old Cornish stock.

FIG. 88.   HUMPHRY DAVY

His father, Robert Davy, was a wood-carver by trade, but had retired early from business on inheriting a small income from Humphry's grandfather, a successful builder. Davy's mother was Grace Millett, the third and youngest daughter of a mercer of Penzance, and was ' remarkable for the placidity of her temper and the amiable and benevolent tendency of her disposition '. There was nothing particularly striking about Robert Davy. The fact that, with but a small income, he was, even whilst a comparatively young man, content to do nothing to supplement it speaks pretty much for itself.

Humphry was the eldest child of his parents, and was bright and healthy from the outset. At the age of five his mother sent him to his first school to learn to read and write. It was a small private school. After a year here, Humphry was passed on to the Grammar-school at Penzance. The head master of this school was the Rev. J. Coryton, an easy-going man who was not very helpful to his pupils. Davy tells us that he ' enjoyed much idleness at Mr. Coryton's school ', and that on the whole it was a good thing for him that this was so, since he was compelled to exert his own will and his own intellect in making good the deficiencies of his master. ' What I am, I have made myself ; I say this without vanity, and in pure simplicity of heart,' wrote he on the same occasion.

That he was both sharp and witty as a boy is illustrated by the following incident. Apparently Mr. Coryton's notion of ' applied discipline ' consisted in a habit of pulling the boys' ears. Davy came in for a large share of this, and, apparently having come to the conclusion that he must do something to put an end to the practice, he appeared at school one morning with his ears all plastered up. His master asked him what was the matter, whereat Davy gravely explained that the plaster was there to prevent mortification.

From his mother, Davy had developed a vivid imagination and a love of poetry. He never tired of listening to both his mother's and his grandmother's endless stocks of stories, or to their readings from books of poems, and, being naturally quick-minded, he soon developed a keen facility for story-telling himself. Although he at all times easily mastered his lessons, he was a natural boy and never devoted more time than necessary to them. After school, this youngster, not yet nine, would gather around him a willing audience of schoolmates, to whom he would repeat story after story, some of which he would invent for himself. He was as natural a leader amongst his playmates then as he was a leader amongst men of science in later life.

When he was nine years old his parents left Penzance and went to live at Varfell, but in order not to interrupt Humphry's studies, such as they were, he was left behind, and lived with Mr. John Tonkin, a local surgeon and apothecary. In view of the great influence which this kindly man exerted on young Davy's future, a word or two regarding him is advisable. This kindly old man was held in high esteem locally, and chance had decreed that he should have been lodging in the house of Mr. and Mrs. Millett, the parents of Davy's mother, at the time of their deaths (Mrs. Millett died within a week of her husband). Mr. Tonkin befriended the orphan children as far as he was able. A relative came to keep house for them, but Tonkin continued in the occupation of his rooms, and he practically ' supplied the place of a father to them '. He never ceased to take an affectionate interest in them, and hence it is not surprising that Humphry should stay with him when his parents left Penzance, and when Humphry was fourteen years of age, Mr. Tonkin sent him at his own expense to the Truro Grammar-school for a year.

So far we may say of young Davy that while he showed general ability, he displayed no special bent, except perhaps that he was inordinately fond of lecturing. No audience was necessary. He would just mount a chair in a room, and ' hold forth ' to the four walls. Yet in a vague way he was ambitious, and he would spend hours in solitude, dreaming, Dr. Paris tells us in his biography, of fame.

In appearance there was little in him to suggest the embryo genius. He was diminutive in stature, somewhat insignificant in manner, round-shouldered, and his countenance ' in its natural state, was very far from comely '.

2. *Youth*

For a year after leaving Truro Davy spent his time somewhat aimlessly, though perhaps not unintelligently. There was no purpose in his movements and he gave no thought to the future. But in December 1794 his father died unexpectedly, and Humphry found himself suddenly forced to take stock of his position. His father had left behind him a small income of about £150 per year and a big debt of £1,300, and Humphry, eldest of the five children, loved his mother dearly, and quickly decided that the days of idling were over. What was he to do ? His mother had returned to Penzance, and together they sought the kindly advice of Mr. Tonkin. As a result Davy was apprenticed in February 1795 to a Mr. Bingham Borlase, who like Mr. Tonkin was a surgeon and apothecary.

Davy was very pleased with himself. He felt he had made a move in the right direction, and he determined, by hard work and deep study, to attain success. He was full of enthusiasm and high spirits, and when alone would frequently give loud vent to his innermost feelings. This habit of declaiming was very strong in him, and we are told by Dr. John Davy, his brother, that on one occasion, during his apprenticeship, he was ' on his way to visit a poor patient in the country, and in the fervour of declamation, he threw out of his hand a phial of medicine which he had to administer, and that when he arrived at the bedside of the poor woman he was surprised at the loss of it. The potion was found the next day in a hayfield adjoining the path '.

His note-book gives clear proof of the wonderful, though very unbalanced, energy this youth displayed.

' It opens with " Hints towards the Investigation of Truth in Religious and Political Opinions, composed as they occurred, to be placed in a more regular manner hereafter ". His first essay is " On the Immortality and Immateriality of the Soul " ; the second bears the title of " Body, organized matter " ; and his third is " On Governments ". Then there follows a variety of essays on metaphysical and moral subjects . . . but besides these there are some verses and the beginning of a romance, called " An Idyll ", which is in the form of a dialogue, the characters being "Trevelis, a warrior and friend of Prince Arthur ", and " Morrobin, a Druid " ; the scene " A cliff at the Land's End in Cornwall ".'

Throughout this period Mr. Tonkin was an invaluable friend, adviser, and teacher to Humphry, and it was not very long before, under his wise influence, superfluous subjects of study were discarded, and gradually the lad's true bent became manifest. In the years 1796 and 1797 he studied mathematics and chemistry, his starting-point for the latter subject being Lavoisier's *Elements of Chemistry*, a book which deeply impressed him. He took to experimenting, using the garret in Mr. Tonkin's house as his laboratory, and soon his inventive genius asserted itself. Text-book experiments were left behind, and he attempted others of his own—his days of research had begun.

As luck would have it, Davy now began to make acquaintances who were to be the means of providing for him the opportunities to develop his talents. One of these was Gregory Watt, son of the famous engineer, whom ill-health had brought to the mild climes of Penzance. The two met, found much in common, and became fast friends. Another was Davies Gilbert, who was later a President of the Royal Society, and who developed an interest in Davy through hearing that he was ' fond of chemical experiments '. Through the influence of these two new-found friends Davy was offered a post as laboratory assistant to Dr. Beddoes, founder and director of the Pneumatic Institution at Clifton, Bristol, the function of which was the curing of ailments by the administration of gases. To Davy, with his chemical turn of mind, this seemed a splendid opening. To old Mr. Tonkin, conservative in his medicine as he was in everything else, it was a disastrous mistake. He was all against it, and as a result was temporarily estranged from the lad whom he loved, and whom he had so greatly befriended.

In spite of this Davy accepted the offer. Mr. Borlase, to whom he had been apprenticed, kindly released him from his indentures, and so in October 1798 he said farewell to his mother and to his friends, and set out for Clifton.

3. *Manhood*

There was every encouragement at Clifton for Davy to make good his ambition. The director, Dr. Beddoes, treated him kindly, and with his wife made Davy's leisure hours sufficiently pleasurable to afford him healthy stimulus for work. Here was an institution whose functions called for a detailed study of gases and their physical, chemical, and physiological properties, and for this purpose there was a well-stocked laboratory. For a keen experimentalist such as Davy it was a glorious opportunity,

and he made the most of it. He had got over the ' speculation '
phase through which he had inevitably passed, and had come
to recognize that ' one good experiment is of more value than
the ingenuity of a brain like Newton's '.

Davy worked well and with success. His most important
researches in physics will be described more fully later, but it is
interesting to note that he instituted the study of anaesthesia
by his successful tests with nitrous-oxide, or laughing-gas, as it
is more popularly termed. A well-known physician of the time,
Dr. Mitchell, had declared this gas to be very poisonous, and
Davy was curious to try its effect for himself. He inhaled it
in small quantities, and satisfied himself that Dr. Mitchell's
statement was exaggerated. He now increased the dose, and
found himself able to breathe it for several minutes, till he
lost consciousness. He awoke without injury, and recorded
with delight his pleasant dreams during the period of uncon-
sciousness. The publication of these results aroused widespread
attention and Davy's name began to receive prominence. He
turned his attention to other gases, but with some of them he
was not quite so fortunate, and he became seriously ill through
inhaling nitric oxide and carburetted hydrogen.

For two and a half years Davy laboured on at Clifton, working
hard, achieving much, and winning the respect and admiration
of all with whom he came into contact. Once again he was to
reap his reward, and take another, and this time much more
effective step, to that fame and honour which he had openly
proclaimed to be his aim.

One of the outstanding figures in the world of science at this
time was Benjamin Thompson, Count Rumford, soldier, states-
man, and scientist. Born in Massachusetts in 1753, he had, in
his early days, fought on the side of the English in the American
War of Independence. Later he had settled in Bavaria, where
he had been ennobled for his services, and in 1798 he was sent
to England as Minister Plenipotentiary of the Court of Bavaria.
As a British subject, however, he could not be received in this
capacity, but he resolved to stay on in England for a few years,
during the course of which he took a prominent part in the

foundation of the Royal Institution. The scheme of this famous institution was very extensive, and amongst its more prominent features were the provision of a school of technical education and an organized investigation into the management of fuel. A lecture room and laboratory were to be built, and equipped with the most up-to-date apparatus and appliances for the study of ' all the mechanical arts as they apply to the various branches

FIG. 89. THOMAS YOUNG

of manufacture ', and public lectures were to be given. The institution was granted a Royal Charter on the 13th of January 1800, and Dr. Garnett was appointed the first Professor of Physics and Chemistry. But Count Rumford, who was throughout the moving spirit amongst the managers, was unable to get on with him, and as a result of a disagreement over his proposed syllabus of lectures, he soon resigned his professorship. He was succeeded by Thomas Young, the brilliant physicist.

One of the posts created with the foundation of this Institution was that of Director of the Chemical Laboratory and Assistant Editor of the Journals, and the question of this appointment now came prominently to the fore. We shall see shortly that one of Humphry Davy's most successful research experiments of his Clifton days was by way of verification of a theory of heat which had been advanced by Count Rumford in opposition to the then current ' caloric ' theory, and the publication of this had naturally given great satisfaction to Count Rumford. Consequently, when some friends urged upon him the advisability of offering to Davy the vacant appointment, he was well disposed to the suggestion, although the two had never yet seen each other.

The managers met and it was resolved that Davy be appointed to the post, and ' that he be allowed to occupy a room in the house, and be furnished with coal and candles, and that he be paid a salary of one hundred guineas per annum '. We can well imagine with what delight Davy received the news, particularly when he learnt that his duties would leave much leisure time for research. He accepted the appointment, and on the 11th of March 1801 he entered upon his new duties. Rumford was at first disappointed with him. Davy was, as has been before mentioned, none too prepossessing in appearance, and he was but twenty-two years old. ' Pert, smirking, and boyish ', the interview had an irritating effect on Rumford, who would not permit him to lecture in public until he had heard him in private.

Such a test was all that Davy needed. To one who had been a lecturer since he was a child, even though his audience varied from blank walls to a street-corner gathering of playmates, and who was burning with the fire of ambition, the giving of a ' show ' lecture in private was no ordeal—it was a pleasure. Rumford was at once won over, and in June 1801, two months after his first appointment, he was promoted to be Lecturer in Chemistry, and the entire resources of the Institution were placed at his service.

Davy was a brilliant success from the outset. As a popular lecturer he was unsurpassed, and his first course of lectures was a series of triumphs in exposition and demonstration. Intellectual and fashionable London flocked to hear him, and he achieved both popularity and fame at a bound. His language was so eloquent that Coleridge openly declared that he attended the lectures ' to increase his stock of metaphors '. Davy's star was truly in the ascendant.

But Davy's name has not been handed down to posterity on the score of his success as a lecturer. His fame rests on his achievements in chemical and physical research. It has been pointed out that his duties left him much leisure time for his own experimental work, and this he employed with all the enthusiasm of a mind dedicated wholly to the service of science in the interests of mankind.

Two years after his appointment as Director of the Institution, Thomas Young resigned. Brilliant man of science as he was, he was no popular lecturer, and he felt his inability to ' get at ' a lay audience. Added to this he was a physician with a private practice of a sort, and the public did not approve of a physician taking duties outside his practice. So Young gave up his post and Davy was promoted in his stead.

Our young philosopher was now at the zenith of his power, and the full force of his brilliant mind began to assert itself. He lectured in his theatre, and he laboured in his laboratory, with an apparently inexhaustible fund of energy, and the result was seen in a brilliant series of researches extending over a wide range of subjects.

What did he achieve ?

FIG. 90. One of Accum's Chemical Lectures.

4. *Rumford, Davy, and the Dynamical Theory of Heat*

The views universally accepted at the end of the eighteenth century as to the nature of heat were embodied in what was called the ' caloric ' theory. It was essentially a statement that heat was something material, and it really arose as a result of a theory of combustion which had been advanced by a famous seventeenth-century chemist named Georg Ernst Stahl (1660–1734), of the University of Halle. This philosopher declared that when a body burns it gives off a substance which he called ' phlogiston '. Since burning and heat are ideas which are necessarily related, it is not surprising that a corresponding view developed with regard to heat, and that it, too, was considered to be a material substance. As to the properties of ' caloric ', as this material substance was called, there was much vagueness. It was held to be highly elastic, and its particles were supposed to repel each other. As afterwards developed the property we speak of to-day as ' capacity for heat ' was explained by the supposition that the heat particles attracted ordinary matter, and that ' the heat was distributed amongst bodies in quantities proportional to their mutual attractions ', and hence to their capacities for heat.

It will be remembered that even as far back as the end of the seventeenth century, Boyle, Bacon, and others had held views on the nature of heat contrary to this, but the caloric theory persisted nevertheless, and it is interesting to note that when in 1738 the French Academy of Sciences offered a prize for an essay ' on the nature of heat ', the three winners, one of whom was the famous mathematician Euler, all favoured the materialistic theory ; and strange to relate even as recently as 1850 the article on ' Heat ' in the eighth edition of the *Encyclopaedia Britannica* advanced the caloric theory in preference to the modern dynamical theory.

For the starting-point of the overthrow of the caloric theory we have to look to the researches of Count Rumford in 1798. He had for many years been closely interested in the properties of heat (the study of fuel-economy, it will be recalled, was one of the prime functions of the Royal Institution), and when in the course of his duties, at Munich, he was engaged in the boring of cannon in the military workshops, he was very much surprised to notice the great heat which the grinding of the boring-tool against his gun was producing. Whence, he asked himself, came all this heat ?

Rumford began to consider the phenomenon in the light of the caloric theory. A body giving out heat should be losing some of its caloric. He therefore experimented with a view to ascertaining if in fact the gun, the chips, or the borer had lost anything. But of this he could find no sign. He next argued that if he went on generating heat by boring long enough, there ought to come a time when all the available caloric in the material he was using must be exhausted, since there was never a suggestion that the quantity of caloric in a body was inexhaustible. But experiment showed him that there seemed no end to the heat which could be produced ; he had merely to go on boring to get just as much heat as he liked.

Did the heat, then, come from the air ? Rumford repeated the experiment under water, and still the heat was produced, making the water itself get warm. He now began strongly to suspect that the caloric theory was all wrong, and he at once recalled the theory of Bacon, Locke, Boyle, and others, that heat is some form of manifestation of the setting up of vibrations in a body, and if this were so, then, he argued, by sufficient friction he should be able to create any quantity of heat he wished. He was thus led to the experiment for which he is most famous.

Rumford fitted a blunt steel borer into the partially scooped-out end of a cannon-shaped piece of brass, and he caused the borer to press down on the brass by placing on it a weight of ten thousand pounds. The whole was immersed in a box containing about a gallon of water, into which also dipped a thermometer. By suitable mechanism worked by two horses, he arranged for the brass cylinder to rotate at a speed of thirty-two revolutions per minute. As a consequence, the borer 'worked its way violently ' into the brass. The initial temperature of the water was 60° F., yet in one hour the temperature had risen to 107° F., and in one hour and a half it had reached 140° F., and finally, after two hours and twenty minutes, the water actually began to boil ! ' It would be difficult ', wrote Rumford, 'to describe the surprise and astonishment expressed in the countenances of the bystanders on seeing so large a quantity of cold water heated, and actually made to boil, without any fire. Though there was, in fact, nothing that could justly be considered as surprising in this event, yet I acknowledge fairly that it afforded me a degree of childish pleasure which, were I ambitious of the reputation of a *grave philosopher*, I ought most certainly rather to hide than to discover.'

Rumford's conclusion that heat was not material, but was due to motion, was given in the following terms : ' It is hardly necessary to add that anything which any *insulated* body, or system of bodies, can continue to furnish *without limitation* cannot possibly be a *material substance* ; and it appears to me to be extremely difficult, if not quite impossible, to form any distinct idea of anything capable of being excited and communicated in the manner the heat was excited and communicated in these experiments, except it be *motion*.' Writing to a friend later, he said : ' I am persuaded that I shall live a sufficient long time to have the satisfaction of seeing caloric interred with phlogiston in the same tomb.'

This was the stage at which Davy took up the same subject. Like Rumford, his work was essentially that of the production of heat by friction. His materials and his experimental details, however, were different. He began by taking two pieces of ice, and by rubbing them together he was able to make them melt even though all external warmth was excluded from them. Three alternatives offered themselves by way of explanation. Either the heat came from the ice, or it came from the air surrounding the ice, or it came from the rubbing. There could be no other alternative.

The first of these possibilities, Davy realized, could be at once dismissed. The heat could not come from the ice, since ice is cold, and, therefore, contains less heat than the water which the rubbing produced. So Davy turned his attention to the second alternative. Did the heat come from the air surrounding the ice ? Rumford had asked himself this question with regard to his experiment, and it will be remembered he answered it by repeating the experiment under water. But this was not a complete answer. It merely transferred the difficulty from the air to the water. It was evident to Davy that to supply a complete answer not only must the air be removed from the surroundings of the experiment, but also nothing else must be substituted for it. In other words, the experiment must be carried out *in vacuo*.

This was the crucial test, and Davy arranged his apparatus accordingly. Two pieces of ice were introduced into the receiver of an air-pump. The contact surface of one was concave, and of the other convex. The rubbing movement was controlled by clockwork. As a further aid to a conclusive decision, Davy kept the temperature of the receiver itself below freezing-point, so that there was absolutely nothing whatever in the surroundings of the ice from which the heat could be derived. Nevertheless, the ice steadily melted as the rubbing went on. Davy was perfectly satisfied that there was only one possible source from which the heat could come. It must have been derived from ' the rubbing '.

' Friction ', said Davy, ' causes vibration of the corpuscles of bodies, and this vibration is heat.'

So, by the joint labours of Rumford and Davy, the first onslaughts on the caloric theory were made, and a new stage in the world's knowledge of the subject of heat was begun. In 1807, Thomas Young launched a trenchant attack on the caloric theory in his *Natural Philosophy*, but it required another fifty years for the final acceptance of the new doctrine.

5. *Further Researches by Davy*

Let us turn now to other directions in the realms of physics in which the world is indebted to Davy's researches. We shall see that in the main his work lies in the direction of electrical researches, and particularly in those branches most associated with chemistry ; for it must be borne in mind that Humphry Davy was really one of the giant pioneers of chemical research, and that in a book devoted to the history of chemistry his name would find an even more important place than it does here.

Much of his work required that his apparatus should be *in vacuo*, and since he found that the various forms of exhaust pumps were unable to produce a sufficiently rarefied atmosphere for his purposes, it is not surprising to find that Davy turned his attention to the problem of high vacua, and that he solved it in characteristic fashion.   He employed chemical means as a supplement to the ordinary type of exhaust pump.   His method was both ingenious and simple.   Into the vessel to be exhausted he introduced some caustic potash, and then filled it with carbonic acid gas.   He now placed the vessel on the receiver of the air-pump, and exhausted it of as much of the gas as the pump would permit.   There was still, of course, some residual gas in the vessel. All, however, that was now required was to seal the vessel and to leave the caustic potash chemically to absorb the carbon dioxide.   Thus he obtained a highly rarefied atmosphere.   A modern alternative is to introduce copper filings into the vessel, and then to fill with oxygen and exhaust.   The copper combines with the residual oxygen.   By these means it is possible to obtain vacua of less than a millionth of an atmosphere pressure.

Turning to Davy's researches in electricity, we may note by way of introduction that there was available for his use at the Royal Institution the most powerful battery then in existence. It was made up of 200 porcelain cells, each containing ten double-plates, virtually making a battery of 2,000 cells.   With this unique equipment Davy in 1801 made a far-reaching discovery the results of which are seen in the electric lighting of to-day.

It is common knowledge that with almost any battery, on causing the terminal wires to touch each other for an instant, and so completing the electrical circuit, a spark is observed.   Davy had noticed this, and in the case of the powerful battery at the Royal Institution, he further found that on drawing the terminal wires apart after first contact, so as to leave a little air gap, the sparking continued across the gap, forming a stream of fire from one pole to the other.   He noticed at the same time that the tips of the wires were intensely heated. This interested Davy very much indeed, and he tried the effect of using different conductors, and the effect was most marked when he used two pencils of charcoal attached to the two terminal wires. When these were brought together they sparked, and on drawing them apart, a brilliant stream of light resulted across the air gap, and the points of the carbon sticks became white hot. When the discharge took place horizontally, the stream of light was seen to bend upwards like a bow, owing, of course, to the rising of the heated air, and because of this Davy spoke of the phenomenon as the *arc* discharge.

He noticed that during the course of the discharge particles of carbon are carried across from the positive stick to the negative stick, causing the former to be used up at about twice the rate of the latter, and causing a crater-like cup to form at the end of the positive carbon. It was the interior of this crater which Davy found to be the most intensely luminous, and the temperature developed therein was without doubt the highest yet obtained by artificial means. It was estimated to be about 3,000° C., and in it platinum was found to melt and run like wax ; refractory minerals such as sapphire, quartz, and magnesia were fused, and bits of diamond seemed to evaporate. Thus was initiated the electric lighting which forms so prominent a feature of twentieth-century comfort.

An allied observation of Davy's which it is convenient for us to notice here is concerned with the relative radiating powers of a luminous body in air and *in vacuo*. ' I find ', he wrote in 1809, ' the radiation *in vacuo* from ignited (meaning incandescent) platina is to that in air as three to one.'

We come now to Davy's greatest achievement : that of the applications of electricity to chemical research. It had been observed by Nicholson and Carlisle in 1800 that when the two terminal wires of a battery were dipped in water, bubbles of gas began to rise from them. Further examination and experiment showed these two investigators that whilst the gas emanating from the one wire extremity was oxygen, that from the other was hydrogen. They were unable to say, however, whence came these gases—whether from the electrical current, the battery, or the water.

Further tests brought to light additional complications in the phenomenon. Damp litmus paper applied at the positive pole was seen to turn red, whilst at the negative pole it turned blue. Clearly an acid was appearing at the positive end, and an alkali at the negative end, at the same time as the oxygen and hydrogen were being evolved. Now Cavendish had shown in 1784 that pure water was composed of oxygen and hydrogen only, and it therefore became evident that the passage of an electric current through water was forming something in the water, and it became important to find out what exactly was the effect of the current on the water.

This was the problem which Davy took up and solved in 1806. The patience and care exercised by him in these investigations afford an excellent example of the reward which must inevitably come to the worker who leaves nothing to chance.

It was necessary for him to be governed in his experimental methods by some preliminary hypothesis. Davy did not believe at first that the electric current produced anything in the water. His idea was that both acid and alkali were being derived in some way from the vessels which were being employed. His plan, therefore, was to use apparatus which, on this hypothesis, would prevent such formations from taking place. So he used distilled water, placed in cups made of agate, only to find that the cups were chemically affected by the current. He now replaced the agate cups with ones made from pure gold. But in spite of all precautions, he still found acid appearing at the positive end, and alkali at the negative end. Davy now decided that the distilled water was unsatisfactory, since there was always an element of possibility that in process of distillation some salt was carried over with the water. He accordingly substituted for it water which had been evaporated very slowly, and was pleased to find that the acid produced was weaker, although the alkali was as strong as ever before. He began to feel that he was moving in the right direction.

There was, however, a further possibility for which he had not allowed. Might not the air surrounding the apparatus have something to do with the effects produced ? So he placed the gold cups in a vessel over the receiver of an air-pump, and completely exhausted the vessel, afterwards filling it with hydrogen to ensure that no other gas could be left in. He was delighted to find that he was now getting almost pure oxygen alone at one pole, and almost pure hydrogen at the other.

It was a most important result. In the first place it confirmed in a striking manner Cavendish's original discovery as to the composition of water, but in addition to this the experiment succeeded in establishing a totally new method of analysis of substances, namely by decomposition by electrolysis.

Davy now proceeded to apply the lessons of the above experiment. What, he asked, will be the effect of the passage of electricity through other substances ? Potash and soda were, in particular, two substances which had interested him for some time. The current belief was that these were elements, and, therefore, incapable of decomposition. Davy, however, had long had his doubts. Here was a new means of testing the point. He took some pure potash and heated it in a platinum spoon till it was quite liquid. He now connected the two extremities of the spoon by means of wires to the terminals of a battery and so passed an electric current through the potash. Almost immediately the liquid showed signs of agitation, and soon bubbles began to form. Presently, beautiful silver globules came to the surface, some of which burst into flame. ' Davy's delight when he saw the minute shining globules like mercury burst through the crust of potash and take fire as they reached the air, was so great that he could not contain his joy—he actually bounded about the room in ecstatic delight.' For the first time in history pure potassium, as he named the new substance, had been isolated. Owing to its strong affinity for oxygen, causing it so readily to burst into flame, and to its extreme lightness (it floats in and combines with water), Davy had great difficulty in collecting the globules, but eventually he gathered some together and placed them in naphtha, where he was able to examine them at his leisure. In the same way he later separated out sodium. Thus

Davy was a pioneer in the study of electrolysis, a study which has led to such present-day activities as copper, silver, and gold refining, electroplating, electrotyping, and a hundred other commercial processes of utility to mankind.

There are many other discoveries of first-class importance which this brilliant man achieved, but most of them dealt with chemistry, a subject outside the scope of this work. Nevertheless we cannot avoid mention of his classic of the principle of the miner's safety-lamps.

We are told that, even as a boy, Davy was touched at the tales of disaster due to the explosions in mines, and as a young student he had made up his mind that one day he would free the miner from the terrors of these underground disasters. Unfortunately, as the pit-workings in various colliery undertakings reached a greater depth below surface, these explosions were found to be more frequent, and the trouble became so serious that in 1813 there was formed a ' Society for the Prevention of Accidents in Mines '. The society very properly sought the assistance of men of science ; at first, however, the suggestions which came in were of little use.

FIG. 91. The First Davy Safety Lamp.

The autumn of the year 1815 was an exceptionally bad one, and there was a series of heart-rending disasters in the mines of the north. Davy was in Scotland at the time, and to him the mine-owners now appealed. He at once responded, and journeyed to Newcastle for the purpose of obtaining samples of fire-damp. For a fortnight he was busily employed studying the properties of this gas. As a consequence he was able, on the 9th of November 1815, to present his safety lamp having a wire gauze surrounding the flame, a result of the principle he had discovered ' that explosive mixtures of mine-damp will not pass through small apertures or tubes ; and that if a lamp or lanthorn be made air-tight at the sides, and furnished with apertures to admit the air, it will not communicate flame to the outward atmosphere.'

There is, of course, an important physical principle involved in this. Who is not familiar with the experiment in which a fine wire gauze is held over a Bunsen burner? Provided the gas be lighted below the gauze, there is no flame above it, and if the gauze be raised or lowered, the flame rises and falls with it; whilst if the gas be lighted only above the gauze, there is no

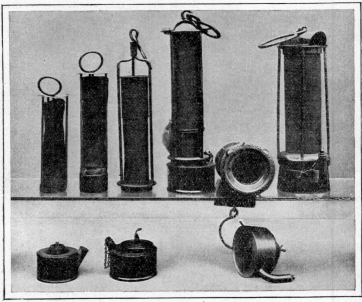

FIG. 92. Davy and Stephenson Safety Lamps.

flame below it. Yet the fact remains that gas is coming through the gauze, and can be ignited if a flame is applied.

What is the explanation? It is all a question of conductivity. The material of the gauze is so good a conductor, and the gauze itself supplies such a large effective area of metal surface exposed to the cold air, that the heat on the 'flame' side is rapidly conducted away in all directions over its surface, leaving the temperature on the other side *below the temperature of ignition of the gas*, and of course, it is only at temperatures at or above the ignition temperature that a flame is at all possible.

Hence Davy's idea was to have the flame from the oil-lamps surrounded by gauze. The necessary air to maintain the flame would then have to filter in through the gauze, and although the inflammable fire-damp would pass through to the flame with the air, and would of course ' catch fire ' inside the lamp, yet the flame would be unable to strike back through the gauze again.

But note carefully how Davy's invention matured. He studied his gas, discovered a principle, and devised his lamp as a result of the principle. Almost at the same time George Stephenson, of steam-engine fame, had also invented a safety-lamp, using at first tubes instead of gauze to transmit the air, and in his case the converse is true—namely, that he invented the lamp and from it discovered the principle. It is a striking illustration of the contrast between two lines of research of which scientific history affords many other examples. There was much controversy at the time as to which of these two could justly claim priority for the invention, but there is no doubt that as far as the *principle* underlying the invention is concerned the honours go to Humphry Davy, and he fully merited the address of thanks and the service of plate presented to him by the coal-owners of Northumberland and Durham.

6. *Further Biographical Details*

Let us now return to further details of Davy's career. It will be recalled that we referred to him as having succeeded Thomas Young as Director of the Royal Institution. In this capacity he was so far successful that he converted what had been intended primarily as an institution for popular instruction into an institution for research. Scarcely a week passed by without Davy's being able to announce some fresh discovery. He was working almost literally at fever heat.

All this time he was in high favour with everybody. Society made much of him. Davy was young and, alas, was not proof against the flattery and the vain compliments which showered on him. In his leisure hours he threw himself as energetically into the life of fashion as he did into his work by day. Such a life is bound to leave its mark, and Davy must have felt that the freshness and the frankness of his nature were in jeopardy, for in May 1803 he wrote thus :

' Be not alarmed, my dear friend, as to the effect of worldly society on my mind : for the age of danger has passed away. There are in the intellectual beings of all men paramount elements —certain habits and passions that cannot change. I am a lover of Nature, with an ungratified imagination. I shall continue to search for untasted charms, for hidden beauties. My *real*, my *waking* existence is amongst the objects of scientific research. Common amusements and enjoyments are necessary to me only as dreams, to interrupt the flow of thoughts too nearly analogous to enlighten and vivify.'

Nevertheless he continued to burn the candle at both ends. Often, we are told, he would leave himself so little time between leaving his laboratory and going out to dinner that he would not have time to change his clothing, and he would put a clean shirt on over the soiled one, and similarly with his stockings. Such a life could have but one result. Following on the hard work entailed by his researches on the isolation of sodium and potassium, he broke down, and for some weeks he lay seriously ill. It was perhaps as well. For although on his recovery he continued to work hard in his laboratory, he led a saner social life.

Meanwhile he had been elected a Fellow of the Royal Society, and by 1809 he was its secretary. A signal compliment was paid to him, too, by France. These were Napoleonic days, and England and France were anything but friendly. Yet in spite of this fact Davy's contributions to scientific knowledge called forth from the Institute of France the award of its gold medal. There were those who did not hesitate to invite Davy to refuse the award, and it is to Davy's infinite credit that he accepted the offer. ' If the two countries or governments are at war,' he said, ' we men of science are not.'

At home, too, although, as we know, Davy never went to a university, honorary degrees were conferred on him, and on the 10th of April 1812 he was knighted. The honour came most appropriately, for on the following day he was married. His wife was a wealthy Scottish widow, whom Davy had first met two years previously. They spent their honeymoon in Scotland, and here Davy was able to indulge in his favourite recreations of shooting and fishing.

In 1813, with his wife, he began a period of Continental travel, his itinerary embracing France, Italy, Switzerland, Germany, and home via Ostend. It was in many respects a tour of triumph, for his reputation was now worldwide and he was everywhere enthusiastically received. There is no doubt, however, that he was a disappointment to those with whom he came into contact. There was something in Davy's manner and bearing which irritated—a mixture of flippancy, haughtiness, and no doubt a want of appreciation of the foreign temperaments amongst which he moved. Such instances as the admiring of a fine alabaster statue as a remarkable specimen of stalactite when the hearer was looking for an appreciation of the artistry of the thing was hardly calculated to impress favourably. His biographer assures us that in fact what looked like the swollen-headedness of youthful success (Davy was but thirty-five at this time) was in reality the outward concealment of an inward timidity and nervousness ; and, indeed, it is but charitable so to regard it.

It was April 1815 when Sir Humphry Davy returned to England, and as we have already seen, the latter portion of this year was busily spent by him in the problem of the safety-lamp. Although he had solved the problem in principle by the end of the year, he continued working at it with a view to effecting practical improvements in the lamp, and this kept him well occupied till 1817, and in October of the following year, as areward for his services to the nation in this connexion, he was created a baronet. Finally, in November 1820, he was accorded the highest honour it was in the power of his scientific colleagues to confer on him, election to the office of President of the Royal Society.

The next few years were busy ones for Davy, but in 1826 his health began to fail. A life lived at top-speed as was his could not continue without some abrupt physical disaster, and towards the end of the year he was seized with apoplexy, and although he partially recovered, he knew himself to be a doomed man. Acting on medical advice, he spent his winters in Rome, ' a ruin amongst ruins ', and employed his enforced leisure in writing *The Consolations of Travel*, and towards the end, when he was unable to write, he dictated the passages to his brother, Dr. John Davy, who was with him.

Davy faced death as he had faced life—courageously, confidently, and hopefully. ' Behold me ', he wrote, ' on the couch of death, my senses lost, my organs falling towards that state in which they will be resolved into their primitive atoms ; still is my mind unconquered, still all my passions, all my energies are alive ; still are all my trains of thinking complete. Philosophy has warmed me through life ; on the bed of death she does not desert her disciple. . . . I feel and believe that the genial warmth of the sun of immortality which has shone through this frame with feeble light shall be more permanent in the region of bliss.'

And so he felt to the very end. At his own desire, he was moved from Rome to Geneva, where he died on the 29th of May 1829.

Scientists there have been whose memories are revered by their colleagues for the work they have done. But Davy belongs to the illustrious few whose names and memories are household words for the service they have accorded to the whole of mankind. Sir Humphry Davy's life stands as an example to the world of the true spirit and service of science. The monetary value of much that he achieved *could* have been enormous, but he scorned so to use his talent, and no better tribute need we pay to his memory than to conclude with his own pronouncement to his friend, John Buddle, when the latter urged him to take out a patent for his safety-lamp and so secure for himself an easy five or ten thousand pounds per annum in royalties. ' No, my good friend,' answered Davy, ' I never thought of such a thing. My sole object was to serve the cause of humanity, and if I have succeeded, I am amply rewarded on the gratifying reflection of having done so.'

XIII

GEORG SIMON OHM AND HIS FAMOUS LAW

1. *Early Life and Progress*

WE have seen how the study of electrostatics began to develop qualitatively under the stimulating researches of Franklin and others, and quantitatively through the efforts of such men as Coulomb and Cavendish : we have also seen how Galvani and Volta initiated the quali- tative study of the electric battery, of how Oersted and Ampère carried the work far- ther into the realms of elec- tro-magnetism, and Davy into the field of electro-chemistry. We shall now see how Georg Simon Ohm, struggling against the almost overwhelming odds of poverty, isolation, and lack of recognition, discovered the law with which his name is so honourably associated, and so

FIG. 93.   GEORG SIMON OHM

laid a lasting foundation for the quantitative study of current electricity.

Georg Simon Ohm was a German.   He was born on the 16th of March 1789, at Erlangen, in Bavaria, and was the elder of the two sons of a master locksmith.   Simon's father was a man of common sense and understanding.   It so chanced that when a lad there had lodged in his house a young student of the University of Erlangen.   This student had given the lad who was afterwards Simon's father lessons in mathematics in part pay- ment of the rent, and these lessons had left in the mind of the recipient a true appreciation of the value of learning.

Consequently, although it was his wish that his two sons, Georg and Martin, should both in due course become locksmiths like himself, he had no intention of denying them the privileges of education. At first he sent them to the elementary school, but from this he passed them on to the local secondary school, or Gymnasium, as this type of school is called in Germany. Here they were able to learn the rudiments of mathematics and science. Both brothers displayed ability, the elder in science and the younger in mathematics, and Charles de Langstorff, a man of discernment and an eminent mathematician, who was in 1804 appointed to the chair of mathematics at the Gymnasium, predicted for the two brothers a brilliant future, and likened them to the famous Bernouilli brothers.

In the face of such a pronouncement, Ohm felt himself unable to insist on making locksmiths of his two boys, although as a matter of fact, living at home as they did, they were rapidly picking up the rudiments of their father's trade. Ohm was a poor man, but with some friendly assistance he managed to give his sons three terms each at the University of Erlangen. Three terms meant an incomplete course, but the young men were thus enabled to make for themselves an opportunity of completing their courses later, and this is indeed what happened.

For a time Simon maintained himself as a private tutor in Switzerland, and by 1811 he had managed to save sufficient money to return to Erlangen to finish his course and pass his examinations at the University. He now obtained his first real teaching appointment at a school in Bamberg. Being a teacher by instinct, he settled down to what he regarded as a satisfactory beginning to his career, and looked forward to the time when he could repay his father, now growing old, for the love, care, and self-sacrifice he had displayed in his endeavours to do well for his sons.

It was a hope doomed to disappointment; for before very long a series of difficulties caused the closing down of the school, and the staff was dismissed. It was an unfortunate time. Europe was in the throes of the Napoleonic wars, and Germany was deeply committed. Ohm found himself unable to obtain another scholastic appointment, and very dejectedly he returned to

Erlangen. He had, however, no intention of being a drag on his father, and so he helped him in the only way now possible—by working at the vice in the locksmith's shop.

There can be no doubt that our future philosopher must have found the work distasteful ; but there was nothing else for it. Necessity and duty held him to his task, but he never lost hope of returning to his beloved teaching. It was his ambition one day to be a university professor, and he never doubted, through all this trying time, but that one day he would achieve his aim.

At last his opportunity came. In 1817 he published an ' Essay on Geometry ', ' written in a room without a fire ', and as a result of the notice this received he was offered, and, as we may be well sure, he eagerly accepted, the post of teacher of mathematics and physics at the Jesuit High School in Cologne. Here he spent nine and a half successful years as a teacher, and here it was that he carried out those researches which made him known. As a teacher he was an undoubted success. His lectures were clearly thought out, well delivered, and popularly received, and many of his students made their mark in after life, notably, for example, Lejeune-Dirichlet, the mathematician.

Ohm's ambition, however, went beyond mere teaching. He was deeply interested in problems of current electricity, and he wanted to engage in research, but there were difficulties in the way. His scholastic duties left him little time for experimental work, and his slender purse rendered the acquirement of books and apparatus an extremely slow process. Nevertheless, there were two other factors which enabled him to triumph in spite of these difficulties—his iron determination to carry through, and his mechanical skill derived from his father's workshops. As a result of the latter he was able to construct much of his apparatus for himself ; and so, without hurry, quietly, but persistently, he worked on in such spare time as he possessed, and gradually built up an edifice of experimental work which enabled him by 1826 to set forth what he had done, and show a result which, later, was to bring him and his country honour.

Let us consider briefly what was this series of experiments, and whither it led.

2. *Ohm's Researches in Current Electricity*

In 1822 Joseph Fourier published an epoch-making work entitled *La Théorie analytique de la Chaleur*. It was an important contribution to mathematical physics, and attracted the attention of the whole of the scientific world. It was valuable not only for the sake of the important matter which it contained, but also for the marked stimulus it gave to experimental inquiry.

One of its chief features was its discussion of the subject of the ' heat conductivity ' of materials ; that is to say, the relative abilities of different substances to transmit heat along themselves when one extremity is subjected to higher temperatures than that of the remainder ; and Fourier's conclusion was that the ' flux of heat ', i. e. the total quantity of heat which flows in a given time, is in direct proportion to the difference of temperatures between its two ends.

This was a conclusion which set Ohm thinking. He thought he saw much that was similar between the problems of the flow of heat along a metallic bar, and the flow of electricity along a metallic conductor. He compared the idea of the flux of heat with the idea of strength of current in electricity, and Fourier's conclusion that the flux was proportional to the difference of temperatures suggested to Ohm the corresponding idea of current strength being proportional to the difference of potential at the two terminals of a battery.

As a starting-point Ohm began to experiment on the effects of using different conductors. He took a number of wires of different materials but each of the same thickness, and beginning with copper, he varied the lengths of the different conductors he used, so as to get the same effect on the galvanometer in his circuit. That is to say, he was experimenting on the effect of length on the conductivities of the different materials.

His results are as follows. Taking the length of the copper conductors as 1,000, the lengths of substances required to give the same flow of current were :

copper	.	.	.	1,000	iron	.	.	.	174
gold	.	.	.	574	platinum	.	.	.	171
silver	.	.	.	356	tin	.	.	.	168
zinc	.	.	.	333	lead	.	.	.	97
brass	.	.	.	280					

and this gave Ohm an idea of the relative electrical conductivities of these different substances. It is interesting to notice, however, that his result for silver was very faulty, since it is actually a better conductor than copper, although the above figures show it to be poorer.

Later Ohm discovered the reason for the error. The trouble arose from the fact that in the process of drawing the silver wire, it had been covered with oily leather, as a result of which the wire appeared to be greater in cross-section than it really was. Now Ohm's next series of experiments was on the effect of varied cross-sectional areas on the conductivity, and he found, using wires of the same materials, that the conductivity was unaltered if the cross-sectional area was kept proportional to the length. This at once told him that his result for silver in the first series of experiments must be wrong if the cross-section was too small, and subsequent experiments with silver gave him a more correct value.

The results of Ohm's researches thus far may be summarized as follows. The conductivity of a given specimen of wire is governed by three factors : (1) its length ; (2) its sectional area ; and (3) the material of which it is composed. Looking at the problem from the reciprocal point of view, the wire offers a natural *resistance* to the passage of the electric current, and this resistance, which we denote by the symbol R, is directly proportional to the length l, inversely proportional to the cross-sectional area a, and is also proportional to a constant ρ, the value of which varies from material to material.

$$i.\ e. \qquad R = \rho \frac{l}{a}.$$

It is not difficult to realize why the resistance of a wire to an electric current is greater for a narrow than for a stout wire. Although it is a very loose sort of comparison, we have a similar phenomenon in the case of a pipe conveying a current of water ; a wide pipe offers little resistance to the flow, whereas a narrow pipe offers considerable resistance.

The symbol ρ in the above equation gives us what is called the specific resistance, or more shortly, the *resistivity* of a given material, and therefore the reciprocal $\dfrac{1}{\rho}$, usually denoted by k, would give us the specific electrical conductivity of a given material.

We now come to the second stage of Ohm's researches. It should be mentioned that he had sent accounts of his observations to a scientific journal conducted by Schweigger, the famous inventor of the galvanometer, and also to Poggendorf's 'Annalen ',

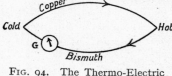

FIG. 94. The Thermo-Electric Circuit.

and in the course of these he explained that he had been much troubled in his experiments by the vexatious variations in current which he experienced from his batteries. To this Poggendorf replied with the suggestion that he should dispense with the batteries altogether, and substitute for them a thermo-circuit.

This was a sound suggestion, and Ohm adopted it. Let us consider briefly what is meant by a thermo-circuit. The ordinary type of battery or electric cell is not the only means of producing a current. In 1821 Thomas Johann Seebeck, a Russian scientist resident in Berlin, had discovered that if a strip of copper be joined to a strip of bismuth so as to form a closed circuit, then, if one junction be subjected to a higher temperature than the other, a current of electricity at once flows round the circuit and continues so to flow as long as the difference in temperature between the two junctions exists. The presence of the current is indicated by a deflexion in the needle of a galvanometer, G (Fig. 94), introduced into the circuit. The strength of the current, of course, is proportional to the temperature difference. This phenomenon is true for any pair of metals, and in Seebeck's original experiment the mere holding of one junction in the hand was sufficient to produce a current which he could measure.

This was the principle which Simon Ohm employed in the place of his troublesome batteries, and he did so with great success. He was now at work upon the experiment which established his famous law. His idea was to study the factors which affected the strength of current in any given circuit. We have already seen how Fourier's work on the flow of heat suggested to him the influence of the potential difference between the two battery terminals as one factor. The resistance offered by the circuit to the passage of the current was, he realized, the other factor. But he saw further. The resistance was made up of two portions.

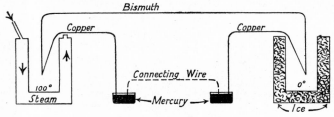

FIG. 95.   Ohm's Apparatus.

There was, first, the resistance of the conductor joining up the battery terminals ; this he spoke of as the external resistance. Secondly, there was the resistance of the battery itself ; this he called the internal resistance. So long as Ohm used batteries this internal resistance was a continual trouble, for it could not be directly determined as could that of a wire conductor, that is to say the formula $R = \rho \, \dfrac{l}{a}$ could not be conveniently supplied.

Here, then, was an additional reason for discarding batteries, and for using thermo-circuits instead ; for, besides being no longer troubled by current variations in the battery, he was also able to dispense with the consideration of internal resistances other than those he could directly determine. Let us see how Ohm set to work. He used a thermo-circuit of bismuth and copper. One junction was maintained at a temperature of

100° C. by immersion in a steam jacket ; the other junction at 0° C. by immersion in an ice-jacket. The copper was in two disconnected portions, the extremity of each dipping into a cup of mercury (Fig. 95), and Ohm could either ' make ' or ' break ' his circuit by introducing or withdrawing the ends of a connecting wire between these two cups.

To measure the strength of the current produced, Ohm did not use the ordinary form of galvanometer. Instead he used a torsion-balance made by one of his assistants. This consisted of a magnetic needle suspended from a graduated brass-head by means of a flattened wire, five inches long. The circular brass-head was radially divided into a hundred parts, and each ' centesimal ' of a circle was further divided into quarters. The theory of the galvanometer is applied in part. When the needle is placed under the copper wire, and the circuit closed, the resulting current produces a deflexion of the magnetic needle, the magnitude of which depends on the strength of the current. But, instead of measuring this deflexion, the brass-head is rotated so as to bring back the needle to its zero position, and it is the angle through which the head is rotated which is observed. One advantage of this method is that it reduces that ' bugbear ' of experimenters—the personal equation.

Ohm used in succession eight samples of copper wire, each of equal thickness, but of lengths 2, 4, 6, 10, 18, 34, 66, and 130 inches. The following were the results he obtained in an experiment he carried out on the 8th of January 1826 :

Length of copper conductor (inches)	Restoring angle of torsion-head in centesimal divisions
2	$326\frac{3}{4}$
4	$300\frac{3}{4}$
6	$277\frac{3}{4}$
10	$238\frac{1}{4}$
18	$190\frac{3}{4}$
34	$134\frac{1}{2}$
66	$83\frac{1}{4}$
130	$48\frac{1}{2}$

Ohm's conclusion was that ' the above numbers can be represented very satisfactorily by the equation

$$X = \frac{a}{b+x},$$

where X designates the intensity of the magnetic effect of the conductor whose length is x, a and b being constants depending on the exciting force and the resistance of the remaining parts of the circuit.'

Let us interpret his language in present-day terms. Ohm talks of X as the intensity of the magnetic effect of the conductor, but we know that the extent of this magnetic effect depends upon the strength of the current, being essentially the 'Oersted' effect referred to in the last chapter. Hence X is replaced nowadays by the symbol C, denoting the strength of the current in the circuit. Again, Ohm says a is the constant 'depending on the exciting force'; this exciting force is what to-day we call the 'electromotive force', and it is that which sets up the difference of potential, so causing the flow of the current. We denote it by the symbol E. Finally, as to the denominator $b + x$, a very little consideration will suffice to show that this expression really gives a measure of the total resistance of the circuit to the passage of the current; for x is the length of the copper conductor, and, as Ohm clearly showed in his first series of experiments on conductivity, the resistance of a conductor is directly proportional to its length (see p. 236); and b is a constant 'depending on the resistance of the remaining parts of the circuit'. A reference to Fig. 95 will show to what portion of the circuit this refers, namely, to the rod of bismuth, the two cups of mercury, and the connecting wire; these remained unchanged throughout the whole series of experiments, and consequently Ohm was able to assign to b a definite and a constant value. The quantity $b + x$ is therefore a measure of the total resistance of any given circuit, and in the case of an ordinary battery circuit, using the nomenclature usual to-day, it consists of the external resistance R of the wires, and the internal resistance r of the battery itself.

Hence we see that, substituting for every term in Ohm's original expression the symbols of to-day, the expression reduces to

$$C = \frac{E}{R + r},$$

or, expressed in words, for any given electrical circuit,

$$\text{Current} = \frac{\text{Electromotive Force}}{\text{Total Resistance}}.$$

This relation is universally spoken of as Ohm's Law.

Returning to the formula, $X = \dfrac{a}{b+x}$, Ohm assigned to the exciting force a the value 7285, and to the external resistance b the value $20\frac{1}{4}$, and, using these values, his results were undoubtedly excellent. Taking at random, for example, the length of the copper conductor as 10 inches, X works out to $\dfrac{7285}{20\frac{1}{4}+10} = \dfrac{7285}{30\frac{1}{4}} = 240\cdot86$, whereas experiment gave $238\frac{1}{4}$; or again, for $x = 6$, the theoretical value gives $X = 277\cdot53$, as compared with the experimental result $277\frac{3}{4}$.

Ohm next consolidated his results by varying his experimental conditions, using brass instead of copper, and in another series using thermo-junction temperatures of $0°$C. at one end and room temperature at the other end. These, of course, altered both current strength and electro-motive force, and also the internal resistance, but his formula still held good.

So was established the famous law upon which all modern electrical computations are based. Current electricity, as Ohm found it, was a qualitative study to which numerical notions were hardly applicable. As he left it, accurate definitions of current strength, of electrical resistance, and of electro-motive force, were clearly laid down, and the numerical relationship between them conclusively established. It was a fine achievement, and, coming as it did from this quiet, unassuming German scientist, it deserved the united acclamation of a grateful Germany for the honour he brought his country.

Yet how, in fact, did his countrymen receive his work?

3. *How Ohm's Results were received*

Ohm had published occasional notices of his experimental work in the scientific journals conducted in Germany by men like Schweigger and Poggendorf. These notices had not attracted much attention, but in 1827 Ohm had applied for, and had been granted, leave of absence to go to Berlin, where library facilities were so much better, to complete his experiments and publish his results. Accordingly in that year there appeared his book entitled *The Galvanic Chain, Mathematically Worked Out*. This work was in effect supplementary to his articles in that it set forth a theoretical deduction of his law from 'first principles'.

It is difficult to realize why it should be so, but the fact remains that the book was badly received. Many who should have known better simply ignored it altogether. To some extent the trouble was due to the fact that very few people appeared to have noticed his articles setting forth his experimental results, and consequently, when they saw in the book what appeared to be a purely theoretical argument unsupported by experiment, it was regarded as the creation of a warped fancy. Ohm's theory, to quote one critic, was 'a web of naked fancies', which could never find the semblance of support from even the most superficial observation of facts; 'he who looks on the world', proceeds the writer, 'with the eye of reverence must turn aside from this book as the result of an incurable delusion, whose sole effort is to detract from the dignity of nature'.

Ohm's disappointment was bitter and deep. For nine years he had laboured at Cologne, building up a reputation as an earnest teacher and a sincere seeker after truth. He had developed legitimate aspirations. His ambition was to become a university professor, and he had naturally thought that this work upon which he had been engaged, based as it was on the irrefutable logic of experimental fact, would win him his desired goal. Yet now that it was completed, where he had looked for commendation he found at best complete indifference, and at worst open abuse and derision.

More was yet to come. Amongst his critics was a certain school official with whom in some administrative capacity Ohm must have come into contact. This person was at all times an opponent of the experimental school of thought, and, with this initial bias against Ohm, he now became particularly hostile to him. The influence of this opposition reached the Minister of Education himself, and he, speaking officially, definitely pronounced it as his opinion that 'a physicist who professed such heresies was unworthy to teach science'.

This truly was a very severe blow, and in the depth of his

misery Ohm took the only course consistent with his self-respect. He resigned his appointment at Cologne.

It is inevitable to wonder why it was possible that in a country so well represented in the world of science by men of eminence and knowledge a series of investigations the searching character of which could admit of no doubt, culminating in the discovery of a law so obviously fraught with significance and importance, should have been received with such shameful disregard and with such obvious violation of the instincts of justice. The fact remains that for the next six years this much-wronged man was withdrawn from a useful activity which might have resulted in further benefits to humanity, and was thrust into the obscurity of casual coaching in Berlin, and during the whole of this time the only certain source of income which he could ' enjoy ', apart from such occasional private tuition as was asked of him, was the giving of some three lessons a week in mathematics in a school at a minute yearly salary.

4. *Ohm's Later Career*

Fortunately, the situation was so grotesquely illogical that it could not persist. Ohm's work was sound and it existed in black and white. It embraced a subject which was *bound* to receive the attention of the world of science. Gradually it began to be talked about. Ohm luckily was not entirely lost in obscurity. During these six years of scientific exile, occasional articles bearing his name found their way into Schweigger's periodical, and although these were of minor importance, they at least helped to set going rumours of a possible value in the work which had brought him such unmerited disgrace.

It is no credit to Germany that first recognition of Ohm's work was to come from abroad. Such great men as Lenz in Russia, Wheatstone in England, and Joseph Henry in America, were all at work on problems of current electricity, and sooner or later it was inevitable that they should come up against the rumours of Ohm's researches. In 1833 Henry asked Dr. Bache, ' Can you give me any information about the theory of Ohm ? Where is.

it to be found ? ' Yet Dr. Bache could tell him nothing, and it was only in 1837, when Henry was on a visit to England, that he was able to get access to the information he sought.

In 1833 Ohm's luck changed. He obtained an appointment under the Bavarian government at the Nuremberg Polytechnic School, and in this position found himself better able to face the future. Indeed his day was soon to come. Even in his own country Poggendorf and Fechner were beginning to insist on the high value of his work, but abroad, and particularly in England, open admiration began to be expressed for his researches, which now began to attain a wide publicity.

A culminating point came in 1841, in which year the Royal Society of London conferred upon Ohm the award of the Copley medal in recognition of his eminent services to science by the discovery of his now famous law. This award, coveted by scientists all the world over, and coming as it did from a foreign country, deeply affected Ohm. It was a proud moment for him, and it repaid him, no doubt, for all that he had suffered at the hands of his own countrymen. It served, too, as a stimulus to further effort, and he determined that he would carry on with his researches with a renewed vigour and enthusiasm.

The next few years saw Ohm steadily at work, and although most of what he did was outside the scope of electrical research, it was none the less useful. His work on acoustics was especially valuable, including as it did the theory of the siren and a dissertation on the analysis of sounds by the ear. Some researches which he seriously contemplated, and which he actually began, in molecular physics, on a somewhat grandiose scale, in which it was his intention to emulate Sir Isaac Newton in the 'parallel' study of celestial mechanics, however, did not mature. In 1849 he received the first real mark of recognition in his own country in the shape of an appointment at the University of Munich as professor, and the various duties which were assigned to him in this capacity left him little time for his own unofficial work.

This appointment was no ordinary incident in Ohm's life. It had been his great dream to become one day a university professor, and it was an ambition which had never left him. Now, at the age of sixty years, his dream had come true. He had won his place. His name was honoured throughout the world of science. He had earned the respect of his colleagues and the love of his students and he was content.

Duties multiplied : he had charge of the library and of the museum : he became councillor of the telegraph administration. What little spare time he had he devoted to the writing of a text-book in physics.

Further recognition came in the shape of various orders, but these in no wise spoilt him. Never a man of fashion, society, rank, or pretence, he remained to the end the simple, quiet, truth-loving man of science he always was. In appearance he was somewhat short and plump and with a kindly, retiring look. He seldom spoke except when addressed, and lived contentedly alone and unmarried. To his colleagues and his critics he was always the essence of courtesy and of generosity of thought. He died in 1854, continuing his official duties almost to the last.

We have already mentioned that in 1881 the International Congress of Electricians at Paris paid homage to the memory of Ampère by naming the practical unit of electrical current after him. It was but fitting that the same congress should extend similar honour to the memory of Georg Simon Ohm, after whom they named the practical unit of electrical resistance.

In 1889, one hundred years after his birth, the Royal Bavarian Academy of Sciences at Munich convened a special gathering of scientists for the purpose of paying tribute to Ohm's splendid services, and we cannot do better in conclusion than quote the following fine passage from Professor E. von Lommel's address :

' The deeds of a man of science are his scientific investigations. Truth once discovered does not remain shut up in the study or the laboratory. When the moment comes, it bursts its narrow bonds and joins the quick pulse of life. That which has been discovered in solitude, in the unselfish struggle for knowledge, in pure love of science, is often fated to be the mighty lever to advance the culture of our race. When, nearly a hundred years ago, Galvani saw the frog's legs twitch under the influence of two metals touching, who could have suspected that the force of Nature which caused those twitchings would transfer the thought of man to far distant lands, with lightning speed, under the waters of the ocean—would even render audible at a distance the sound of the spoken word ? That this force of Nature— after man by ceaseless investigation had learned vastly to increase its strength—would illuminate our nights like the sun. This enormous development of electro-technology could only be accomplished upon the firm foundation of Ohm's law. For only he can govern a force of Nature who has mastered its law. Ohm, by wresting from Nature her long-concealed secret, has placed the sceptre of this dominion in the hands of the present.' [1]

[1] From Sir R. Gregory's *Discovery*, p. 184.

FIG. 96. The first Membership Ticket of the British Association.

XIV

MICHAEL FARADAY

1. *Early Life*

THERE are two facts which make one marvel that Michael Faraday should have made himself what he did. The first was his parentage. The late Professor John Tyndall, an intimate friend of Faraday, tells us :

FIG. 97. MICHAEL FARADAY

' Believing, as I do, in the general truth of the doctrine of hereditary transmission — sharing the opinion of Mr. Carlyle, that a really able man never proceeded from entirely stupid parents—I used the privilege of my intimacy with Mr. Faraday to ask him whether his parents showed any signs of unusual ability. He could remember none.' [1]

The other fact is that throughout his career he knew little or no mathematics. He was not a mathematician, and indeed he once boasted that he never made a mathematical calculation in his life except once when he turned the handle of a Babbage calculating machine.

This latter was indeed a most remarkable fact, for there is no doubt but that a mathematical equipment, even though of a meagre kind, is a wonderful weapon of assistance to the physicist. Yet such was Faraday's brilliance that his mind was independent of this weapon. He was in the truest sense of the term a master experimentalist. Experimentalists there have been who, looking to the mathematics for the basis of a theory, have applied successfully the test of experiment to that theory :

[1] Tyndall's *Faraday as a Discoverer.*

others there have been, too, who, starting without either theory or hypothesis, have by patient repetition of experiment built up results the statistics of which have led them to great truths. But Faraday belongs to neither of those groups. In him there was that subtle sense which time after time suggested to him the possibility of some physical truth, and he would at once proceed to apply to it the test of the laboratory—and almost always with astonishing success.

Michael was the son of James Faraday, a Yorkshireman of humble parentage, and a journeyman blacksmith by trade. James had married in 1786 a farmer's daughter named Margaret Hastwell, and shortly after, the couple migrated to London, living for a time at Newington. Here four children were born to them, of whom Michael, born on the 22nd of September 1791, was the third. The mother was an almost illiterate woman, but what she lacked in education she made up in neatness, frugality, and love, and the children were accordingly as well cared for as circumstances permitted.

On the whole they were poor circumstances indeed. When Michael was five years old, the family moved from Newington into some rooms over a coach-house in Jacob's Well Mews, Charles Street, Manchester Square, and here the ill-health to which James Faraday was repeatedly subject, together with the severe industrial depression from which the country suffered at the beginning of the nineteenth century, served to make the lot of the Faraday family a hard and difficult one. Dr. Bence Jones, Michael's chief biographer, tells us that in 1801, ' when the price of corn rose above £9 a quarter, the family obtained public relief, and Michael's portion was a loaf, which had to serve him for a week.'

This, then, was the atmosphere in which Michael was brought up. It might, perhaps, have been worse, since at least he had a roof over his head, and the Faradays were a united family. So Michael lived the life of the average London street boy. ' My education ', he writes, ' was of the most ordinary description, consisting of little more than the rudiments of reading, writing, and arithmetic, at a common day-school. My hours out of school were passed at home and in the streets.' We know nothing in particular, at this period of his life, to suggest that there was in this boy either special ambition or ability. He was merely average, but without doubt this was only because the opportunity was lacking.

The first taste of the world beyond his streets came at the age of thirteen, when he was given a job by a Mr. George Riebau, a bookseller and bookbinder, as errand boy. One of Mr. Riebau's activities was the hiring out of papers of various kinds, and these Michael used to deliver and collect. He gave his master such satisfaction that after a year, in 1805, Mr. Riebau accepted him as an apprentice to the bookbinding trade without a premium. This brought Michael for the first time into intimate contact with books, and, fortunately, he needed little encouragement to make the most of his opportunity. There was innate common sense in the lad, and Watts's *Improvement of the Mind*, which he read as he bound the book, appealed to him. He then read through Mrs. Marcet's *Conversations on Chemistry*, and the article on ' Electricity ' in the *Encyclopaedia Britannica*, which he was also binding, and he found himself irresistibly drawn to a study of the facts of science.

He spent what few pence he could spare on odds and ends of apparatus for a few home-made experiments, but he felt he must get more information and instruction. Where was it to come from ? Those were not the days of organized evening classes, but to a small extent private enterprise supplied what public spirit lacked. When Faraday was nineteen he saw an advertisement in a shop window announcing that a Mr. Tatum, of Dorset Street, Fleet Street, was delivering a course of lectures in Natural Philosophy at his private residence at eight o'clock on certain evenings, admission one shilling per lecture. To Michael, with his slender resources, it was a lot of money ; but with the help of his elder brother Robert, by now a working blacksmith like his father, he was able to raise the necessary amount, and so he attended the lectures.

Another circumstance helped him considerably. Lodging at Mr. Riebau's house was a French refugee, a M. Masquerier, an artist. This gentleman had noticed with some pleasure that Michael had exhibited a taste for drawing, and he encouraged him with hints and with the loan of Taylor's *Perspective*. As a consequence, when he came to write out careful notes of Mr. Tatum's lectures, he was able to illustrate them very fully, and to bind them together into four volumes when they were completed.

This course of lectures not only brought to Faraday some of the joys of scientific knowledge, but it also brought him into contact with people of similar taste. He thus made friendships, but at the same time he began to develop a feeling of unrest. The future of a routine of bookbinding which a year or two before he had regarded as rosy with promise was now becoming increasingly distasteful to him. The call of science had begun.

2. *Faraday and Davy*

Then came that little circumstance which was to become the turning-point in his life. One of Mr. Riebau's customers was a Mr. Dance, a member of the Royal Institution. Various visits to the bookshop had made this gentleman aware of Faraday's liking for science, and he resolved to invite Michael to attend the last four lectures of a course which Sir Humphry Davy was concluding at the Royal Institution. The lectures were a revelation of delight to Michael, and only served to increase his longing to abandon trade and give himself up to the service of science. But how? He knew no one who might help him. Nevertheless the period of his apprenticeship was nearly at an end, and he felt that he must do something. In his ignorant helplessness he wrote to the President of the Royal Society, and no doubt the letter found its way fairly quickly to the presidential waste-paper basket.

Our heavy-hearted, discontented Michael came to the end of his apprenticeship. On the 8th of October 1812 he became a full-fledged journeyman bookbinder, his age now being twenty-one years. He was none too lucky in his employer, an ill-tempered Frenchman, and the rather long hours of his employ prevented him from devoting any leisure time to the science he had come to love ; trade and the atmosphere of business were becoming more and more hateful to him, and he felt he must make one more effort to break away from his nauseating surroundings.

Then came the happy thought which brought him ultimately to the desired goal. Why not write to Sir Humphry Davy himself ?

' My desire to escape from trade, which I thought vicious and selfish, and to enter into the service of science, which I imagined made its pursuers amiable and liberal, induced me at last to take the bold and simple step of writing to Sir H. Davy, expressing my wishes, and a hope that, if an opportunity came in his way, he would favour my views ; at the same time I sent the notes I had taken of his lectures.'

The letter clearly made some impression on Davy. The appeal rang with sincerity, and the lecture notes showed ability. Davy consulted the famous Mr. Pepys, a descendant of the great diarist and one of the original managers of the London Institution. ' Pepys,' he said, ' what am I to do ? Here is a letter from a young man named Faraday ; he has been attending my lectures, and wants me to give him employment at the Royal Institution—what can I do ? ' ' Do ? ' replied Pepys, ' put him to wash bottles ; if he is good for anything he will do it directly, if he refuses he is good for nothing.' ' No, no,' replied Davy, ' we must try him with something better than that.'

So it was that our delighted Michael one day saw Davy's carriage drive up to his home, and the following letter was handed to him :

' SIR,

I am far from displeased with the proof you have given me of your confidence, and which displays great zeal, power of memory, and attention. I am obliged to go out of town, and shall not be settled in town till the end of January ; I will then see you at any time you wish. It would gratify me to be of any service to you. I wish it may be in my power.

I am, sir,

Your obedient humble servant,

H. DAVY.'

As luck would have it, the situation of assistant in the laboratory of the Royal Institution fell vacant shortly after, and Davy
sent for Faraday. In the same letter to Dr. Paris, from which
we have just quoted, Faraday writes of this interview :

' At the same time that he thus gratified my desires as to
scientific employment, he still advised me not to give up the
prospects I had before me, telling me that science was a harsh
mistress, and, in a pecuniary point of view, but poorly rewarding
those who devoted themselves to her service. He smiled at my
notion of the superior moral feelings of philosophic men, and said
he would leave me to the experience of a few years to set me right
on that matter.'

As a result, at a meeting of the managers of the Royal Institu-
tion on the 1st of March 1813 it was resolved ' that Michael
Faraday be engaged to fill the situation lately occupied by
Mr. Payne, on the same terms '.

Faraday's duties were of a very humble kind, but he was very
happy. He had got his chance. His main work was to assist the
lecturers and keep the apparatus and the laboratory clean. He
was provided with quarters at the top of the building, and he
received twenty-five shillings per week. He quickly showed
himself to be capable of better things, and it was not long before
he was assisting with minor experiments (at first mainly in
chemistry) and in acting as amanuensis to Davy. Further, he
became a regular member of the City Philosophical Society,
a weekly gathering which had developed from the private science
class of Mr. Tatum. Here he made a few friends, who constituted
themselves a sort of sub-society, meeting at Faraday's rooms
for discussion and mutual improvement.

Faraday rapidly established himself in the full favour of his
chief, Sir Humphry Davy, and when the latter set out, in October
1813, on his Continental tour, he invited Michael to accompany
him as amanuensis and general assistant (and incidentally, as it
turned out, owing to the last-minute defection of Davy's personal
servant, as unofficial valet), and although the intimate contact
between two such totally different minds and personalities gave
rise to various ' incidents ', it was for Faraday a wonderfully
helpful and educative tour. It brought him into new countries

and amongst new peoples, and above all he had the inestimable privilege of meeting many of the great philosophers of Europe, men who were afterwards to become his close and admiring friends.

3. *Further Career*

The tour lasted till the spring of 1815, and on his return Faraday was reinstated to his former position as laboratory assistant at the Royal Institution, but at the augmented salary of thirty shillings per week. The managers were justified in the granting of the extra five shillings. Faraday was now beginning to experiment in earnest, though still, of course, in quite an elementary way, carrying out simple analyses. This was his period of learning ; the days of creation had yet to come.

Meanwhile his attendance at the meetings of the City Philosophical Society continued regularly, and on the 17th of January he delivered to its members his first address, the subject being on the general properties of matter. The same year, too, saw the publication of his first paper, on an analysis of caustic lime, in the *Quarterly Journal of Science*, the official organ of the Royal Institution, and from this time onwards, for the next few years, various papers of minor importance appeared at intervals.

We now come to 1820, in which year for the first time he gained the ear of the Royal Society, by a paper ' on the new compounds of chlorine and carbon, and on a new compound of iodine, carbon, and hydrogen '. The paper was well received, and seemed to provide a fitting starting-point for the life-long series of researches which now followed. The year 1820 was epoch-making in the history of electro-magnetism, for it saw Oersted's great discovery of the magnetic effect of the electric current, and Ampère's subsequent researches on the subject. Dr. Wollaston took the subject up in England and unsuccessfully attempted an experiment, to which we shall later refer, at the Royal Institution. Faraday was present, and the proceedings excited his interest profoundly. He very properly realized that before attempting anything similar himself, he must first make a careful study of what had been done, and so he began an intensive course of reading and experiment which culminated in his publication of *A History of the Progress of Electro-Magnetism*.

Finding himself now properly equipped with the facts of the situation he set to work to achieve that which Wollaston had failed to accomplish. The experiment was performed in December 1821 and succeeded magnificently, and we are told that by way of celebration the author of it treated himself to a visit to the pit at Astley's Circus.

We now come to one of the happiest events in Faraday's long life. He was a member of a small sect known as the Sandemanians, and through his attendance at their place of worship he gained an introduction to the family of Mr. John Barnard, one of the elders, and a silversmith by trade. Faraday wooed, and won, the third daughter of this gentleman, and he married Sarah Barnard on the 12th of June 1821. It was, by his wish, the simplest of ceremonies. He desired that the day should resemble any other day as far as possible, and so he just married the lady and brought her to his rooms at the Royal Institution. It was a happy union. Twenty-five years after he recorded an entry in what was by then a voluminous book of diplomas.

'25th January, 1847.

Amongst these records and events, I here insert the date of one which, as a source of honour and happiness, far exceeds all the rest. We were *married* on June 12, 1821. M. FARADAY.'

He had by this time been promoted to superintendent of the laboratories, and his researches now began to assume first-class importance. He carried out, in collaboration with Mr. Stodart, some experiments on the alloys of steel, as a result of which ' he was accustomed in after years to present to his friends razors formed from them, and in 1823 he performed some important experiments on the liquefaction of gases, through which he was able to establish that all gases could be considered as the vapours of their corresponding liquid, possessing very low boiling-points. These experiments, involving as they did the subjection of glass vessels to very high pressures, were not without risk to the experimenter, and on one occasion an explosion caused no less than thirteen pieces of glass to enter his eye.

Faraday had by now thoroughly established himself as a scientist of high order, and on the 8th of February was elected, unfortunately not without some jealous opposition from Sir Humphry Davy, a Fellow of the Royal Society. The jealousy, however, could only have been but a transient feeling on Davy's part, since, through his influence and recommendation, Faraday was in 1825 promoted to the position of Director of the Laboratories, at the same time as Mr. Brande was promoted from Lecturer to Professor of Chemistry. One of Faraday's first acts in his new capacity was to organize Friday evening gatherings of those members who were interested in science, and these quickly developed into those weekly discourses which became so noted a feature of the activities of the institution.

The next few years saw our philosopher (he always had a leaning towards that title, preferring it to either ' scientist ' or ' physicist ') busily engaged on research on optical glass, and his services were beginning to be increasingly in demand as consultant from various outside sources. It brought him up against the big moral fight of his life. What was his position ? As Director he was in receipt of a salary of £100 per annum, plus lodgings, fuel, and light. It was, of course, an absurdly small amount. Yet, in 1830, occasional consultations and various analyses brought in something over a thousand pounds in fees, and in 1831 it was greater still. Here he was, then, at the parting of the ways. For while on the one hand there was ahead of him the prospect of a vast avenue of research with nothing in the shape of reward other than the honour and glory of work nobly and unselfishly done, he had on the other hand only to call a halt to research, to have the whole of the commercial world at his feet, and so enjoy in fees an almost unlimited income. ' While once conversing with Faraday on science, in its relation to commerce and litigation,' wrote Tyndall, ' he said to me, that at a certain period of his career he was forced definitely to ask himself, and finally to decide, whether he should make wealth or science the pursuit of his life. He could not serve two masters, and he was therefore compelled to choose between them.' His choice, like that of Humphry Davy on a former occasion, leaves the world eternally grateful to his memory. The facts speak for themselves. In 1831 his income derived from fees was £1,090 4s. ; in 1832 it fell to £155 9s. ; it was nil in 1838, and thence till 1845 it never exceeded £22.

The cash value of research to the scientist is wellnigh nothing. But to the general public, whom the research student serves, it is wealth untold. Huxley once put the matter thus :

' I weigh my words when I say that if the nation could purchase a potential Watt, or Davy, or Faraday, at the cost of a hundred thousand pounds down, he would be dirt cheap at the money. It is a mere common-place and everyday piece of knowledge that what these men did has produced untold millions of wealth in the narrowest economical sense of the word.'

Faraday died a poor man. ' But his was the glory of holding aloft among the nations the scientific name of England for a period of forty years.'

4. *Faraday's Researches in Electro-Magnetic Induction*

The work which above all things has made Faraday famous was his researches in electro-dynamics. We have already mentioned that in 1821, when the world of science was still ringing with the news of Oersted's discovery of the magnetic effect of an electric current, and of Ampère's further discoveries in the same subject, Faraday succeeded in carrying the problem to a further stage of solution by an experiment which had previously been attempted, without success, by Wollaston at the Royal Institution. What was this experiment ?

Oersted had shown that a magnetic needle in the neighbourhood of a current tends to set itself at right angles to the conductor conveying the current. This, as we know, is due to the fact that a north pole tends to move along the ' lines of force ' in a magnetic field in which it is placed. If we arrange a wire from a battery B (Fig. 98) to be vertical, and to pass through the centre of a horizontal piece of cardboard C, then, if we sprinkle iron filings on the cardboard and gently tap the edge, the filings will set themselves in lines which indicate the direction of the magnetic force at any point. This is the direction along which a magnetic pole would tend to move if free to do so. In this case we find that the 'lines of force', as these magnetic lines are called, are in

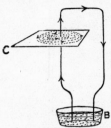

FIG. 98. Lines of force round a wire carrying a current.

the shape of concentric circles round the wire, and so it is that a north pole will tend to rotate round the wire in a right-hand direction, and a south pole in the opposite direction.

Wollaston's view, with which Faraday agreed, was that since action and reaction are equal and opposite, if a magnetic pole tends to rotate round a current, there must be an equal tendency for a conductor carrying a current to rotate round a magnetic pole. It is all a question of which is free to move, and which is fixed and so unable to move.

Faraday's experiment is shown diagrammatically in Fig. 99. Placed in an electrical circuit are two mercury cups A and B. Current enters A through the wire a, and leaves B through e. A and B are connected by means of the wire c. m and m_1 are two

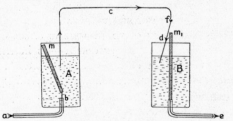

FIG. 99. Faraday's experiment on mutual rotations of magnet and wire carrying current.

magnets, m in A being free at one end and pivoted at b, and m_1 being rigidly held. Dipping into B, however, there is a portion of wire d suspended from c at f. Hence the left-hand half of the apparatus was a test of the rotation of

a movable pole m round a fixed conductor c, whilst the right-hand half of the apparatus was a test of the rotation, in the opposite direction, of a free conductor d round a fixed magnet m_1.

The experiment succeeded admirably, and we are told that when Faraday saw the needle and wire revolve round each other, he danced about them with childlike delight, exclaiming, ' There they go, there they go ! '

It was in 1831 that Faraday's next and perhaps most far-reaching discovery was made, whereby he was in effect able to produce electricity from magnetism, and thus open up a new branch of the subject, known to-day as electro-magnetic induction. It was the culminating result of some years of careful thought and experiment.

Let us consider what was the general nature of the problem as it presented itself to the mind of our philosopher. We have seen that a current is surrounded by a magnetic field, as a result of which it attracts a magnet. Further, Ampère showed that a conductor carrying a current attracts or repels *another* conductor carrying a current. It was also known that a body carrying a static or stationary charge could *induce* a similar charge in a conductor brought into its neighbourhood. Why, thought Faraday, should it not be possible for a dynamic charge, i. e. a *current* of electricity, to have a similar effect, and induce a current in a conductor brought into its own neighbourhood ? Looking at it from another angle, Faraday asked himself why it should not be possible to produce or induce an electric current from magnetism, seeing that Oersted and Ampère had produced magnetic effects from a current of electricity.

Faraday first began thinking on these lines in 1824, and in 1825 he arranged a wire carrying a current to lie alongside another connected with a galvanometer, but he got no result. At this time he was busy on researches on optical glass, and he was unable to follow up the subject of electricity, but in 1828, he tried the experiment again, still without result.

It was not till another three years had elapsed that Faraday met with success, but the year 1831 was probably for him the most brilliant of his whole career. It will be recalled how Ampère had shown that a solenoid carrying a current behaves as though it were a magnet, and that a rod of iron placed in the solenoid at once becomes magnetized by induction. Faraday hit on the happy idea of utilizing this effect, and on the 29th of August 1831 he took a soft wrought iron ring about six inches in diameter and seven-eighths of an inch thick, and round each half of this he wound coils X and Y (Fig. 100), X being connected to a battery of ten cells B, and Y to a galvanometer G. On depressing the key K to close the battery circuit round X, the galvanometer needle swung completely round four or five times, and then came to rest in its original position, and later, on disconnecting K, the needle was *again* disturbed though in the opposite direction.

Faraday afterwards realized that the magnetism which was produced in the iron ring by the current round X was the cause, at the moments of starting and stopping the current only, of a momentary electric current round Y, thus producing the galvanometer 'kicks'.

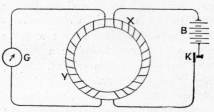

FIG. 100. Faraday's discovery of Electro-Magnetic Induction.

But at the time he did not fully realize the significance of this. On the 23rd of September he wrote as follows : 'I am busy just now again on electro-magnetism, and think I have got hold of a good thing, but can't say. It may be a weed instead of a fish that, after all my labour, I may at last pull up.'

Thinking over the experiment we have just described, Faraday felt that he must assure himself that this was definitely a case of magnetism producing electricity. Accordingly he repeated the experiment, substituting for the iron a ring of 'non-magnetic' copper, and he was pleased to find that the effect was greatly reduced.

His next experiment carried the results a stage farther. Instead of deriving his magnetism from an electric current, he went direct to a magnet. He took a short cylinder B (Fig. 101) and wound his wire round it, connecting the ends to a galvanometer. He then took two bar magnets, in contact at one end A, and placed B between the two opposite poles N and S of the other ends. ' Every time the magnetic contact N and S was made or broken, there was magnetic motion at the indicating helix (i. e. at the galvanometer needle G), the effect being as in former cases, not permanent, but a mere momentary push or pull. . . . Hence here (was) distinct conversion of magnetism into electricity.' [1]

Here, then, was the direct converse of Oersted's effect. Oersted found a magnet to be excited by an electric current : Faraday found an electric current which had been excited by a magnet.

It will be noticed that in all the experiments above described, Faraday got a reading momentarily from his galvanometer only at the instant of *making* contact, and at the instant of *breaking* contact. During the normal passage of the current itself, or in the last experiment during the normal ' flow ' of magnetism in the magnetic circuit ANS, the galvanometer was perfectly steady, showing no deflexion whatever.
It only registered a ' kick ' during the actual moment when a *change* of conditions was operating. This was a most important point. Faraday, with that wonderful intuition which

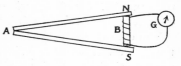

FIG. 101. Faraday's experiments on Electro-Magnetic Induction.

was so powerful an asset to him in his experimental work, rightly felt that it was, in fact, the governing factor.

On the 1st of October 1831 he proceeded to his next famous experiment. Hitherto he had used some direct source of magnetism—first from an electro-magnetic iron ring, and then, as we have just described, from an iron bar in contact with the poles of two magnets forming a magnetic current. He now dispensed with any such direct source of magnetism, and this time wound his two reels of wire, each 203 feet long and of copper, round a *wooden* rod or bobbin. As before the ends of one wire were connected with a battery of ten cells, and of the other to the terminals of a galvanometer. Again on making the circuit there was a momentary kick of the needle of the galvanometer, and on breaking, another kick on the opposite direction.

It was now quite clear to Faraday that the essential factor for the production of an induced current in any given conductor is that there must be a *relative change of conditions* between the

[1] B. Jones, *Life and Letters of Faraday.*

primary, as he called the conductor connected to the battery, and the secondary, or wire carrying the induced current ; and in the case of electro-magnetic induction, here again the essential factor is *change*, for regarding the source of magnetism as being surrounded by a ' field of force ', the current will only be induced in the conductor when it ' cuts ' the lines of force in the magnetic field, i. e. when the conductor is in motion relative to the field. Faraday obtained a striking verification of this by taking a coil or solenoid of copper wire, and connecting the ends to the terminals of a galvanometer. He used no battery whatever in this case, but merely took a bar magnet and suddenly plunged it into the coil. There was at once a kick of the galvanometer needle. On withdrawing the magnet he again got a transient current through the coils, but this time in the opposite direction.

The evidence was practically complete. So much so, indeed, that there was little more for other people to do than to develop the practical applications of the new discoveries. Faraday's researches had been very thorough. He realized, for example, that since the earth is itself a big magnet, a coil in rapid rotation would cut the earth's magnetic lines of force, and so induce a current in the coil, and this phenomenon of earth inductance, as it is called, he was also able to demonstrate.

Lenz, a Russian, supplemented what Faraday had done by pointing out what has since been incorporated as part of the law bearing his name, that in every case of induced current due to a relative change in the magnetic conditions, the *direction* of the induced current is always such as to tend to oppose the change. It is, so to speak, Nature's natural remonstrance against change, and is (in a very vague way, no doubt) somewhat analogous to the idea of the principle of inertia in motion.

There is one other discovery by Faraday in connexion with electro-magnetic induction to which we must refer, and which did in fact indicate one very important direction along which the practical application of his researches would go. On the 8th of February 1832 he succeeded in obtaining a spark from the induced current. It is known that if an electrical current is broken by a very small air-gap, then provided the difference of potential between the two ends of the broken wire producing the gap is sufficiently great, the current will ' bridge ' the gap with a spark. This is particularly the case when the circuit is broken at the moment that the current is actually passing. In this case the heat generated at the ends volatilizes the metal and forms a medium of metallic vapour, and this conveys the current with sparking. Faraday's difficulty was to break the circuit during the passing of the induced current, since it will be remembered that the induced current is itself of but moment-ary duration, once at the beginning, and once at the end, of the passage of the current in the primary circuit. However, he got over the difficulty by cutting the wire of his secondary circuit, and arranging the cut ends to overlap lightly so that the slightest shock would separate them. Instead of having a battery for his primary, he had the secondary coil wound round a short rod of iron the ends of which protruded beyond the coil. This rod was held over the poles of a magnet, and was then released. Its motion through the magnetic field between the poles generated an induced current (due to the cutting of the magnetic lines of force), but the slight shock of the impact of the rod on the magnet at once separated the broken ends of the wire, and to Faraday's delight, a spark at once appeared across the gap. It was an im-portant discovery, upon which the modern system of electric light is largely based. Faraday subsequently greatly improved on the brightness of the sparking by using points of charcoal on the wires ; and thus Davy's original observations of the electric arc were supplemented by a further discovery, and the problem of electric lighting began to assume a practical character.

Gladstone, great in statesmanship but somewhat narrow in scientific vision, once asked Faraday, on seeing one of his famous experiments terminate in an effect which, to the non-scientific man, was very uninspiring, of what use his discovery could be. ' Why, sir,' answered Faraday, ' you will soon be able to tax it.' It is quite understandable that the mere momentary movement of a galvanometer needle could not be of much significance to the old lady who also innocently asked Faraday what good such an experiment could be. Yet Faraday's reminder of Franklin's answer to such a question, ' Madam, of what use is a new-born child ? ' is full of significance. For out of the small galvanometer deflexion which first showed Faraday the existence of electro-magnetic induction, there has developed for the use and comfort of mankind the electric light, the electric motor, the dynamo, and the hosts of modern inventions which have followed in their wake.

5. *Further Researches in Electricity and Magnetism*

We have by no means concluded the tale of Faraday's dis-coveries, for his researches in electricity extended far beyond the subject of electro-magnetism.

In 1835 Faraday interested himself in showing that the elec-tricity derived from friction was identical with that derived from the voltaic cell. Davy had opened up the subject of electrolysis, or the analysis of compounds by the electric current. Faraday showed that just as potassium iodide could be decomposed into its constituents by the passage of a voltaic current, so he could also obtain the same effect by using instead the current from a frictional machine.

A further observation which confirmed him in his conclusions as to the identity of these two sources of electricity was the fact that the stream of electricity from his frictional machine was able to produce a deflexion in his galvanometer identical with the deflexion obtained from a battery current.

These experiments led Faraday naturally into a quantitative investigation of the *laws of electrolysis*. He introduced termino-logy in this connexion which is now universally adopted. He called the ends or plates in the decomposing cell *electrodes* ; the positive being called the *anode* and the negative the *cathode* ; and he referred to the substance which the current was decom-posing as the *electrolyte*. Faraday's method of work was as follows. He determined to see under what varied conditions he was able to electrolyse a given quantity of water. We speak to-day of a cell in which two electrodes dip into an electrolyte as a voltameter, and Faraday arranged a number of these voltameters having platinum electrodes of varying size, from plates to mere wires. On collecting the gas liberated on each separate pair of electrodes, he found the same quantity in each case. His conclusion was that ' when the same quantity of electricity is passed through a series of cells containing acidulated water, the electro-chemical action is independent of the size of the electrodes '. This remained true, too, whether he used strong currents or weak, or whether the acidulation of the water was varied, and even when he used a stronger acid strength in one voltameter than in another for the same current. He now felt quite definitely *that the amount of chemical action produced depended only upon the quantity of electricity passed.* This is now spoken of as Faraday's First Law of Electrolysis, and is a most important result, for it gives us an additional and an accurate means of measuring current which is totally independent of the use of the magnetic effect. For if we know how much decomposition is produced by a unit amount of current per unit of time, we have only to measure the actual decomposition obtained in a given time to calculate exactly how many units of current must have been employed. This method is frequently used nowadays in standardizing or testing current-measuring instruments of the magnetic type.

Faraday next proceeded to investigate the relationship between the amounts of decomposition of different substances by the same current, and he found that there undoubtedly existed a constant relation between the amounts of the several compounds which are decomposed thereby. It works out to this, that for example a current of one ampère always deposits in an hour 4·025 grm. of silver, whether the electrolyte is silver nitrate, silver cyanide, or any other silver compound. Similarly one ampère will deposit in one hour 1·181 grm. of copper, 1·203 grm. of zinc, and so on. These quantities, 4·025 for silver, 1·181 for copper, 1·203 for zinc, &c., are proportional to what are known as the electro-chemical equivalents of the various substances, and without going into the exact significance of this term (students of chemistry will of course be quite familiar with it), it means in effect that by knowing how much of one substance is deposited by a given current in unit time, we can at once calculate, from a knowledge of these electro-chemical equivalents, how much of any other substance would be deposited by the same current in the same time. This then was another of Faraday's many wonderful achievements, and his Laws of Electrolysis are one of the commonplaces of every text-book on electricity to-day.

Following on this he next turned his attention to electrostatic induction. Coulomb had developed a law of inverse squares as between electrical charges, and in view of the similarity of this to Newton's inverse square law for gravitational forces, he had assumed that the attraction or repulsion between two charges was also, like gravity, a case of ' action at a distance ' ; that is to say, the intervening medium played no part in this. Faraday felt that this was wrong, and that, on the contrary, the medium played a vital part in the propagation or transmission of this force. He spoke of the medium as a ' dielectric '. Action at a distance presupposes the mutual attraction to take place along the straight line joining the two charges, but Faraday's investigations showed that, as a matter of fact, the lines of induction are curved, and these he called ' lines of force '. But what is equally important, he showed that the actual value of the force between two charges differed according to the medium intervening between them, and so he discovered the property which he termed ' the dielectric constant ' of the medium, and which we now speak of as the ' specific inductive capacity '. Henry Cavendish, it will be recalled, had discovered this long before, but his eccentricity and the retiring, hermit-like life he led had not made for publicity, and so Faraday, like most other people, knew nothing of his work.

Faraday used in his experiments two concentric spheres, and he filled the space between them with various media in succession. He compared the electrical attraction or repulsion through them with the results he obtained for air. He published his results in 1837. Taking air as unity, he got 2·26 for sulphur, 2·0 for shellac, and 1·7 for glass.

We pass on now to the year 1845 for Faraday's next great discovery. With his delicate vision and somewhat vivid imagination, he had for a long time been feeling his way to a unification of the various phenomena of nature, and in that year he succeeded in showing by a beautiful experiment a definite relationship between electricity and light. On the 24th of November 1845 he submitted to the Royal Society a memoir entitled, ' On the Magnetization of Light, and the Illumination of Magnetic Lines of Force '. It was a vivid title, and no one quite knows what was in his mind at the time. However the definite experiment which it recorded, and the lesson it taught, were clear enough at any rate. ' I have long ', wrote he, ' held an opinion, almost amounting to conviction, in common, I believe, with many other lovers of natural knowledge, that the various forms under which the forces of matter are made manifest have one common origin ; in other words are so directly related and mutually dependent, that they are convertible, as it were, to one another, and possess equivalents of power in their action. . . . This strong persuasion extended to the power of light.'

Faraday's experiment was on the effect of magnets upon a particular condition of light known as polarized light. In the ordinary way light waves may be regarded as the ' passing on ' of ether vibrations much the same as water waves are the passing on of water vibrations, but in the case of light the plane of vibration is not restricted, and consequently a ray of light may consist of waves in every conceivable plane. Fig. 102 may serve to show the meaning of this a little more clearly. If we look ' edgewise ' behind a single wave, we merely see a short straight line showing the extremes between which the vibration takes place. In the figure, we are looking ' end on ' along a ' bunch ' of five light waves (the language employed here is unfortunately very loose from the scientific point of view, but it will serve), and the planes of their vibrations are seen to be all different—wave (1) is vertical, wave (4) is horizontal, and the others are variously inclined, but *all* are moving forward into the plane of the paper.

Now there are certain transparent or partially transparent substances which have a remarkable effect on such a bunch of waves when their surfaces are exposed to light. When the bunch of waves impinges on the surface, *all are stopped except the waves of one plane only*, so that the light which emerges—of considerably less intensity, of course, than that which enters the medium—is such that there is one, and only one plane of vibration. It is just as though the interposing medium were a set of railings, shown dotted in the figure, parallel to the plane of vibration of any ray (2) in the bunch. All the other rays will be stopped by the obstacle, but ray (2) will pass on between the rails quite easily. Such emergent light is spoken of as plane-polarized light, and many substances will have the effect of polarizing the light which passes through them, tourmaline being a notable example.

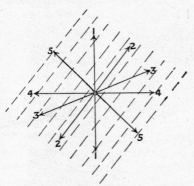

FIG. 102. Unpolarized Light-waves, showing various inclinations of the plane of vibration.

We are now in a position to be able to appreciate the nature of Faraday's experiment. He employed as his polarizing medium a piece of heavy glass known as silico-borate of lead. The light which entered this glass was unpolarized ; but that which emerged from it was polarized, and the direction of the plane of polarization was carefully noted by means of a ' Nicol prism '—a split piece of calcite which could be rotated, and which accordingly acted just like rotating a second set of the railings already mentioned ; that is to say, since the light was already polarized by the glass, until the direction of ' the rails ' coincided with the plane of polarization, no light could penetrate the Nicol prism at all, but at a certain point in the rotation, the ' rails ' now coinciding with the plane of polarization, the light bursts through the prism suddenly, and the angle at which this occurs can be noted.

Having done this, Faraday now placed the arrangement between the poles of a powerful magnet, so that the magnetic lines of force were in the same direction as that in which the light was travelling through the heavy glass medium. The immediate effect was that where before the polarized light was passing through the Nicol prism, it suddenly ceased to do so, until the nicol was rotated to a different position, when the light again burst through. This clearly proved *that the effect of the magnetic field was to rotate the plane of polarization of the light*, and as soon as the magnetic field was removed, the light was restored to its original plane of polarization. Faraday subsequently obtained similar results by substituting for the magnet a coil of wire carrying the current, with the glass medium at the centre.

So for the first time in history there was established a definite connexion between light and electricity, and the problem of the ultimate meaning of all forces was notably advanced. Tyndall refers to it as the 'jewel in the casket', and adds, 'I should liken (it) to the Weisshorn among mountains—high, beautiful, and alone'.

But Faraday's scientific record is not complete without reference to one further discovery, a consequence of the experiment we have just described. He gave his discovery in a paper before the Royal Society on the 18th of December 1845, entitled 'On the Magnetic Condition of All Matter'. He had long been struck with, as he thought it, the incongruity of the existence of only two magnetic substances, iron and nickel. He began to suspect that other substances ought to exhibit magnetic phenomena under suitable conditions. So he set to work testing various substances, and before long he was able to add cobalt to iron and nickel. But on the 4th of November 1845 he suspended from a silk thread a bar of heavy glass, and this he placed between the poles of a powerful electro-magnet. Now if the bar had been of iron, we know that on account of its permeability to magnetism it would have set itself parallel to the lines of force, that is to say, in the direction of the line joining the north and the south poles of the magnet. Imagine Faraday's surprise, therefore, when he found that his rod of glass set itself at *right angles* to the magnetic lines of force joining north and south poles and therefore indicating a magnetic repulsion instead of a magnetic attraction. This phenomenon Faraday called diamagnetism, and the reason why he had not discovered it before was because his magnets had not been sufficiently powerful. He extended his observations and satisfied himself that *all* substances are either para-magnetic or dia-magnetic, and that examples of the latter group are sulphur, india-rubber, asbestos, and human tissue. Referring to this last substance he says : ' If a man could be in the magnetic field, like Mohammed's coffin, he would turn until across the magnetic line.'

6. *Faraday's Later Life*

So much for the scientist. Meanwhile what of the man ? Wonderful as a thinker, his private life was simplicity itself. He had no children of his own, but for ten years from 1830 to 1840 his niece, Miss Jane Barnard, came to live with Faraday and his wife, and from her we get the following interesting story of the philosopher's daily routine :

' We often found him hard at work on experiments connected with his researches, his apron full of holes. If very busy he would merely give a nod, and aunt would sit down quietly at a distance, till presently he would make a note on his slate and turn round to us for a talk ; or perhaps he would agree to come upstairs to finish the evening with a game at bagatelle, stipulating for half-an-hour's quiet work first to finish his experiment. He was fond of all ingenious games, and he always excelled in them. For a time he took up the Chinese puzzle. . . . Another time, when he had been unwell, he amused himself with papyroplastics, and with his dexterous fingers made a chest of drawers and pigeon-house, &c. When dull and dispirited, as sometimes he was to an extreme degree, my aunt used to carry him off to Brighton, or somewhere, for a few days, and they generally came back refreshed and invigorated. Once they had very wet weather in some out-of-the-way place, and there was a want of amusement, so he ruled a sheet of paper, and made a neat draught board, on which they played games with pink and white lozenges for draughts. . . .

' Often of an evening they would go to the Zoological Gardens and find interest in the animals, especially the new arrivals, though he was always much diverted by the tricks of the monkeys. We have seen him laugh till the tears ran down his cheeks as he watched them. He never missed seeing the wonderful sights of the acrobats and tumblers, giants and dwarfs; even Punch and Judy was an unfailing source of delight.' [1]

Faraday was at all times neat and punctual in his habits. In his laboratory everything not only had its place, but had to be in that place. He breakfasted at eight, spent his mornings in the laboratory, dined at half-past two, and retired to his study in the afternoons to write his papers and to prepare for his next day's work. Like his predecessor, Sir Humphry Davy, he was a most successful and fascinating lecturer, and his discourses were always delivered to a crowded and a delighted audience. He himself always enjoyed lecturing, particularly when he was addressing a juvenile audience, for he always loved children.

The strain of his work began to tell very seriously on his health, and between the years 1838 and 1841 he repeatedly broke down, but the loving care of his devoted wife saved him, though for a period of two years he had to abandon completely even the reading of science. In 1841 his wife took him to Switzerland, and they were accompanied by her brother, George Barnard, an artist. During this period he was in a very low condition, and even conversation was painful to him, but he rallied, and returned to England fit and well in 1843.

Meanwhile learned societies all the world over were electing him to their fellowships, the Royal Society awarded him every medal it was in its power to confer, including the Copley Medal twice over, the universities showered honorary degrees on him, and foreign monarchs conferred various orders. In 1844 France awarded him the ' blue riband ' of international science by electing him one of the eight foreign Associates of the Academy of Sciences. Yet he sought not a single honour. In fact, when the Presidency of the Royal Society fell vacant, and the council of the Society unanimously invited him to succeed to this, the highest scientific position in England, Faraday refused. ' Tyndall,' said he to his old friend and pupil, ' I must remain plain Michael Faraday to the last.'

[1] B. Jones, *Life and Letters*, vol. ii, p. 114.

An incident which occurred in 1835 is well worthy of note. It will be recalled that Faraday, owing to his renunciation of pecuniary benefits which his work could earn for him, was a poor man. Sir Robert Peel, then in power, wished to confer on the great philosopher a state pension of £300 per annum as a mark of the gratitude of the nation for his work. Faraday's first impulse was to decline this, but his friends persuaded him otherwise, pointing out to him that the pension was not a charity, but a reward, and in the nature of a compliment to science.

Before, however, the matter could be settled further Peel left office, and was succeeded by Lord Melbourne, who, taking the subject up as a matter of form (his scientific outlook was very different from that of his predecessor), sent for Faraday. The interview was a very unfortunate one. Melbourne ' in utter ignorance of the man ', used such terms as ' humbug ', and Faraday, deeply hurt, left him and wrote declining to have anything to do with the proposal, stating that he had manifestly mistaken his Lordship's intention of honouring science in his person. The good-humoured nobleman at first considered the matter a capital joke ; but he was afterwards led to look at it more seriously. An excellent lady, who was a friend to both Faraday and the Minister, tried to arrange matters between them ; but she found Faraday very difficult to move from the position he had assumed. After many fruitless efforts, she at length begged him to state what he would require of Lord Melbourne to induce him to change his mind. He replied, ' " I should require from his lordship what I have no right or reason to expect that he would grant—a written apology for the words he permitted himself to use to me." The required apology came, frank and full, creditable alike to the prime minister and the philosopher,'[1] and so eventually Faraday accepted the proffered pension.

White-haired, grey-eyed, kindly of face, and gentle of manner, Faraday was nevertheless by nature very excitable. Says Tyndall, ' Underneath his sweetness and gentleness was the heat of a volcano. He was a man of excitable and fiery nature ;

[1] Tyndall's *Faraday as a Discoverer*, p. 199.

but through high self-discipline he had converted the fire into a central glow and motive power of life, instead of permitting it to waste itself in useless passion.' [1]

The last years of this great philosopher were years of peace. In 1862 he began to feel his declining powers somewhat keenly, and he told his audience at the Royal Institution that he had been before them too long. He was over seventy years old, and both his brain and body were tired ; so he gave himself over to the loving care of his wife and niece, and they, with the willing assistance of a host of affectionate friends, made his last years a period of tranquillity and patient resignation for the end.

Towards the close of the year 1865 he had an attack of illness from which he never recovered, and slowly an advancing though painless paralysis gained on him. Much of his time was passed in sleep, but his waking hours were always peaceful. He rarely saw any one, though inquiries were legion. ' Tyndall,' he had once said, ' the sweetest reward of my work is the sympathy and goodwill which it has caused to flow in upon me from all quarters of the world.' So it had been during the period of his scientific activity, and so it continued when he lay dying. The end came on the 25th of August 1867. ' Slowly and peacefully he sank towards his final rest, and when it came, his death was a falling asleep. In the fullness of his honours and of his age he quitted us ; the good fight was fought, the work of duty—shall I not say of glory—done.' [2]

[1] *Ibid.*, p. 45. [2] *Ibid.*, p. 203.

S

XV

LORD KELVIN AND APPLIED SCIENCE

1. *Early Record*

THE scientific pre-eminence of Lord Kelvin in the latter half of the nineteenth century is beyond dispute. The number and

importance of his contributions to original research and discovery are truly remarkable. Yet on most of these we must needs be silent. For Kelvin was a brilliant mathematician, and the abstruse nature of most of his researches, bound up as they are with the arguments derived from higher mathematics, places them far beyond the reach of most people. Such readers must therefore content themselves with an aspect of Kelvin's career which, even though it represents but a portion of his eminent services to mankind, nevertheless suffices to mark

FIG. 103. WILLIAM THOMSON, afterwards Lord Kelvin, 30 April 1856

out a unique position for him : we refer to his work as an ' applied physicist '—that is to say, as one who taught and practised with consistency that the best performance of the everyday occupations of mankind are those to which the principles of science are rigidly applied. It was Kelvin's great influence which assured to the world for all time that the best type of engineer, for example, is at the same time a true man of science.

William Thomson was born at Belfast on the 20th of June 1824. He was the second son of James Thomson, Professor of

Mathematics at the Royal Academical Institute at Belfast, who had risen to this position from relatively humble beginnings by sheer hard work and determination. William's mother was a Miss Gardiner, the daughter of a Glasgow merchant, so taking into account the fact that the Thomsons were original emigrants from Scotland escaping religious persecution in the days of the Covenant, it is not surprising that, with all the natural pride of Irish birth which both William and his father possessed, there was much of the Scotsman in them, and as such they are proudly regarded by all men born north of the Tweed.

Certainly, the proverbial seriousness of outlook and hardiness of development typical of the average Scots family was present in the Thomsons. There were four sons and three daughters, and unfortunately, whilst all were still young, Mrs. Thomson died, and the professor accordingly had the main responsibility for their upbringing. He threw himself into the task, and combined keen affection with stern discipline with such success that all his sons eventually achieved distinction in their respective spheres of activity.

In 1832, when William was but eight years old, his father was offered the post of Professor of Mathematics at Glagsow University, and so the whole family migrated to Scotland. Thus began an association with Glasgow which lasted, in one form and another, until William's death in 1907. It is amusing to note that at his new post Professor James found himself one of many professors of the name of Thomson. There was Thomas Thomson the chemist ; William Thomson of Materia Medica ; Allen Thomson of Anatomy . . . Dr. James Thomson of Mathematics, &c., and the university was not infrequently referred to as the ' Thomsonian University '.

Life during this period was for William and his elder brother James a stern round of hard study varied by long family holidays during the vacations. Both showed early signs of unusual ability, and, remarkable to relate, when William was but ten years old they passed their matriculation examination at the Glasgow University. Further, the two brothers more than held their own amongst their fellow students, it being quite usual for

William to come out top and James a close second. Nor must it
be thought that the course of study was in any sense easy.
Lagrange's *Theory of Functions* in mathematics, Newton's
Principia, and Laplace's *Mécanique celeste* in natural philosophy,
and commensurate studies in logic, Latin, Greek, moral philosophy, and chemistry were all included in the course. In all of
these both brothers did well in spite of the competition of such
men as John Caird, afterwards to become the Principal of the
University.

In the summer of 1840 the professor took his two sons for
a holiday tour in Germany. He wanted the boys to study the
German language, but William had come into the possession of
a copy of Fourier's famous *Théorie analytique de la Chaleur*, that
same book which had so inspired Simon Ohm in his electrical
researches in 1826 (see p. 236). The originality of the mathematical methods employed in this book greatly fascinated William,
and he spent far more time on the book than he did on the study
of German, and indeed his first paper, a defence of Fourier
against the criticisms of a Professor Kelland on some of the
conclusions of the book, was actually begun at Frankfort in
July 1840, and was completed in Glasgow in the following year.
The reading of Fourier's book was a distinct event in William
Thomson's life, for the whole of his later career shows very
definitely how his work was constantly influenced by Fourier's
methods.

In October 1841 Thomson was admitted a student at St. Peter's
College, Cambridge. His father realized fully that, however
useful the course at Glasgow might be, the best road to an
academic career was via the Cambridge Mathematical Tripos.
The person who came out top in the Tripos lists was known as
the Senior Wrangler (the lists are only published alphabetically
nowadays), and it was not long before Thomson's name became
freely mentioned as both the prospective Senior Wrangler and
as the coming Smith's Prizeman—another of the highest of the
mathematical honours of the university. There seemed just
grounds for this belief. He worked under William Hopkins,
most renowned of tutors ; he contributed a series of able and

original papers to the Cambridge Mathematical Journal ; and
he obviously outshone the majority of his fellow students. By
way of diversion from work, he kept himself physically fit by
walking, rowing, and swimming ; and mentally fresh by the
devotion of occasional hours to music, for he was, indeed, an
active member and later President of the University Musical
Society.

There is no doubt that as the date of the Tripos Examinations
drew near, William Thomson became a little anxious. He knew
how very keen was his father on his success, and he was most
anxious not to disappoint him. Professor Thomson was ambitious
for his son. There was to be a vacancy shortly at the University
of Glasgow in the professorship of natural philosophy, and
James Thomson felt that if William could but do well enough
at Cambridge, his chance of obtaining the appointment at Glasgow was probably very good. On the other hand, the peculiar
requirements of the examiners involved William in much irksome drudgery of a kind that would be of little use to him in
after life, and his studies were somewhat distasteful to him on
this account.

In due course the examination results were published, and it
was seen that William Thomson came second. He was beaten
by Parkinson of St. John's. Shortly after, these two were again
rivals for the Smith's Prize, and this time it was Thomson who
was first, and Parkinson second. As to the actual merits of our
Smith's Prizeman and Second Wrangler, it must surely suffice
to note the comment which one of the examiners is reported to
have made to the other, ' You and I are just about fit to mend
his pen.'

Following on these examinations in the early part of 1845,
Thomson went to London and met Faraday, and subsequently
passed on to Paris to study physics under the famous Regnault,
then at work on his wonderful series of experiments for the
determination of the various constants in the theory of heat.

In May 1846 the aged Dr. Meikleham, Professor of Natural
Philosophy at Glasgow University, died. The Faculty met on
the 11th of September and, ' having deliberated on the respective

qualifications of the various candidates, unanimously appointed Mr. William Thomson, B.A., Fellow of St. Peter's College, Cambridge', to the vacant professorship. He was twenty-two years of age, and from now onwards began a professional career which lasted for over sixty years, and which brought him world-homage.

2. *Early Researches in Electricity*

Professor William Thomson's inaugural lecture was delivered in November 1846. It was ' a carefully prepared introductory lecture on the scope and methods of physical science '. The delivery suffered somewhat from the lecturer's nervousness : but he soon got over this. There was never, however, much of the natural teacher about him. He was too deeply steeped in problems of research. Many of his students were Arts students for whom attendance at the natural philosophy class was compulsory, and on these much of what Thomson had to say was lost. Nevertheless it was both fascinating and inspiring to all to watch him digress as he frequently did, to develop an idea which his remarks might suddenly bring to his mind, and he would then completely forget his class, and fill the board time after time with what was in fact a real exhibition of ' research in the making '. A somewhat extreme example of the abstruse nature of his lectures is that of a student who once remarked, ' Well, I listened to the lectures on the pendulum for a month, and all I know about the pendulum yet is that it wags '. Yet from the outset Thomson was the practical physicist seeking for a clear physical meaning, where the stereotyped text-book gave only a mathematical statement. Thus Dr. A. Russell, the Principal of Faraday House, tells us that when he was asked by Professor Thomson the meaning of the symbol $\frac{dx}{dt}$, he said ' with much complacency, that it was the limiting value of the ratio of the increment of x to the increment of t when the latter increment was indefinitely diminished '. This was of course, the stock mathematical meaning, but it did not satisfy Thomson.

'That's what Todhunter [1] would say,' said he. 'Does nobody know that it represents a velocity?'

The session of a Scottish University of those days lasted only six months, and this left Thomson much leisure for research. His earlier activities were in the direction of statical electricity. Coulomb's well-known laws of electrostatic attraction had been challenged by W. Snow Harris, an experimentalist of high repute, and Thomson boldly attacked Harris in defence of Coulomb. The outcome of this controversy was that Thomson successfully developed a new method for the investigation of this class of problem, known as the 'method of electrical images'. We do not propose to go into this method and into his many ingenious applications of it, but it will suffice here to point out that as a consequence Thomson was able triumphantly to vindicate Coulomb's theory. Another of Thomson's achievements was the 'absolute' determination, by mechanical methods which have now become mere commonplaces of a laboratory course, of the volt and ampère. These are respectively the practical units of potential difference (i. e. of electromotive force) and of electrical current. We are all familiar with the gold leaf electroscope. There is a difference of potential and therefore a force of attraction between the leaves and the inner walls of the electroscope and as a consequence the gold leaves fly apart. Between any two plates or surfaces, in fact, which are at different electrical potentials will there be a natural force of attraction, and Thomson first worked out the value of this attraction in terms of the size of the two surfaces, and of their distances apart. If for any given set of conditions there corresponds a definite force of attraction to a given difference of potential, then by *measuring* this force the corresponding difference of potential, or voltage, is at once found.

The devising of the necessary experimental details was but a step from this, and Thomson developed two forms—the 'attracted disk' form and the 'quadrant electrometer'. In the former there are two parallel plates. The lower one is charged

[1] Todhunter was the universally-read author of the mathematical text-books of those days.

up to a voltage which it is required to measure, and it attracts the upper light disk (connected to the earth to bring its potential to zero, since we regard the earth's potential as zero) with a force which is directly measured by springs or counter-weights such that they just counteract the electrical force between the plates. In the quadrant electrometer the attraction between the plates of different potentials is made to produce rotation the extent of which is proportional to the potential difference. This is arranged for by having two flat boxes, *A* and *B*, shaped as

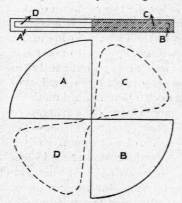

the two opposite quadrants of a circle (Fig. 104). In place of the remaining quadrants *C* and *D*, there is a figure-of-eight-shaped plate of thin aluminium, suspended horizontally from a graduated head by means of a torsion fibre in such a way that on setting up a potential difference between the plate and boxes, the oblique attraction swings *D* into *B* and *C* into *A*. The angle of swing is measured by the graduated head, and from it the necessary potential difference can be calculated.

Fig. 104. The principle of the Quadrant Electrometer.

The great advantage of this lies in the fact that the value of the volt as so obtained depends only upon a measured mechanical force and upon the linear dimensions of the apparatus. That is to say, it makes the volt independent of any other electrical quantities, and so gives us what is known as an *absolute* determination of the volt. This is invaluable, and Thomson extended the idea further in finding in a similar manner an absolute determination of the unit of current—the ampère. This he accomplished by using the fact that between two coils of wire carrying a current there is a mechanical attraction or repulsion. He arranged for the same current to flow through each coil, and literally *weighed* the attraction between them.

Finally, to obtain the standard ohm, it was only necessary

for Thomson to apply to his absolute measurements of the volt and the ampère the consequences of Ohm's Law. He so adjusted a coil of wire as to carry a current of one ampère with a difference of potential between its ends of one volt. Then it followed from Ohm's Law that the resistance of this coil was one ohm.

One other important piece of work amongst Thomson's earlier researches in electricity must not be omitted from our record, since it shows him to have been an unconscious pioneer of that most dramatic of all discoveries of twentieth-century science—viz., wireless telegraphy.

FIG. 105. HERMANN VON HELMHOLTZ

In 1847, Hermann von Helmholtz, a brilliant physicist, had drawn attention to some puzzling observations by Riess in connexion with the discharge of a Leyden jar. Riess had wound a wire round a knitting-needle, and he arranged for the current of discharge of a Leyden jar to pass round this wire. He expected of course to find his needle magnetized as a result, but what he did not expect to find, yet what nevertheless proved to be the case, was that through a course of experiments sometimes one end of the needle became the north-seeking pole, and sometimes it was the other end which was so left. This was very puzzling, as was also a corresponding observation by Wollaston, who on using the current of discharge from a Leyden jar to decompose the water by electrolysis found that instead of getting his oxygen at one electrode and his hydrogen at the other he obtained instead a *mixture* of both gases at each electrode.

Helmholtz, with characteristic brilliance of vision, suggested that these observations could be explained by the assumption that the Leyden jar discharge was *oscillatory* in character, and in 1853 Thomson took up this point in a paper ' On the Oscillatory Discharge of a Leyden Jar ' which he communicated to the Glasgow Philosophical Society, in the course of which he not only proved mathematically that this was so, but he also developed a formula for determining the rapidity with which the oscillations were taking place.

The discharge of a Leyden jar may be likened in some respects to the ' letting go ' of a pendulum ball which has been pulled to one side. As the ball swings down to its lowest position it gains in kinetic energy at the expense of the store of potential energy which had been supplied to it by the hand which drew it to one side, and this kinetic energy gives to the ball a speed which carries it past its lowest position, and the ball sweeps upwards on the other (and shall we say the *negative*) side, once more losing its kinetic energy and regaining its potential energy. The ball now repeats its oscillatory journey, this time from the negative side to the positive, again surging past its lowest position ; but gradually the resistance of the air reduces the swing, till the ball eventually comes to rest at its lowest position ; and the denser the medium in which the ball is swinging, the quicker does it come to rest, and indeed if the medium were sufficiently viscous, the ball would probably never get past the lowest position on its first journey downward. Similarly, in a sense, with a Leyden jar, which, it will be remembered, consists essentially of a glass jar coated inside and outside with layers of tinfoil. To charge up, we connect the inner coating to the positive terminal and the outer coating to the negative terminal of an electrical machine, and so induce on each charges which are equal but opposite in sign. To discharge we bring a wire from the inner coating up to a wire from the outer coating, and so great is the potential difference between the two that the discharge begins before the wires touch, a spark leaping across the intervening air-gap with a loud noise or snap. The whole thing appears to be instantaneous, but in fact it is not so, but takes a minute fraction of time. Not only so, but as with the pendulum, the current of one sign surges from, say, the inside of the jar to the wires and so on to the outside of the jar, thus momentarily re-charging the jar in the opposite way, and then

the charge surges back again along the wire, and then forward
again, each time with diminished energy owing to the resistance
of the wire and the heating at the tips, until it dies away, leaving
insufficient energy ultimately to carry the current across the
air-gap. In the best of cases this all takes but a fraction of
a second, but frequently the resistance and the heat generated
suffice even to prevent
a single complete os-
cillation.

We owe the knowledge
of all this to William
Thomson, and the ulti-
mate results were beyond
even his wildest dreams.
For working on this far-
ther, Clerk Maxwell,
another brilliant con-
temporary of Thomson,
showed in an epoch-
making piece of research
that if these oscillations
are sufficiently rapid,
much of the energy
stored in the Leyden jar

FIG. 106. JAMES CLERK MAXWELL

can be radiated out into space in the form of electro-magnetic
waves : and Hertz, following on this, not only produced such
waves, but devised a means of detecting or receiving them, and
so wireless telegraphy became a scientific possibility : and, in
the hands of such men as Sir Oliver Lodge, Signor Marconi,
and Professor Fleming, has now become one of the normal
adjuncts of civilization.

3. *Researches in Heat*

We turn now to another important subject upon which the future Lord Kelvin turned the light of his genius—the subject of the dynamical theory of heat, or thermodynamics.

We have mentioned at some length the researches of Count Rumford and Sir Humphry Davy in showing the relation between heat and mechanical work, and it will be recalled that these men attacked the caloric theory of heat, which had hitherto been universally accepted and remained in possession of the field right through the first half of the eighteenth century.

In 1824, impetus was given to the study of thermodynamics by the publication, by Nicolas Léonard Sadi-Carnot, of a work called *Réflexions sur la puissance motrice du feu*. In this work Carnot tried to determine mathematically how much mechanical work could be performed by a steam engine, and from this he went to the more purely theoretical consideration of the amount of work which could be performed by an ideal heat-engine. Carnot introduced the idea of a complete cycle of operations and of the principle of reversibility. Starting with a source of heat maintained at a high temperature (i. e. a boiler), he takes heat from this source and utilizes it by converting part of it into mechanical work, restoring the remainder of it to a condenser kept at a low temperature. Then (arguing theoretically of course), taking the reverse cycle, by performing *on* the engine an equal amount of work to that previously performed by the engine, he is able to extract the heat again from the condenser, and restore it to the original boiler or source. In effect, Carnot realized that not only was it possible to convert mechanical work into heat but also that the *reverse* was possible, namely, to convert heat into mechanical work ; and also that to a given amount of mechanical work there corresponds a definite amount of heat. He did not, however, actually measure the amount of this ' mechanical equivalent of heat ', as it is now called, and for many years the extreme importance of Carnot's work was not recognized, until William Thomson drew the attention of the scientific world to it in a paper which he published in 1849, entitled 'An account of Carnot's Theory of the Motive Power of Heat, and Numerical Results from Regnault's Experiments on Steam'.

Meanwhile various workers were attempting to establish the doctrine of the conservation of energy, namely, that the total energy in the universe is constant, and that when energy disappears in one form, e. g. heat, it must reappear in another form, e. g. mechanical energy. No such speculations could have any final value until the actual mechanical equivalent of heat had been determined, and for this we are indebted to James Prescott Joule, a young Manchester brewer and scientific amateur. This remarkable young man had spent years in studying the relations between the various forms of energy, his researches culminating in that famous experiment in which he converted the mechanical energy of a falling weight into the heat produced by the rotation

FIG. 107. J. P. JOULE

of a baffle-plate in a vessel of water, giving him a result of 778 foot-pounds of work as the mechanical equivalent of the pound-degree Fahrenheit.

Yet no one would listen to Joule. In April 1847 he gave a popular lecture on the subject in Manchester. Most of the newspapers ignored it, the *Manchester Guardian* being a notable exception ; as in the case of Carnot, it again remained for William Thomson to force recognition for Joule from a reluctant world of science. Joule was due to read a paper on the subject of his experiments before the British Association at Oxford in June 1847, but the Chairman, to whom the paper seemed unimportant, asked him to be brief. ' I can never forget ', said Thomson, when as Lord Kelvin he was unveiling a statue of Joule in Manchester in 1893, ' the British Association at Oxford in 1847, when . . . I heard a paper read by a very unassuming young man, who betrayed no consciousness in his manner that he had a great idea to unfold. I was tremendously struck with the paper. . . .' As to what happened on the conclusion of his reading, we may turn to Joule's own account. ' Discussion not being invited, the communication would have passed without comment if a young man had not risen in the section, and by his intelligent observations created a lively interest in the new theory. The young man was William Thomson.'

In the light of the researches of both Carnot and Joule, William Thomson was now able to make an important contribution to the subject of thermometry. No thermometer can be perfectly reliable as an absolute measurer of temperature which is dependent upon the behaviour of a substance. For example, no two specimens of glass expand in precisely the same way. So in the case of mercury-in-glass thermometers, which depend for their reading upon the physical property of the expansion of both glass and mercury, the probability is that there are as many scales as there are thermometers, since there can be no absolute uniformity ; similarly with gas thermometers, in which temperature changes follow the physical properties of pressure and volume changes ; so also with electrical thermometers, which depend upon the physical property of the variation of electrical resistance with temperature. In fact, no thermometer can be absolutely reliable unless it is totally independent of the physical properties of any substance whatever, and Thomson saw in Carnot's cycle of operations with the ideal engine a means of obtaining a scale of temperatures which would be independent of all physical properties.

We have seen that a steam engine may be regarded as a heat engine which takes in heat at boiler temperature and converts *some* of this heat into work by utilizing the expansion of the steam in the cylinder to move a piston to and fro. The diminished heat of the cooled steam is now passed to the condenser and is changed into liquid form. Consequently the heat which has been converted into work is the difference between the heat taken from the boiler and the heat returned to the condenser.

It is not necessary for us to regard steam as the only substance for such a cycle of operations. Carnot taught that theoretically, in the ideal engine, *any* substance may be made to do mechanical work by expansion so long as we regard it as passing between a source of heat (like the boiler) and a *receiver* (like the condenser). Now Thomson pointed out that the amount of work which can be done by such an engine depends upon two things— firstly upon the difference of temperatures between source and receiver (that is to say, if the boiler temperature is 150 degrees higher than the condenser temperature, more mechanical work could be done than if the difference were only 100 degrees), and secondly, upon the absolute values of these temperatures. Thus the mechanical work which would be done between the temperatures of 200° C. and 100° C. is not the same as would be done between 150° C. and 50° C., or between 100° C. and 0° C.

So far as the first of these conditions is concerned we may say that if a quantity of heat Q_1 be put in at the higher temperature T_1, and if a quantity of heat Q_2 be put out at the lower temperature T_2 then the ratio of these temperatures is fixed by the relation

$$\frac{T_1}{T_2} = \frac{Q_1}{Q_2}.$$

Keeping the boiler heat fixed, that is to say, keeping T_1 and Q_1 constant, suppose we utilize the whole of this heat Q_1, and convert it all into mechanical work. Then Q_2 becomes nil, and therefore T_2 becomes nil too. This fixes in fact a zero of temperature on this new scale of temperature measurement, namely, that condenser temperature at which *all* the heat from the boiler is converted into work. *It is impossible to conceive of a greater degree of cold than this,* and so Thomson spoke of it as *the absolute zero of temperature,* and he denoted it by $0°$ *Absolute*, or $0°$ A.

As to the value of this absolute zero on the ordinary thermometer scales of daily use, we must turn to the second of the conditions above referred to. Here Thomson showed that, working between boiler temperature of $100°$ C. (the temperature of boiling water) and condenser temperature of $0°$ C. (i. e. of freezing water), *for every* 373 *parts of heat put in at* $100°$ C., *the engine will return* 273 *parts into the receiver, converting* 100 *parts into mechanical work.* This means that $\dfrac{Q_1}{Q_2} = \dfrac{373}{273}$ and therefore the ratio of temperatures on the absolute scale will also be $\dfrac{T_1}{T_2} = \dfrac{373}{273}.$ To make an easy comparison with the Centigrade scale, Thomson next decided that the length of the degree on his new scale would be arranged so that there should be 100 of them between the melting-point of ice and the boiling-point of water. He had in fact to determine T_1, and T_2, such that $T_1 - T_2 = 100,$ and $\dfrac{T_1}{T_2} = \dfrac{373}{273}$, and a simple calculation shows that this gives $273°$ A. as corresponding to $0°$ C., and $373°$ A. as corresponding to $100°$ C., and $0°$ A. as corresponding to $-273°$ C. Thus his scale was complete, and it is now universally known as Thomson's *absolute thermodynamic scale.* It is solely concerned with the work done by the thermometric substance employed, and it is totally independent of all its physical properties · and so it is without exception the most satisfactory scale of temperature known. In addition it is very simply related to all the other temperature scales in daily use.

4. *Ocean Telegraphy*

Let us now consider one of the many examples of Thomson's service to mankind in the rôle of applied physicist and consulting engineer—the laying of the Atlantic cable. We have already seen how the researches of Oersted, Ampère, Arago, and others had paved the way to the invention of the electric telegraph by

Cooke, Wheatstone, and Morse, and by the end of 1840 commercial telegraphic undertakings were in operation in both England and America. By 1850, improvements had been so generally perfected that telegraphy by land was possible over hundreds of miles, and the problem of submarine telegraphy emerged from the realms of discussion into the reality of a Dover to Calais line successfully laid by Crampton, and followed soon after by other short lines connecting England with Ireland, and with Holland.

The natural ambition of all telegraph engineers was, however, the establishing of telegraphic communication between England and America. Why was this regarded as such a formidable undertaking? When, in August of 1850, the Dover to Calais line was first laid, the cable used was a copper wire surrounded by gutta-percha insulation, and it was at once noticed that the signals received were 'extraordinarily sluggish' as compared with the clear signals usual to overland telegraphy. Two hours later the line was severed by the anchor of a fishing-smack. So far as the latter of these troubles was concerned the remedy was obviously the strengthening of the cable, but so far as the question of sluggish signalling was concerned the remedy was not so immediately obvious.

Fig. 108. Five-needled instrument patented by Messrs. Cooke and Wheatstone in 1837.

From a general discussion, however, the fact soon emerged that such a cable was really in effect an elongated Leyden jar of great capacity, the copper acting as the inner lining, the salt water as the outer lining, and the gutta-percha as the ' glass ' of the jar ; and when a battery is connected up to one end of the core, the ' Leyden jar ' gradually gets charged up, first at the battery end, and gradually farther and farther along the wire, and so to the other end ; and similarly when the battery is withdrawn (or the circuit broken), the discharge is equally gradual.

In May 1855, William Thomson took up the discussion in a paper communicated to the Royal Society, entitled ' On the

FIG. 109.   Sections of the second and third Atlantic Cables.

Theory of the Electric Telegraph ', in the course of which he established a most important law governing the retardation of the electrical impulse along a cable.   He showed the retardation to be proportional to (*a*) the ' capacity ' and (*b*) the ' resistance ' of the cable.   Now each of these quantities is proportional to the length, and so it follows that the time retardation of a signal is proportional to the square of the length.   Thus ' if a cable 200 miles long showed a retardation of $\frac{1}{10}$th second, one 2,000 miles of similar thickness would have a retardation 100 times as great, or 10 seconds '.[1]   The enormous difficulty of a trans-Atlantic cable is therefore very evident, and it now remained for Thomson to show how this could be overcome.

Essentially he recommended two things—the employment of a copper cable of as low a resistance (and therefore of as high

[1] S. P. Thompson's *Life of Lord Kelvin*, vol. i, p. 329.

a conductivity) as possible, and the use of as thick a cross-section as possible.

Considerable opposition was offered to Thomson's theory, but ultimately his view prevailed, and in 1858 the newly-formed Atlantic Telegraph Company, of which William Thomson was a director, successfully laid its first cable. The signals from such a long cable were, however, so weak that ordinary methods of receiving messages were of no avail, and so Thomson invented the famous mirror galvanometer, now regarded as part of the normal equipment of all scientific laboratories. In this the magnet at the centre of the coil of the ordinary galvanometer is attached to a vertically suspended small spherical mirror which of course swings with the magnet whenever a current passes round the coil. A spot of light from a lamp is reflected from this mirror on to a distant scale, and provided the scale is sufficiently far away, a very small movement on the part of the magnet and mirror will cause a *big* swing of the spot along the scale and so the mirror galvanometer is very sensitive to small current changes. By this means the feeble currents received at the receiver of the cable were successfully recorded. Alas, after a few weeks' precarious work, the messages ceased, and the cable would not work. Nevertheless, inasmuch as during these few weeks no less than 732 messages, some of them of first-class importance, had been sent through, the project could not altogether be regarded as a failure.

It was decided to try again, and Thomson busied himself with the plans for the new venture forthwith. A cable ship, the *Great Eastern*, was designed to take the whole length of cable required, and to have the necessary freedom of manœuvring which the difficulties of laying required, and in 1866, after two attempts, not only was the line successfully laid, but the original line was once more rendered serviceable. As electrical engineer to the expedition, William Thomson was knighted, and on his return was presented with the freedom of the city of Glasgow.

Shortly after he replaced his mirror galvanometer by his still more sensitive siphon recorder, in which a ' small and delicate pen was formed by a piece of very fine glass tube in the form of

FIG. 110. The *Great Eastern* leaving Sheerness with the Atlantic Telegraph Cable on board, July 1866.

a siphon, of which the shorter end dipped in an ink bottle, while the other end wrote the message in little zig-zag notches on a ribbon of paper drawn past it by machinery. The siphon was moved to and fro by the signalling currents which flowed in a small coil hung between the poles of an electromagnet, excited by a local battery, and the ink was spurted in a succession of fine drops from the pen to the paper. This was accomplished by electrifying the ink-bottle and ink by a local electrical machine, and keeping the paper in contact with an uninsulated metal roller. Electric attraction between the electrified ink and the unelectrified paper thus drew out the ink drops, and the pen, which never touched paper, was quite unretarded by friction'.[1] The siphon recorder is in use to this day.

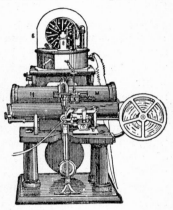

FIG. III. Lord Kelvin's Early Siphon-recorder.

It was probably his activities in this direction that caused Thomson to turn his attention to the many other applications of science to the problems of engineering. He definitely took up the commercial side by entering into partnership with Mr. C. F. Varley and Professor Fleeming Jenkin, and the firm of Thomson, Varley and Jenkin took up all phases of telegraphic engineering with great success, and to them are due most of the up-to-date inventions which have made submarine telegraphy the pronounced success which it is to-day.

[1] Gray's *Lord Kelvin*, p. 270.

5. *Research in Navigation*

Thomson's years of research on ocean cables brought him naturally into intimate contact with some of the urgent problems awaiting solution in the science of navigation. It is therefore a matter for little surprise that here, too, he achieved wonders.

There was, for example, his invention of the sounding-machine. One of the first requisites in the organization of the laying of the Atlantic cable was a proper charting of the ocean bed, and the method which he found in vogue was somewhat primitive and very laborious. A sinker was lowered attached to an inch-and-a-half-thick rope. This required many hands and in deep water the ship had to be stopped for the operation. As a first measure, Thomson suggested the use of pianoforte wires as being of great tensile strength, but the problem which required solution was to find a means whereby, with a minimum of both labour and time, a weight could be lowered and kept vertical, and a measure of the depth obtained. Accordingly he invented a winding-machine fitted with a brake to prevent both kinking and the too rapid running out of the wire. Only two men were needed to handle the apparatus. One of the sinkers was in the form of a cylinder containing a long, narrow, glass tube the inside of which was lined with chromate of silver. The deeper this sinks, the further up the tube does the sea-water penetrate, and in so doing it reacts chemically on the chromate of silver, producing a discoloration. On rewinding, the length of discoloured tube is at once a measure of the depth. The usual length of cable used to-day is 300 fathoms, the wire being of steel and made up of seven strands.

In this connexion it is related that Joule once found Sir William surrounded by coils of pianoforte wire, and he inquired what they were for. He was told they were for sounding. ' For sounding what note ? ' inquired Joule. ' The deep C,' was Sir William's reply.

As to its value to seamen, Admiral Sir W. R. Kennedy once wrote thus :

' Some years ago I left a port on the coast of Patagonia in the

Ruby. We shaped a course for Golfo Nuevo for the night. At 8 p.m. the navigation officer came to my cabin and showed me the position of the ship, well clear of the land and 100 fathoms no bottom, marked on the chart.——" All right ", I said.—— " Throw Thomson overboard."——The navigator looked at me to see if I was joking. " Why, there 's no bottom at 100 fathoms, sir." " Well, heave Thomson over." He left the cabin, and presently I heard the whirr of the wire suddenly stop. I rushed on deck. Fifteen fathoms! " Stop her, hard-a-port, leadsmen on both chains ! " Sure enough, 15 fathoms. I hove to all night,—— but had we continued on our course we should have been ashore before daylight.——The coast line was not correctly charted. No wonder that we sailors bless the name of Lord Kelvin.' [1]

We turn next to Sir William's invention of the modern mariner's compass—probably his most popularly-known achievement. In 1870 something prompted him to choose the subject of the mariner's compass for a magazine article, and he discovered that he knew very little about it. So he set himself to study the matter. He quickly realized how unsatisfactory were the forms then in use. The needles were heavy and long (as much as fifteen inches in some cases), and were mounted on large cards for steadiness, but in fact the action was sluggish in fine weather (if the compass did not stick altogether), whilst in stormy weather the instrument was practically useless.

Excellent pioneer work on the theory of compass deviation had been done by Archibald Smith, who was, indeed, the original source of Thomson's inspirations. Working on from Smith's standpoint, Thomson showed that, contrary to the prevailing practice, steadiness of the compass in stormy weather could best be obtained by short needles mounted on a light card. He clearly saw the necessity for a slow horizontal swing to avoid unsteadiness, and for very little friction to prevent sticking. He paid much attention, too, to the problem of shielding his compass from the magnetism due to the ship's ironwork.

As a result of all this, Thomson's marine compass takes the following form. The ' card' consists of an extremely light (less than $\frac{2}{5}$th of an ounce) graduated paper ring, kept circular by

---

[1] Sir R. Gregory's *Discovery*, p. 270.

a light ring of aluminium. Threads of silk extend radially from the rim to an aluminium centre, on the cap of which is a sapphire bearing resting on an iridium point which projects upward from the compass bowl. The 'compass needle' is built up of eight thin magnets of glass-hard steel from $3\frac{1}{4}$ inches to 2 inches long, strung together 'like the steps of a rope ladder' on two silk threads attached to the radial threads. The weight is distributed at a distance from the axis, giving a long period of free vibration

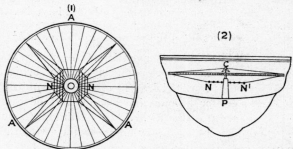

FIG. 112. Thomson's (Lord Kelvin's) Compass.
(1) Frame and Needles.   (2) Section of Compass Bowl.

The Compass Card consists of a broad ring of paper marked with degrees and points, attached to a frame like that in (1) above, where an aluminium ring, A, A, is connected by 32 radial silk threads to a central disk of aluminium, in the centre of which is a round hole designed to receive an aluminium cap with a highly polished sapphire centre worked to the form of an open cone. To direct the card eight short light needles, N, N, are suspended by silk threads from the outer ring. The section shows the mounting of the card on its pivot.

(an important essential for steadiness of action), and the friction at the point of support is very little indeed.

With regard to the question of compass errors due to the ship's magnetism, Thomson's design was based on the fact that part of the ship's magnetism is permanent and due to the permanent iron structures (it does, however, change very slowly, requiring periodic adjustment) and part is 'induced', and alters with change of course and position. The former, which may affect the 'needle' by as much as 20° in ordinary iron vessels, and 30° in war-ships, is corrected for by two sets of steel magnets placed at right angles to each other, with their centres under the binnacle needle, one directed fore and aft, and the other set directed athwartship. The error due to the induced magnetism, which may amount to from 5° to 10°, is corrected for by placing two soft iron spheres one on each side of the compass with their centre line at right angles to the ship's length. This keeps the induced magnetism annulled, since as its value changes, so also does the induced magnetism of the spheres.

It took Sir William many years to overcome the conservatism of the Navy, but eventually he had the satisfaction of seeing the almost universal use of his compass not only in our own Navy, but throughout the merchant service, and in most foreign Navies, though to-day it is beginning to be replaced by the more recent gyro-compass.

The achievements of the sounding-machine and the mariner's compass are wonderful enough, but they by no means exhaust the tale of Thomson's magnificent services to those who 'go down to the sea in ships'. Space only permits of their bare mention. There is his work on the furnishing of lighthouses with distinctive lights to distinguish one from the other, his

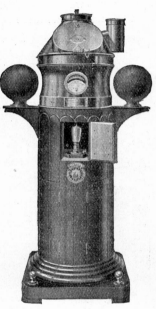

FIG. 113. Standard Mariner's Compass.

work on tides and his invention of the tide-predicting machine, his mathematical investigations on waves in general, and his work on the design of ships. Small wonder, therefore, is it that we read in the standard biography of this great man [1] the tribute of the sailor in the distant seas of the East, ' I don't know who this Thomson may be, but every sailor ought to pray for him every night.'

[1] S. P. Thompson's *Life of Lord Kelvin.*

6. *Further Biographical Details*

Of the scores of further contributions in almost every direction of scientific activity nothing more can here be said than that it is hoped that the interested reader will seek them out in the standard biographies which have been written, and well written, by men who were brought into intimate contact with their subject.

Reference might have been made to the famous collaboration

FIG. 114. Lord Kelvin on board the *Lalla Rookh*, 23 September 1885.

which produced Thomson and Tait's *Natural Philosophy*, and which set a new and high standard in the text-book presentation of the principles of scientific inquiry ; to Thomson's fascinating investigations on the age of the earth and on the age of the sun's heat, developed from a consideration of the laws of cooling—investigations which profoundly stirred the scientific world at the time he made them, though the discovery of radium subsequently considerably modified the value of his results in both these investigations ; and to the famous Baltimore lectures, delivered by invitation to ' professional students in physical science' in 1884 at the Johns Hopkins University, in which he dealt exhaustively with the wave theory of light. Our intention, however, has been rather to lay stress on those portions of his work which served to link up the scientific investigator with the activities of the engineer, and to leave his more purely abstract researches for the further reading of the interested students.

In 1852 William Thomson, then a young professor of twenty-eight, married Miss Crum, a daughter of Walter Crum, a first cousin of his father's. It was a happy union, but Lady Thomson was constantly in delicate health and died in 1870. Four years later he married again. He had visited Madeira the previous summer as consulting engineer for the Western and Brazilian Cable Company, and a fault in the cable had kept him there for sixteen days, during the course of which he met Miss Frances Anna Blandy, daughter of a prominent Madeira citizen. He was drawn to her at first by the promptitude with which she had picked up 'dot and dash' practice, and he returned to the island in the succeeding summer, and the two were married at the British Consular Chapel, Funchal Bay, Madeira. They were devotedly attached to each other to the end.

In 1851 Thomson had been elected a Fellow of the Royal Society. In 1890 he was elected its President, and remained so for five years. It is impossible, however, to record the full number of the honours he received from all the world over. The Royal Society of Edinburgh, of which he was for many years President, awarded him both the Keith Medal and the Victoria Jubilee Medal, and the Royal Society of London the Copley Medal and the Royal Medal : the Institute of France elected him one of their Foreign Associates, the French President made him a Grand Officer of the Legion of Honour, and Prussia a Knight of the Order ' Pour le Mérite '.

In England, apart from the honours bestowed upon him by the brotherhood of science, further recognition came to him at the hands of Queen Victoria, who on New Year's day of 1892 conferred upon him a peerage. He took the title of Baron Kelvin of Netherall, Largs, the name being taken from the Kelvin river, in close proximity to the new University buildings at Glasgow.

The year 1896, however, saw a most remarkable demonstration, world-wide in its character and extraordinary in its sincerity, in his honour. For this was the year of Kelvin's completion of a half-century of illustrious service to Glasgow as the Professor of Natural Philosophy at its University. A great gathering assembled —scientific colleagues of international fame from England, Ireland, the Colonies, and from every civilized foreign country, representatives of kings, princes, colleges, and scientific societies and institutions.

FIG. 115. Telegraph by Semaphore, 1842.

In 1899 Lord Kelvin resigned his professorship. He was now seventy-five years old, and he felt that the time had come when this step was necessary. He was succeeded by Andrew Gray, a former student and assistant, and later author of an able biography of his great master. Yet Kelvin could not altogether sever his long connexion with the University, and with characteristic grace he inscribed his name on the rolls of the University as a research student.

Retirement from his professional duties by no means meant a withdrawal from his scientific activities, and these continued if anything with a renewed vigour and freshness which astonished all his friends. Old as he was, except for occasional bouts of facial neuralgia, his health continued good. He died peacefully on the 18th of December 1907. His grave is alongside that of Sir Isaac Newton. He was buried on the 23rd of December with a stately simplicity which worthily fitted the occasion. ' There he sleeps well who toiled during a long life for the cause of natural knowledge, and served nobly, as a hero of peace, his country and the world.' [1]

In this short record we have said very little of the man himself; of his wonderful vitality, and of the remarkable influence his very presence exerted on both students and colleagues. It is worthy to note that of all the illustrious men some record of whose lives has been given in this volume, Lord Kelvin is the only one of whom it can be said that there are men alive to-day who came under his personal influence as either pupil or colleague. Thus Dr. Russell, in his short volume on *Lord Kelvin*, tells us :

Fig. 116. A Central Telephone Exchange to-day.

' Even in his introductory lectures Thomson soared to heights which made many of his class feel giddy and helpless. He would say, for example, that all motion is relative motion. . . . Having thus unsettled the ideas of his class and awakened their interest, he would point out how easy it is to get the relative motion. . . . Towards the end of the session, owing to the very comprehensive programme that had to be got through, the pace had to be quickened. The last day was always an eventful one, the professor sometimes lecturing . . . to those of the class who could remain, long after the hour was up. The writer was one of those

[1] Gray's *Lord Kelvin*, p. 304.

who remained to the end—a period of over four hours—in 1878. . . .
But even the most enthusiastic of us were beginning to be fagged
before the professor gave any signs of concluding. The memory
of that last lecture is a treasured possession '; and again, ' All
old students look back on their attendance at Kelvin's lectures
as something never to be forgotten and to be treasured deep in
their hearts. . . .' ' Kelvin had a powerful imagination, a strong
inductive faculty, and a power of realizing his conceptions in
practice which has only been equalled by the greatest inventors.
The possession of three such faculties by the same man is probably
unique. His deductions were not of such world-wide importance
as those of Sir Isaac Newton. It is very difficult to make a
comparison between these two intellectual giants, as the ages in
which they lived are so far apart. Newton was more painstaking
and thorough. He published little that was open to criticism.
Kelvin, on the other hand, could hardly wait until his experiments
were finished. There was so much to do and such short time to
do it in. Whatever his hand found to do he did with all his
might.'

From Andrew Gray at Glasgow, we get the following tribute :

' Genius has been said to be the power of taking infinite pains :
it is that indeed, but it is also far more. Genius means ideas,
intuition, a faculty of seizing by thought the hidden relation of
things, and withal the power of proceeding step by step to their
clear and full expression, whether in the language of mathematical
analysis or in the direction of daily life. Such was the genius of
Lord Kelvin ; it was lofty and it was practical. He understood—
for he had felt—the fascination of knowledge apart from its
application to mechanical devices ; he did not disdain to devote
his great powers to the service of mankind. His objects of daily
contemplation were the play of forces, the actions of bodies in all
their varied manifestations, or, as he preferred to sum up the
realm of physics, the observation and discussion of properties
of matter. But his eyes were ever open to the hearing of all that
he saw or discovered on the improvement of industrial appliances,
to the possibility of using it to increase the comfort and safety
of men, and so to augment the sum total of human happiness.'

On the 4th of May 1921 there assembled a gathering of
scientists. The occasion was the first award by the Institute of
Civil Engineers of a newly-created Kelvin Medal. The meeting
was presided over by the great philosopher and politician,
Lord Balfour, and in the course of his address he said :

' Lord Kelvin had in a manner hardly, and perhaps never, equalled before, except by Archimedes, the power of theorizing on the darkest, most obscure, and most intimate secrets of Nature, and at the same time, and almost in the same breath, carrying out effectively and practically some engineering feat, or carrying to a successful issue some engineering invention. He was one of the leaders in the movement which had compelled all modern engineers worthy of the name to be themselves men not merely of practice, but of theory, to carry out engineering undertakings in the spirit of true scientific inquiry and with an eye fixed on the rapidly growing knowledge of the mechanics of Nature, which can only be acquired by the patient work of physicists and mathematicians in their laboratories and studies.'

FIG. 117. Buoys and Grapnels used in recovering the Atlantic Telegraph Cable of 1865.

FIG. 118.   The Growth of Aviation.   An early French print (1798)
contemplating Napoleon's descent on England through the air.

XVI

SCIENCE TO-DAY AND TO-MORROW

I. *Retrospect and Prospect*

IN these pages we have passed the progress of knowledge in review, century by century. The story has been one of steady progress. Truth after truth has been brought to light, law after law has been unearthed, fallacy after fallacy and misconception after misconception have been removed. Gradually there has emerged a glimpse of a grand cosmical scheme of order, law, and method which commands our respect and compels our awe.

Of late the pace has quickened. Discoveries of first-class importance have brought with them inventions of equal import. Wonderful as was once overland and submarine telegraphy to a world accustomed only to postal communication, even wireless telegraphy is to-day regarded as one of the commonplaces of everyday life, and wireless telephony no longer surprises us.

Yet we are still on the threshold of knowledge. Only one small corner of nature's veil of truth has been lifted to the understanding of mankind. Newton, it will be remembered, once wrote : ' I seem to have been only like a boy playing on the seashore, and diverting myself in now and then finding a smoother pebble or a prettier shell, whilst the great ocean of truth lay all undiscovered before me.' We have advanced far since Newton's day, yet at best we can say that a few more pebbles have been rounded, and a few more shells exposed. The infinite ocean of discoverable truth still lies before us.

To-day, with barely a quarter of the century gone, we are already far beyond the point at which Lord Kelvin and his nineteenth-century contemporaries stopped. In more directions than one, events are stirring in the world of science, and already vast possibilities of rapid future development are opening up.

2. *Applied Physics*

What is the general trend of scientific research to-day ? Apart from the normal development of the applications of the already discovered laws of physics in the direction of utility (two of the latest examples of which are the perfecting of wireless telephony and wireless telephotography), in the world of applied physics one of the main features of the twentieth century has undoubtedly been the conquest of the air. So far as the ' lighter than air ' machines are concerned, the fundamental scientific problems have not been very great, though they are by no means to be dismissed.

The problem of the heavier-than-air machine, or aeroplane, has, however, been a much more formidable one. To some extent,

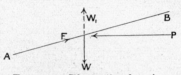

FIG. 119.   Illustrating heavier-than-air flight.

it was the influence of Newton himself which retarded progress, for he worked out a theory which taught that the resistance to a rapidly moving object in the air would be so great that the mechanical power required to maintain such motion was enormous and prohibitive. Pioneer work by Professor Langley, of America, from 1887 onwards cleared away this misconception. He showed that, contrary to Newton's deductions, the more rapid is the motion in horizontal flight of a given plane, the less will be the power required to support it. The problem was further developed on the theoretical side by such men as Bryan, Bairstow, and Lanchester, and on the practical side by such pioneers as the brothers Wilbur and Orville Wright.

Some very slight insight into the fundamental problems involved in the theory of ' heavier-than-air ' flight may perhaps be realized by the following.   Imagine a plane AB (Fig. 119), inclined to the horizontal by a small angle.   Its weight W acts vertically downwards, and to sustain this weight there must be an equal and upward force.   Now suppose that by means of engines and propellers a ' fore and aft ' force F is produced along the length AB, causing the plane to move forwards (on wheels—'taxi-ing', as it is called in aeroplane language). This sets up a horizontal windage pressure P (against the direction of motion) on the under side of the surface, and at the same time creates a partial vacuum on the upper surface of AB, and as a combined result there is developed an upward force or reaction W_1, which increases with the speed of the motion, and which, when it becomes greater than W, will cause the machine to rise at the same time as it is moving forward with the speed due to F, and it then becomes a question of maintaining this speed to preserve this upward thrust. The whole argument is, it will be noticed, independent of the lateral compass direction taken, and so the provision of steering accommodation will thus make directive locomotion possible, while the controlling of the angle AB to the horizontal will enable the necessary variations in the value of W_1 to be made to lift the machine higher or to bring it lower down as desired. No mention has been made, of course, of the hundred and one modifying considerations which are really involved, such as shape, surface area, skin friction, drag, and so on.

3. *Pure Physics*

Turning now to the sphere of pure physics, the feature of present-day research is the investigation of the structure of the atom. It is well over a hundred years since Dalton first enunciated his atomic theory, according to which the atom was the 'last word' in the subdivision of matter. To-day we know that the atom is an exceedingly complicated structure.

The start in this direction may be said to date from 1878, in which year Sir William Crookes, when studying the discharge of electricity through a highly rarefied tube, discovered the 'cathode rays', a stream of minute electrified particles to which the name of 'electrons' was afterwards given. Hertz, of wireless telegraphy fame, showed in 1893 that these rays could penetrate thin sheets of certain metals (including aluminium) placed inside the vacuum tubes, and following this up, Lenard, in 1894, succeeded in passing these cathode rays out into the air by having the end of the vacuum tube of aluminium, thus acting as a window to the rays, which remained luminous in the air, and which were found also to affect a photographic plate.

It may be mentioned in passing that a year later, in 1895, Röntgen, in repeating Lenard's work, discovered almost by accident the existence of X-rays, and worked out their remarkable properties, to the great benefit of mankind in the many subsequent applications to medicine and surgery.

Returning, however, to our main theme, we come to Henri Becquerel's discovery, in 1896, of radio-activity in uranium and its compounds—that is to say, these substances were phosphorescent on exposure to sunlight, and emitted rays which could penetrate materials opaque to light, and would affect a photographic plate.

In 1903 radium itself was isolated by Professor and Madame Curie, and the problem of its remarkable store of energy began to agitate the world of science ; for radium gives out heat and light continuously without evident chemical change, and even radium-salts maintain a temperature of 3° Fahrenheit above that of their surroundings.

Whence comes this apparently inexhaustible store of energy ? According to the Disintegration Theory of Rutherford and Soddy, the rays emitted by a radio-active substance are evidences of the breaking up of its atomic structure, and according to calculation one grain of radium would reduce to half a grain in 1,760 years. Similarly ' radium emanation ', a gas emitted by radium, and much more ' active ' than the radium itself, reduces to one-half in four days. Sir William Ramsay computed that the energy in a ton of radium is equivalent to that of a million and a half tons of coal.

As a development from all this, and from the detailed researches of Sir J. J. Thomson and others on the subject of the electron, there has developed in the past few years a conception of the structure of matter widely different from that which held the field in the nineteenth century. According to the present-day view, instead of the atom being regarded as a single indivisible something, it is considered to be made up of a minute nucleus of positively electrified matter (positive and negative electricity 'slumped together' with a preponderance of the former) surrounded by a number (anything up to 92) of exceedingly minute negative electrons, probably revolving round the nucleus at varying distances much as do the planets round the sun. The mass of the atom is concentrated at the nucleus, the negative electron weighing only about 1/1830 of the weight of the positive nucleus.

In the normal atom, the *amount* of positive electricity on the nucleus is exactly equal to the *number* of negative electrons surrounding it, but this number varies from element to element. It is known as the Atomic Number. Its value for lead is 82, for mercury 80, for gold 79, for oxygen 8, for helium 2, and for hydrogen 1. The physical and chemical properties of the element depend upon this number, and so there arises a vastly important problem for the future—one of those fascinating problems which link up the distant past with the years to come. It is no less a problem than that of the transmutation of the elements.

Mercury has an atomic number of 80 and gold of 79, and all that has to be done is to reduce the charge in the nucleus by one—there is no doubt that an accommodating negative electron would at once also depart—and the thing is done. And about the only way to do it is to bombard the nucleus with a suitably light projectile—a helium atom or a hydrogen atom, for example—which would have to be small enough to escape collision with the surrounding negative electrons. In a million such shots, thousands will so collide, thousands more will go clean through the space between the electrons and emerge on the other side, thousands more will so nearly but not quite hit the nucleus that they will be deflected round it like a comet round the sun, and perhaps only one will actually hit the elusive nucleus, and then it is a question whether it will do this with sufficient energy to produce the necessary disruption. And finally, millions of such successes would be required to get a sufficient amount of transmutation to be appreciable.

Yet it has actually been done, recently, by Professor Rutherford, of Cambridge. His attack was on atoms of nitrogen (atomic number 7), and his 'bombs' were atoms of helium (in the form of high speed particles emitted radio-actively by what is known as radium—*C*, with a speed of 12,000 miles per second). Rutherford showed that from a small percentage of these atoms of nitrogen he succeeded in producing atoms of hydrogen (atomic number 1), and so we get the first really authentic case of artificial transmutation of an element on record.

4. *Einstein and Relativity*

We turn finally to the much-talked-of theory of relativity which is at present holding the attention of all physicists and

FIG. 120.   ALBERT EINSTEIN

mathematicians and with which is associated the name of Albert Einstein. Born in Switzerland, of Jewish parentage, some forty-three years ago, he succeeded Van 't Hoff as an ' akademischer ' professor at the University of Berlin. Gifted with a wonderful creative imagination, a profound knowledge of mathematics and physics, and all the delicate sympathy of a master musician (he is almost as brilliant a violinist as he is a philosopher), he has come to the world with a mission of whose import we have not heard the like since the time of Newton.

We have seen how Huyghens, in opposition to Newton, developed a wave theory of light, as a result of which there grew up a conception of a medium pervading all space, whose function it was to transmit the light waves. This medium is spoken of as the ether, and much controversy and discussion has centred round the problem of its properties. It has proved most elusive. It can be neither felt nor seen, and every attempt to show its actual presence has failed. Clerk Maxwell, one of the most brilliant of the nineteenth-century mathematical physicists, developed his famous electro-magnetic theory of light (after having shown that the same ether which was necessary for the propagation of light waves at a speed of 186,000 miles per second, was also necessary for transmission of electro-magnetic disturbances at *the same speed*), according to which light was itself electro-magnetic in origin, the sensation of light being in fact due to the passage of electric waves through the ether.

Hertz, we know, strikingly verified the relation between light and electricity by showing that the oscillations of the discharge of a Leyden jar set up ether waves at a speed of 186,000 miles a second, and we also saw how Faraday showed a relation between light and magnetism. Zeeman, too, discovered such relationship. A spectrum of sodium light shows two bright yellow lines ; but place the incandescent sodium between the poles of a powerful magnet and the two yellow lines at once give place to *ten* such lines.

The electronic theory of matter, to which we have already referred, developed naturally from all this. The unit of electricity is the electron and a stream of electrons produces an electric current. But at the same time the electronic particle is the ultimate unit of matter, and the vibrations of the negative electrons around the positive nucleus give rise to the phenomenon of light. Now comes one of Einstein's strong contentions. If matter is derived from the electron, and if light is also derived from the electron, then since the former is affected by gravitation, why not the latter also ?

Einstein argued that just as a body shooting past another body must be deflected out of its course by the gravitational influence of the latter, so a ray of light shooting past a body would be deflected out of its course also. With the huge speed of 186,000 miles per second, it would no doubt require a huge body to produce a small deflexion, but Einstein predicted a definite value for the case of a ray of light shooting past the sun. This could be calculated from Newton's law of gravitation, but it is part of the new theory that Newton's law requires some modification ; and working on his own formula, Einstein prophesied a deflexion practically double that which he derived from Newton's formula.

Here was a fitting opportunity, not only to test Einstein's theory—but also to test it against Newton's. One can study the passage of a light-ray past the sun only when there is a total eclipse, as then the sun is blotted out and the stars suddenly appear ; and of course those stars whose ' lines of sight ' just skim past the sun can be photographed, and a careful study should show a slight displacement of their position in the skies from that which they normally occupy when the sun is elsewhere.

The story constitutes one of the romances of science. Einstein, a German-Swiss professor in a recently hostile country, made his prophecy. But ' genius knows no frontier '. England, while the late war was still in progress, arranged the eclipse expedition to Sobral, in South America, and to Principe, off West Africa, to put the matter to the test. The result is well known. It was a triumphant vindication of Einstein's theory.

No longer can we, then, with absolute truth, say of light that it travels in straight lines. No longer can we say convincingly that parallel lines never meet ; nor that the straight line joining two points is the shortest distance between them.

For the exact expressions of the laws of nature which it is the business of the scientist to discover we seek the language of mathematics, for this we regard as being both exact and universal. But unfortunately, as Einstein points out,. the mathematical language employed hitherto has not been absolutely universal, and accordingly could not be regarded as exact. Why is this ? It is because the observer who framed the laws has omitted to allow for his own motion.

All the constituent portions of the universe are in motion in one way or another, and the *relative* effects are different to observers in different parts of the universe. We on the earth are not moving in quite the same way as are the observers on, say, the star Sirius, and as a consequence the facts of nature seem different to the two sets of observers. The scientist on the earth builds up his series of formulae and equations, to express the laws of nature as *he* sees them, and the scientist on Sirius does likewise. But on comparing them (assuming we could), *we find the sets of formulae and equations are different*. Einstein says that so long as this is so the laws *cannot* be regarded as absolute, but only as relative. So we say that the underlying doctrine of Einstein is that the mathematical expression of the laws of nature shall be independent of the state of motion of the observer who frames them.

As a matter of history, assuming that the ether of space really existed, a number of attempts were made by various people by various means to detect the motion of the earth through this ether, and so to allow for its effect on the laws of nature. These attempts all failed, and Einstein boldly asserted that such a motion was, in the nature of things, incapable of detection, and from this view he began to develop his theory, which demands from us a totally different scheme of perception from that to which we have been accustomed.

Where we have regarded matter, space, and time as completely separate conceptions, Einstein asserts that these are, on the contrary, intimately bound up with each other, and that there is only one fundamental fact of experience—a happening or an event. Space and time are inseparable. Events do not occur at a certain point at a certain time—they simply ' are ', and for the full representation of events we must replace the old scheme of three axes of reference at right angles by four axes at right angles, the fourth being a time-axis. On the ' three-axes ' scheme, ten different observers, having of course their different motions, and, therefore, their different outlooks, would give ten different representations of any one event. But on the four-dimensional ' continuum ', as it is called, one event gives one representation, provided the axes of reference are the same for all.

Relativity of space is of course by no means a new conception ; but the time factor in relativity is undoubtedly a new thing. Let us now see in what fundamental respects Einstein differs from Newton. Newton taught that perfectly free matter moves in straight lines, and to explain curved motion he brought in the idea of *force*—in the case of the moon moving round the earth, for example, the force of gravitation. Einstein, too, says that perfectly free matter moves in straight lines, but his contention is that the *moon is* moving in a straight line, only to us it appears not to be so, owing to the fact that ' space in the neighbourhood of matter is modified in such a way that a straight line in it appears to an observer who is unaware of the modification to be curved '. We remarked before that on the new philosophy a straight line is no longer the shortest distance between two points. This might be said to be an Einsteinian fact expressed in Euclidean language. To express it in Einsteinian language, it would be more correct to say that ' a straight line *is* the shortest distance between two points, but the ' distance ' must be taken in the ' four-dimensional continuum ' and not in that relatively selected portion of it which we call space, and which we represent on our old-fashioned three-dimensional framework of reference.

A word of caution is here necessary. The modern theory of relativity has in no sense dethroned Newton. The equations which develop from Einstein's theory show a law of gravitation which so far agrees with Newton's law that we may say that for the ordinary speeds with which we are concerned in most of the problems which confront us the two are practically identical. They begin to differ, however, as the velocities increase, and for those speeds comparable with that of light the divergence becomes very great.

In June 1921 Albert Einstein visited this country to deliver a lecture at King's College, London, and after the lecture he was the guest of honour at a dinner attended by the most eminent English philosophers. Toasting the health of the guest, the Principal, Mr. Ernest Barker, used these fine words :

' We welcome you twice, for discovering a new truth which has added to the knowledge of the universe, and for coming to us from a country that was lately our enemy to knit the broken threads of international science. If at your command the straight lines have been banished from our universe, there is yet one straight line which will always remain—the straight line of right and justice. May both our nations follow this straight line side by side in a parallel movement, which, in spite of Euclid, will yet bring them together in friendship with one another and friendship with the other nations of the world.'

BIBLIOGRAPHY

THE object of this bibliography is to draw the attention of the reader to the general literature in scientific history rather than to the biographies of the scientists.

Scientific Method and General Scientific History.

J. A. Thomson. *Introduction to Science.* Home University Library (Williams & Norgate). 1911. 2s. 6d. net.

F. W. Westaway. *Scientific Method, its Philosophy and its Practice.* (Blackie & Son.) 2nd Edition. 1919. 10s. 6d. net.

Henri Poincaré. *Science and Method*, translated by Hon. Bertrand Russell. (Nelson & Sons.) 1914. 6s. net.

Norman Campbell. *What is Science ?* (Methuen.) 1921. 5s. net.

Charles Singer. *Studies in the History and Method of Science.* Oxford (Clarendon Press). First Series, out of print. Second Series, 1920, 48s. net.

Karl Pearson. *The Grammar of Science.* (A. & C. Black.) 3rd Edition. Part I, Physical. 1911. 10s. net.

Sir R. A. Gregory. *Discovery, the Spirit and Service of Science.* (Macmillan.) 10th Edition. 1921. 7s. 6d. net.

F. S. Marvin. *The Living Past.* Oxford (Clarendon Press). 1920. 5s. 6d. net.

W. W. Rouse Ball. *A Short History of Mathematics.* (Macmillan.) 6th Edition. 12s. 6d. net.

F. Cajori. *A History of Elementary Mathematics.* (Macmillan.) 12s. net.
—— *A History of Physics.* (Macmillan.) 14s. net.

E. Mach. *The Science of Mechanics* (with Supplementary Volume). (Open Court Publishing Company.) 1907. 9s. 6d. net. Supplementary volume, 2s. 6d. net.

Sir O. Lodge. *Pioneers of Science.* (Macmillan.) 7s. 6d. net. Mainly astronomical.

Ancient Science.

J. L. Heiberg. *Science and Mathematics in Classical Antiquity.* Oxford (Clarendon Press). 1922. 2s. 6d. net.

R. W. Livingstone and others. *The Legacy of Greece.* Oxford (Clarendon Press). 1921. 7s. 6d. net. (Chapters on Science and Mathematics by Sir T. Heath, Dr. Charles Singer, and Professor D'Arcy W. Thompson.)

Cyril Bailey and others. *The Legacy of Rome.* Oxford (Clarendon Press). 1923. (Chapter on Roman Science by Dr. Charles Singer.)

Sir T. L. Heath. *Greek Mathematics* (2 vols.). Oxford (Clarendon Press). 1921. 50s. net.

Aristotle.

Charles Singer. *Greek Biology and Greek Medicine.* Oxford (Clarendon Press). 1922. 2*s.* 6*d.* net.

Euclid.

Sir T. L. Heath. *Euclid in Greek.* (Cambridge University Press.) 1920. 10*s.* net. Very interesting notes.

—— *The Thirteen Books of Euclid's Elements.* (Cambridge University Press.) 1905. 52*s.* 6*d.* net.

Archimedes.

Sir T. L. Heath. *The Works of Archimedes.* (Cambridge University Press.) 1907. 17*s.* 6*d.* net.

Science in the Middle Ages.

Hearnshaw. *Mediaeval Contributions to Modern Civilization.* (Harrap & Sons.) 1921. 7*s.* 6*d.* net. The Chapter on 'Science' by Dr. C. Singer gives an excellent survey of mediaeval science.

A. G. Little. *Roger Bacon Essays.* Oxford (Clarendon Press). 1914. 16*s.* net.

J. L. E. Dreyer. *History of Planetary Systems from Thales to Kepler.* (Cambridge University Press). 1905. 12*s.* 6*d.* net.

Charles Singer. *Studies in the History and Method of Science.* Oxford (Clarendon Press). In vol. i, 'The Scientific Views and Visions of Saint Hildegarde', by C. Singer, ably depicts twelfth-century science. In vol. ii are: 'Mediaeval Astronomy', by J. L. E. Dreyer; 'Science in the Thirteenth Century', by R. Steele; 'The Scientific Works of Galileo', by J. J. Fahié; 'Science and the Unity of Mankind', by F. S. Marvin; 'Steps leading to the Invention of the First Optical Apparatus', by C. Singer.

The Modern Period.

A. D. Lindsay. *A Discourse on Method by René Descartes.* (J. M. Dent.) Everyman. 1912. 2*s.* net.

J. A. Thomson. *Progress of Science* (Nineteenth Century Series). (Chambers.) 5*s.* net.

A. MacFarlane. *Ten British Mathematicians.* (Chapman & Hall.) 8*s.* 6*d.* net.

—— *Ten British Physicists.* (Chapman & Hall.) 8*s.* 6*d.* net.

INDEX

320

Index

Printed in England at the Oxford University Press